DESERT AND MOUNTAIN PLANTS OF THE SOUTHWEST

DESERT AND MOUNTAIN PLANTS OF THE SOUTHWEST

by

Dorothy VanDyke Leake

John Benjamin Leake

Marcelotte Leake Roeder

Illustrated by Dorothy VanDyke Leake

University of Oklahoma Press : Norman and London

Also by Dorothy VanDyke Leake
(coauthor, with Henderson Leake) *Wildflowers of the Ozarks* (Little Rock, 1981)

Also by John Benjamin Leake
(coauthor, with Neal J. Holmes) *Gateways to Science* (New York, 1983)

Figures 20, 28, and 123 drawn by Bellamy Parks Jansen.

Library of Congress Cataloging-in-Publication Data

Leake, Dorothy Van Dyke, 1893–1990.
Desert and mountain plants of the Southwest / Dorothy Van Dyke Leake, John Benjamin Leake, Marcelotte Leake Roeder; illustrated by Dorothy Van Dyke Leake. — 1st ed.
p. cm.
Includes bibliographical references (p.) and index.
ISBN 0-8061-2489-X
1. Botany—Southwestern States. 2. Desert plants—Southwestern States. 3. Alpine flora—Southwestern States. I. Leake, John Benjamin, 1923– . II. Roeder, Marcelotte Leake, 1920– III. Title.
QK142.L43 1993
581.979—dc20 92-50716
CIP

The paper in this book meets the guidelines for permanence and durability of the Committee on Production Guidelines for Book Longevity of the Council on Library Resources, Inc. ♾

1 2 3 4 5 6 7 8 9 10

Contents

Preface

This book is a collection of drawings and descriptions of some of the plants that live in the mountains and deserts of the southwestern United States and especially in the part of the Sonoran desert located in Arizona.

Many variables determine the number of plant species found in any location. Chemical composition and acid or alkaline properties of the soils, annual amount and time distributions of precipitation, size of soil particles, opportunities for population introduction and expansion, and the extent and duration of solar radiation are among the more important variables.

Desert plants have limited water available, and the water they do get may be available for only a short time. Therefore, desert plants have two primary properties. They are adapted to conserve moisture and can exist and propagate after long periods of drought. Since precipitation is low, chemicals have not been leached from the soil as badly as in areas where rainfall is high. The result is chemically rich soil. One outcome of this chemical richness is the brilliant colors displayed by desert flowers. Since conditions for growth are harsh, plant mass is low and organic matter is quite scarce. Soils that have little organic matter do not retain water efficiently. Desert plants have adaptations that either allow them to store water or prevent its evaporation from plant surfaces.

Even though precipitation is limited in the desert there are a few locations where the microclimate is humid. One such location is where water flows from the ground in the form of a spring from an underground aquifer. Another type may be a deep valley where, due to limited radiation from the sun, moisture does not evaporate rapidly from the soil surface and water condenses from the air during the cool nights. In locations such as these the plants will be markedly different from those in the desert open spaces.

Elevation also makes a difference in plant populations. Temperatures tend to be cooler as elevation increases. The plants mirror this change in growth pattern and abundance.

Throughout this book reference will be made to the climatic characteristics of specific plants' locations. The healing properties of plants or use of them as food will also be mentioned.

There are several people who should be mentioned for their contributions to and support of this work. Thanks are especially due to Ruth Ashton Nelson, who initiated it and contributed her expertise. During the springtime weeks of 1982 and 1983, Mrs. Nelson went to the desert, accompanied by the illustrator, Dorothy VanDyke Leake, to collect and identify plants. The work of these two years was based at the Boyce Thompson Arboretum near Phoenix, Arizona.

At the end of the second year Mrs. Nelson was not physically able to continue the work. She asked Dorothy Leake to take on the writing as well as the figure drawing. At that point Mrs. Nelson had not done any writing at all, as she was busy with collection and identification. She deposited two identical collections at herbaria—one at the University of Wyoming, the other at the University of Missouri.

Fieldwork was continued in 1984 with the able assistance of Jaqueline Hall Durant. The headquarters for the work in the eastern portion of the Sonoran desert was New York's Natural History Museum's Field Station at Portal, Arizona.

For the central section the work was again based at the Boyce Thompson Arboretum, where Dr. Frank S. Crosswhite and staff helped in its progress.

In 1985 the California desert was explored, with headquarters at the home of Van and Sandra Arnett in Ocotillo, California. These two were a great help in finding and identifying desert plants.

At the same time, Lorraine and Howard Pritchett, science teachers in El Centro, California, were an invaluable help because of their knowledge of desert plants and the fieldwork it takes to find them. The Pritchetts also provided plant specimens that Dorothy Leake was unable to get while working in the desert.

We would also like to thank Dr. Peter Raven, Director of the Missouri Botanical Garden, and his staff, especially George Yatskievych, for their help in the final corrections of this book.

How to Enjoy this Book

Part of the enjoyment of a book of this kind is in learning about the characteristics and names of the plants. Of course, pleasure comes from just leafing through the pages, admiring the pictures and reading the descriptions, but study of the southwestern flora is rewarding too.

The section "Plant Characteristics Illustrated" and Glossary were made to assist in such study. The book includes only a small part of the plant life of the southwestern deserts and mountains, but the works listed in the Bibliography (page 231) can be consulted for additional information. Many library books and magazines have excellent color photographs of plants.

A good way to begin identification is by studying plants of the larger families. The composite family (page 182) would be excellent to examine first because there are so many familiar plants in this family. On page 226 the characteristics of the family are illustrated. The milkweeds (page 129) plants with milky juice, and the mustards (page 52) would also be suitable for the study of plant classification. They are large families as well.

The sequence of plant families in this book, which approximates that currently used in taxonomic literature, begins with the nonseed plants, then goes from the monocots to the dicots. To aid the general reader, the plant families have been categorized according to their most obvious characteristics (especially relative to the flowers) into fifteen groups, listed and described in the "Guide to Plant Families" (p. xi). Families not in the Guide can be identified using conventional keys to classification, some of which are listed in the Bibliography. The most helpful of these are: *Fieldbook of Western Flowers*, by Margaret Armstrong; *Desert Wildflowers*, by Edmund C. Jaeger; *Handbook of Rocky Mountain Plants*, by Ruth A. Nelson; and *Vegetation and Flora of the Sonoran Desert*, by Forrest Shreve and Ira L. Wiggins. The paperback books by Natt N. Dodge and Pauline Mead Patraw have line drawings of plants that are more useful for identification than color photographs because they show more details.

Guide to Plant Families

Group One

These are plants with conductive tissue that do not bear flowers or seeds. These plants are included in a large group, the Pteridophytes (Fern plants). There are two groups: the fern allies and the true ferns. Only one family of fern allies, Selaginellaceae, is included in this work. Other families are the horsetails and the ground pines. Only one family of the true ferns, the Polypodiaceae, is included.

Group Two

Plants bearing seeds are divided into two groups. The Gymnosperms have their seeds on open scales arranged in cones. The Angiosperms have seeds that are enclosed within an ovary. The Gymnosperms included in this work are the Pinaceae, the Cupressaceae, and the Gnetaceae. The Pinaceae (pines) include both evergreen trees and shrubs. The cone is made of spirally arranged scales. The Cupressaceae (cypresses) are also evergreen trees and shrubs. The cones are composed of woody, wedge-shaped scales. The Gnetaceae (joint-firs) have long, fluted joints and small, papery leaves arranged in twos or threes.

Group Three

The Angiosperms are divided into two groups. The monocotyledons have flower parts in threes and sixes. The dicotyledons have flower parts in fours and fives. The term *monocotyledon* means "one seed leaf." The embryo plant within the seed has one leaf, as in corn seeds. It follows that dicotyledons have two seed leaves, as do the beans and peas. Families of the monocotyledons are the Palmaceae (palms), Iridaceae (irises), Liliaceae (lilies), and the Agavaceae (agaves). There is only one palm native to the Southwest, a beautiful tree called the California Palm. One of the irises is named Blue-eyed Grass, but it is not a grass at all. The flower does not look like the tame iris and, unlike the tame iris, grows from a bulb instead of a rhizome. Lilies are typical monocotyledons, with flower parts in threes and sixes. The most conspicuous ones of the west are the Desert Lilies and Mariposa. The agaves are represented in this book by the familiar yucca, which is assigned to the lily family by some taxonomists.

Group Four

The embryo plants of dicotyledons have two seed leaves. An example is the bean embryo, the cotyledons of which are the seed halves pressed tightly together. Group Four includes trees and shrubs with simple, alternate, stipulate leaves. This group is nearly always dioecious with flowers in catkins, like the willows. Also included are the beeches (monoecious trees that have staminate flowers in catkins); the partially parasitic mistletoes; and the parasitic sandalwoods.

Group Five

The flowers have two or more sepals and five or more separate petals, radially symmetric. Stamens number generally more than twenty.

Group Six

The flowers have two, four, or six sepals and four, six, or eight petals. They are radially symmetric. The number of stamens ranges from six to many.

Mustard Family	(Cruciferae)	page 52
Caper Family	(Capparidaceae)	page 57

Group Seven

The flowers have four or five sepals and four or five separate petals. The number of stamens is equal to or double the number of petals.

Pink Family	(Caryophyllaceae)	page 43
Saxifrage Family	(Saxifragaceae)	page 59
Orpine Family	(Crassulaceae)	page 61
Flax Family	(Linaceae)	page 84
Parsley Family	(Umbelliferae)	page 119

Group Eight

The flowers have two, four, five, or six sepals and the same number of separate, radially symmetric petals. Stamens are of the same number or twice as many as the petals. There is only one pistil in each flower.

Purslane Family	(Portulacaceae)	page 41
Caltrop Family	(Zygophyllaceae)	page 85
Rue Family	(Rutaceae)	page 87
Primrose Family	(Onagraceae)	page 111
Mint Family	(Labiatae)	page 144

Group Nine

The flowers have four or five sepals and petals. Petals are usually separate but in some species they may be united. The number of stamens is five or ten.

Pea Family	(Leguminosae)	page 68
Ratany Family	(Krameriaceae)	page 83

Group Ten

The flowers have two, four, or five sepals and four or five petals. Petals are united and radially symmetric. The number of stamens is the same or twice the number of petals. Leaves are usually basal and small; crowded, opposite, or whorled on stem.

Heather Family	(Ericaceae)	page 124

Group Eleven

The flowers have four or five sepals and petals. The petals are united and radially symmetric. Stamens are of the same number as the petals. Leaves alternate.

Group Twelve

The flowers have three, four, or five sepals and petals. The petals are united and radially symmetric. The number of stamens is one to four. Except in the gourd family the leaves are in pairs or whorls around the stem.

Group Thirteen

The flowers have four or five sepals and three, four, or five petals. The petals are united and bilaterally symmetric.

Group Fourteen

The inflorescence is a head, made up of many flowers, of which there are two kinds. One kind, the ray flowers, have a strap-shaped corolla of five fused petals. The other, the disk flowers, have five petals united into a radially symmetric tube. There are genera with ray and disk flowers, ray flowers only, and disk flowers only.

Group Fifteen

This is a list of families represented by only one or two genera. All are trees, shrubs, or vines. Individuals are very distinctive. These plants are mostly thorny and many climb by stems or tendrils.

DESERT AND MOUNTAIN PLANTS OF THE SOUTHWEST

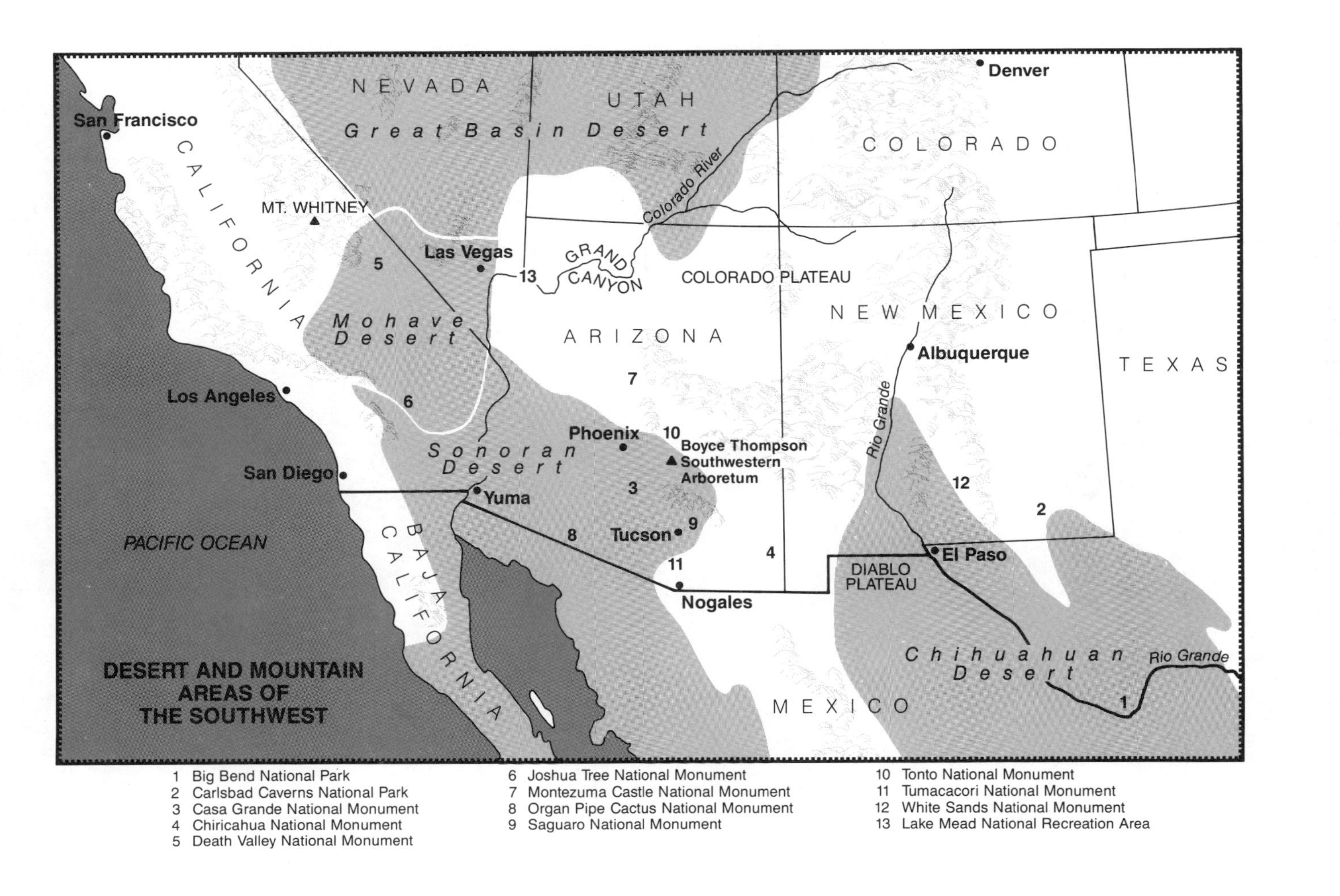
DESERT AND MOUNTAIN AREAS OF THE SOUTHWEST
NEVADA
UTAH
Great Basin Desert
COLORADO
Denver
San Francisco
CALIFORNIA
MT. WHITNEY
Colorado River
Las Vegas
GRAND CANYON
COLORADO PLATEAU
Mohave Desert
NEW MEXICO
ARIZONA
Albuquerque
TEXAS
Los Angeles
Rio Grande
Phoenix
Boyce Thompson Southwestern Arboretum
Sonoran Desert
San Diego
Yuma
PACIFIC OCEAN
BAJA CALIFORNIA
Tucson
El Paso
DIABLO PLATEAU
Nogales
Chihuahuan Desert
MEXICO
1 Big Bend National Park
2 Carlsbad Caverns National Park
3 Casa Grande National Monument
4 Chiricahua National Monument
5 Death Valley National Monument
6 Joshua Tree National Monument
7 Montezuma Castle National Monument
8 Organ Pipe Cactus National Monument
9 Saguaro National Monument
10 Tonto National Monument
11 Tumacacori National Monument
12 White Sands National Monument
13 Lake Mead National Recreation Area

SELAGINELLACEAE

Little Club Moss Family

This is a family of plants belonging to a large group of plants that have conducting tissues, like the seed plants, but no seeds. Neither the little club mosses (Selaginellaceae) nor the larger club mosses, the Lycopodiaceae, belong to the moss phylum, Bryophyta; rather, they belong to the fern phylum, Pteridophyta. The closely related quillworts, water ferns, and equisetums are also fern allies.

1. **Spike Fern** *Selaginella densa* var. *scopulorum*

There is only one genus, *Selaginella*, in this family. The most common species in the genus is *Selaginella densa*. These plants form a moss-like ground cover with upright and horizontal branches. The leaves form a four-ranked spiral around the stems, and the fruiting stems are tipped with cone-like growths. Dry weather turns them dull brown and they turn bright green when rains come.

1
2
3

POLYPODIACEAE

Fern Family

The polypodys are the so-called true ferns. Other families of ferns are the Osmundaceae (Royal Ferns) and the Ophioglossaceae (Adder's Tongue Ferns). All families of ferns have the characteristic mentioned for the club moss family—that of having conducting tissue but no seeds. Reproduction is by spores that develop into inconspicuous male and female plant structures bearing sex organs. Union of the eggs and sperms of these produce conspicuous ferns as we know them. These plants produce the spores.

2. **Forked Spleenwort** *Asplenium septentrionale*

All of the desert ferns listed in Lehr's *Catalogue of the Flora of Arizona* belong to the Polypody family. The genus *Asplenium*, the Forked Spleenwort, is an evergreen fern that grows in rock crevices. Asplenium means "without spleen," which refers to supposed medicinal properties.

3. **Lip Fern** *Cheilanthes fendleri*

Cheilanthes is from the Greek—*cheilos* (a margin) and *anthos* (flower), referring to the position of the sori along the leaf margin, making a lip. The Lip Fern sometimes grows in crevices at the foot of dry cliffs and on plains and foothills. The undersurfaces of the fronds are covered with reddish brown hairs or thin tapering transparent scales.

4. **Bladder Fern** *Cystopteris fragilis*

Cystopteris refers to the inflated covering of the sori—from *cystos* (bladder) and *pteris* (fern). The Bladder Fern or Brittle Fern is very common throughout the world. These are delicate woodland ferns requiring more moisture than the desert affords.

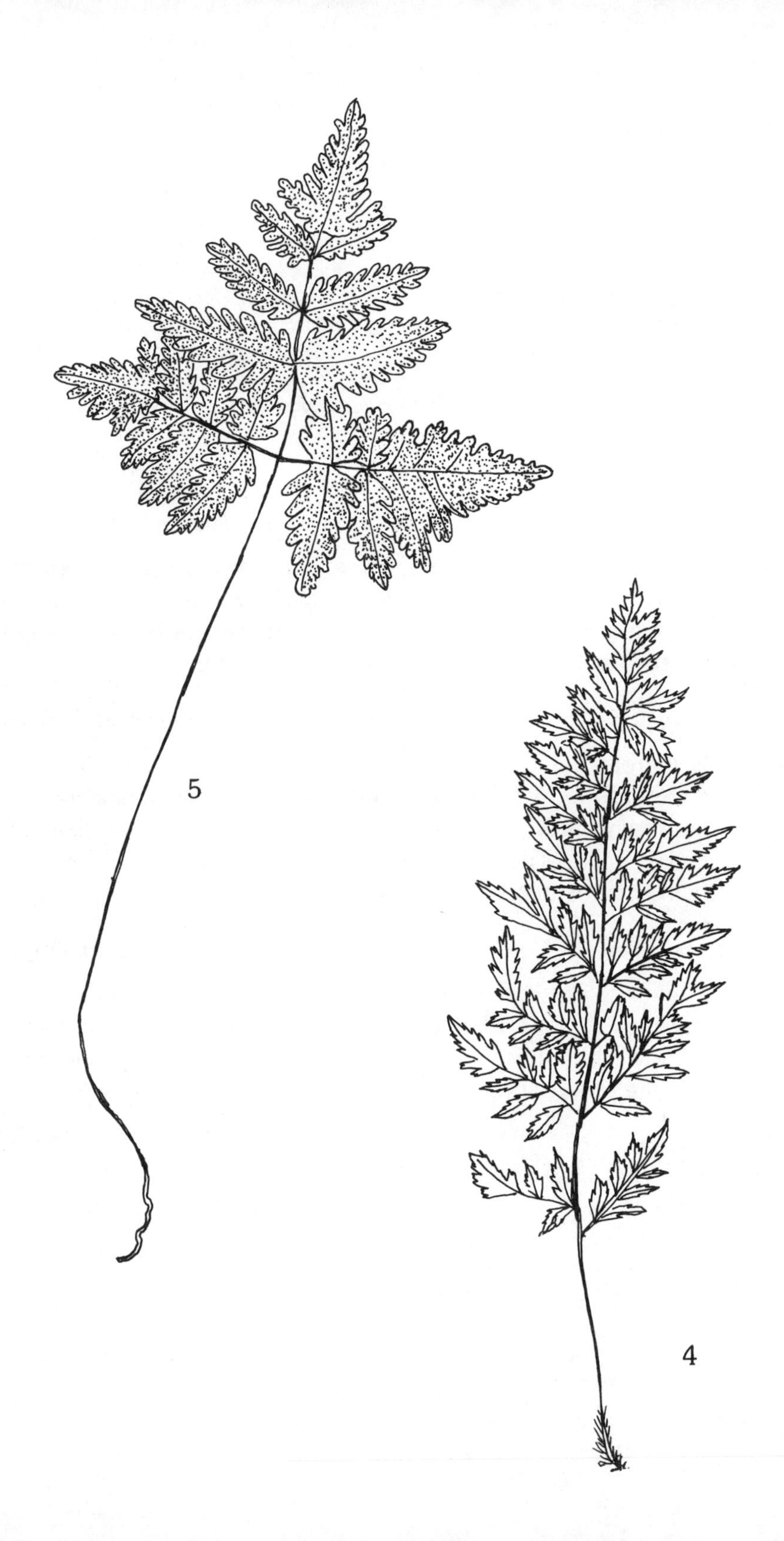
5
4

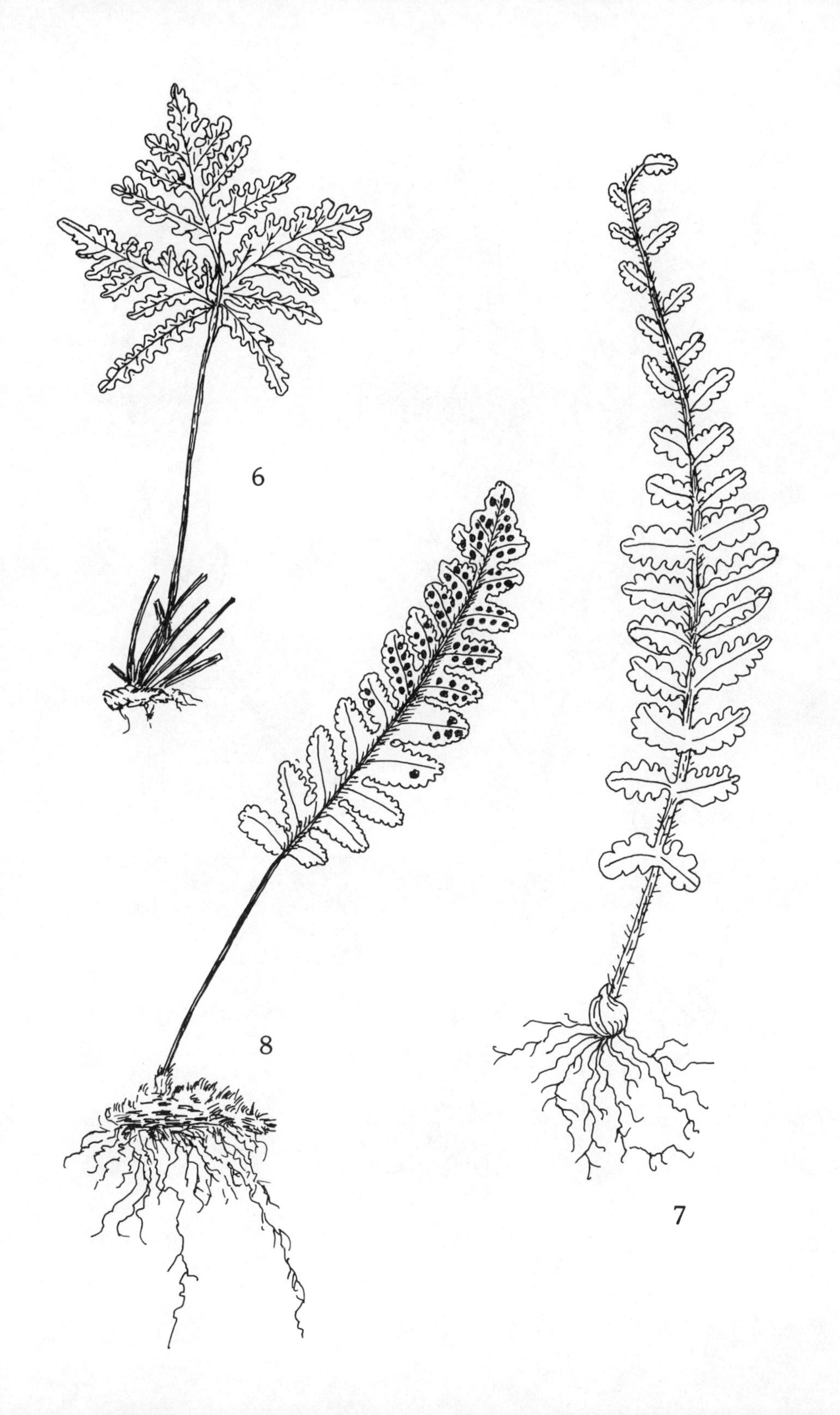
6
8
7

9

5. **Oak Fern** *Gymnocarpium dryopteris*

Gymnos means "naked" and *carpium* refers to the cover of the sorus, the indusium, which is lacking in this fern. Like *Cystopteris* it usually grows in more moist habitats than deserts.

6. **Zig-Zag Cloak Fern** *Notholaena californica*

Notholaena means "false cloak," possibly referring to the yellow powder that covers the underside of the leaf. In the days when children wore long black stockings they would decorate them by pressing the leaf against the leg to leave a lacy yellow print.

7. **Cloak Fern** *Notholaena sinuata*

Instead of having a broad five-angled leaf this Cloak Fern has a slender seven- to ten-inch stem with leaflets on opposite sides.

8. **Polypody Fern** *Polypodium hesperium (P. vulgare)*

Polypody means "many footed"—that is, several branches to the creeping rootstock. As one may see in the sketch, the sori are found on the backs of the upper parts of the fronds.

9. **Holly Fern** *Polystichum lonchitis*

The single-pinnate fronds have a thumb-like division of the leaflets at the bases of their upper edges. The name is from the Greek words *polus* (many) and *stichos* (row), referring to the several rows of sori.

10. **Oregon Woodsia** *Woodsia oregana*

This genus is named for the English botanist Joseph Woods, who died in 1804 at the age of twenty-eight. Lehr's *Catalogue* lists five species of *woodsia.* One needs a good hand lens to study these ferns because an important characteristic for identification is the small size of the filament below the sorus.

10

PINACEAE

Pine Family

This family serves as an introduction to seed plants. The Pinaceae, Cupressaceae, and Gnetaceae, which develop seeds that are not enveloped in a folded leaf, are called Gymnosperms, or naked seed plants. Ovules (eggs) are on an open scale, not enclosed within an ovary. There are two or three stamens. The cone is made up of spirally arranged scales. Seeds are usually winged.

11. **Blue Spruce** *Picea pungens*

Staminate and ovulate cones are produced at the tips of the previous year's growth. A powdery substance on the surface of the needles gives them a bluish color. The short, four-sided needles are very sharp.

12. **Douglas Fir** *Pseudotsuga menziesii*

This is really not a fir. The genus name means "false hemlock." The Douglas Fir is a tree with flat sharp needles. It can attain a height of 100 feet and is usually found in the mountain sections of the desert on north-facing slopes.

13. **Piñon Pine** *Pinus edulis*

The Piñon Pine is a bushy tree of the desert foothills. The nuts of the Piñon Pine have been and still are used by the Indians of the Southwest. Piñon nuts can be bought in the markets and are a staple food of Navaho and Pueblo Indians. The wood is used for fuel, posts, and furniture.

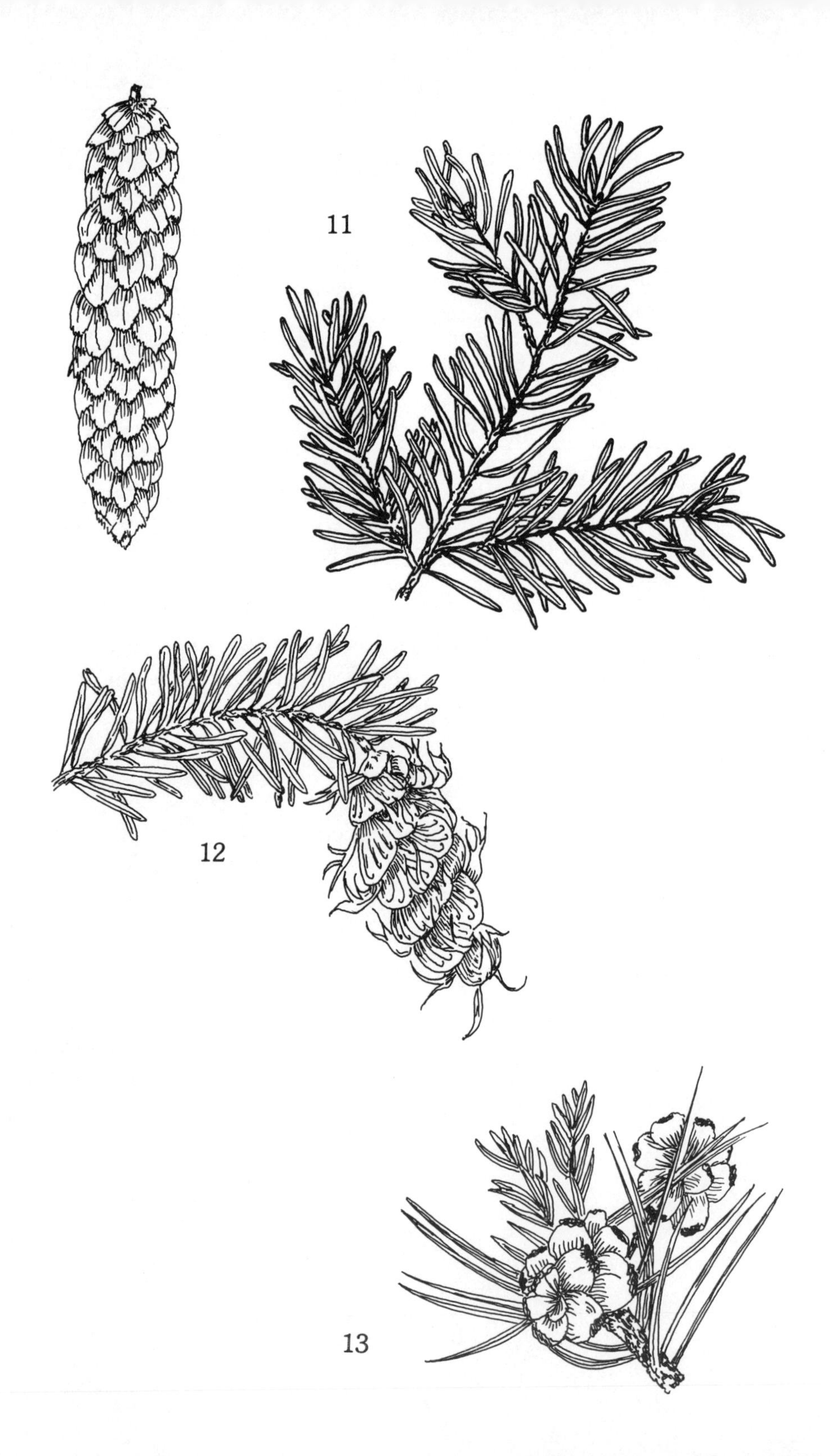
11
12
13

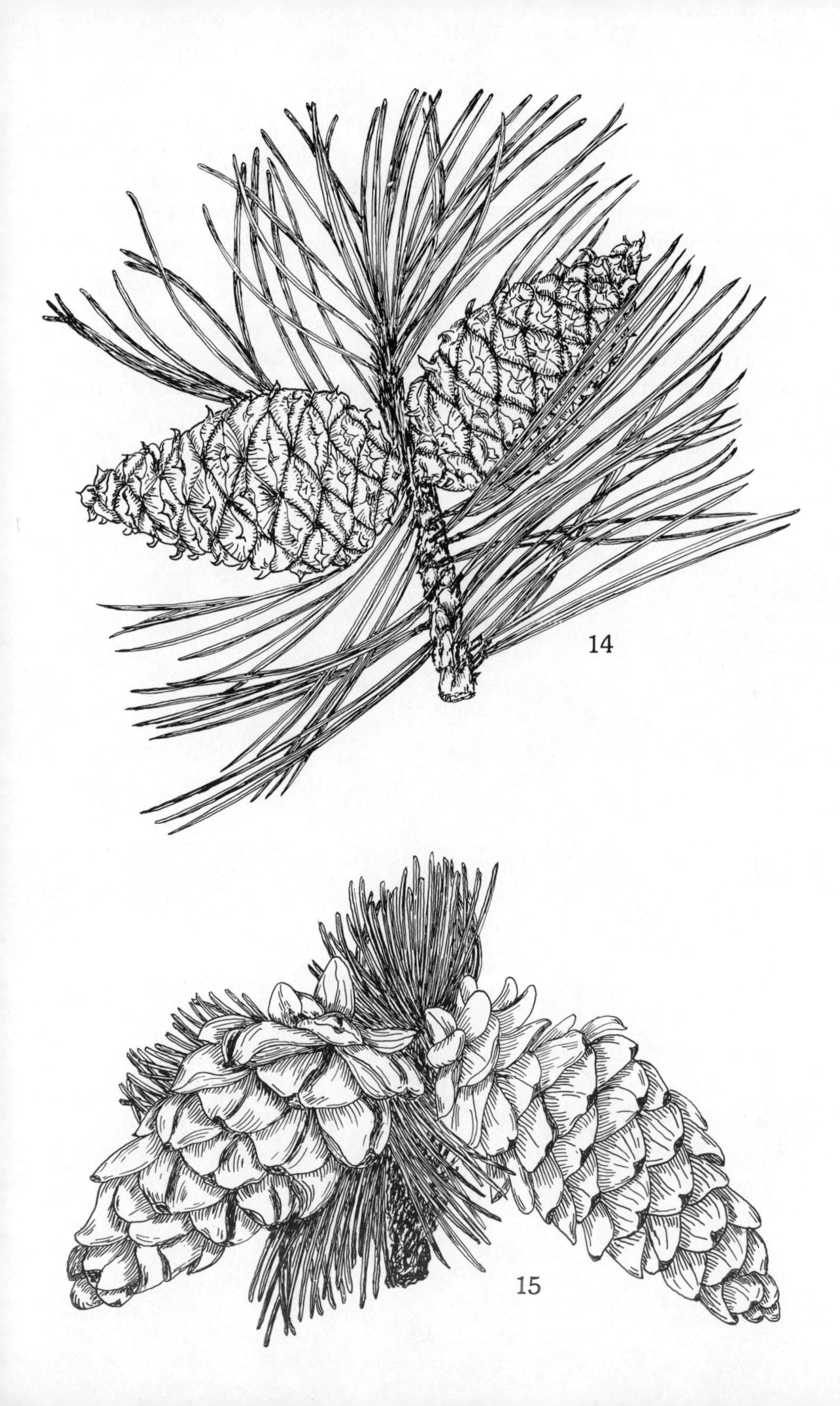
14
15

14. **Arizona Pine** *Pinus ponderosa* var. *arizonica*

The Ponderosa Pine is the most widely distributed of the Rocky Mountain pines, extending along most of the Rocky Mountain range. A very beautiful tree with orange-brown bark, it is the largest of the pines, sometimes reaching a height of 150 feet. The Ponderosas are the most important pines for lumber.

15. **Limber Pine** *Pinus flexilis*

The flexible branches of the Limber Pine give it its species and common names. The cylindrical cone is from four to ten inches long and is usually coated with a pitchy exudate. Sometimes these trees are used to make railroad ties.

CUPRESSACEAE

Cypress Family

Trees of this family are either male or female. The cypresses are evergreen trees or shrubs. Branchlets are covered with small, alternate pairs of scales. The cones are composed of woody, wedge-shaped scales.

16. **Arizona Cypress** *Cupressus arizonica*

This evergreen tree has gracefully drooping branches. It is found in canyon bottoms or on north slopes of desert mountains.

17. **Alligator Juniper** *Juniperus deppeana*

The Alligator Juniper gets its name from the squarish plates, like alligator scales, on the trunks of old trees. The leaves are blue-green and the ripe fruit is dark brownish red.

18. **Utah Juniper** *Juniperus osteosperma*

The Utah Juniper is the common one of the foothills. The leaves have a yellowish green tinge. Berries of some species of junipers are used to make gin or roasted to use as a coffee substitute. In Europe, a pulp is extracted from juniper berries and used as a spread on bread.

GNETACEAE

Joint-Fir Family

Members of this family are the ephedras, or joint-firs. At the nodes of their long, fluted joints are small, papery leaves arranged in twos or threes.

19. **Nevada Joint-Fir** *Ephedra nevadensis*

Ephedra, which means "sitting upon seat," does not seem to be a very suitable name. These plants have had a long history of uses by the southwestern Indians. The Pima Indians and others boiled the stems, which contain tannin, to use for intestinal ailments. The tea was also supposed to be a cure for syphilis. The large black seeds can be roasted for eating. Ground squirrels store great quantities of the seeds for winter food.

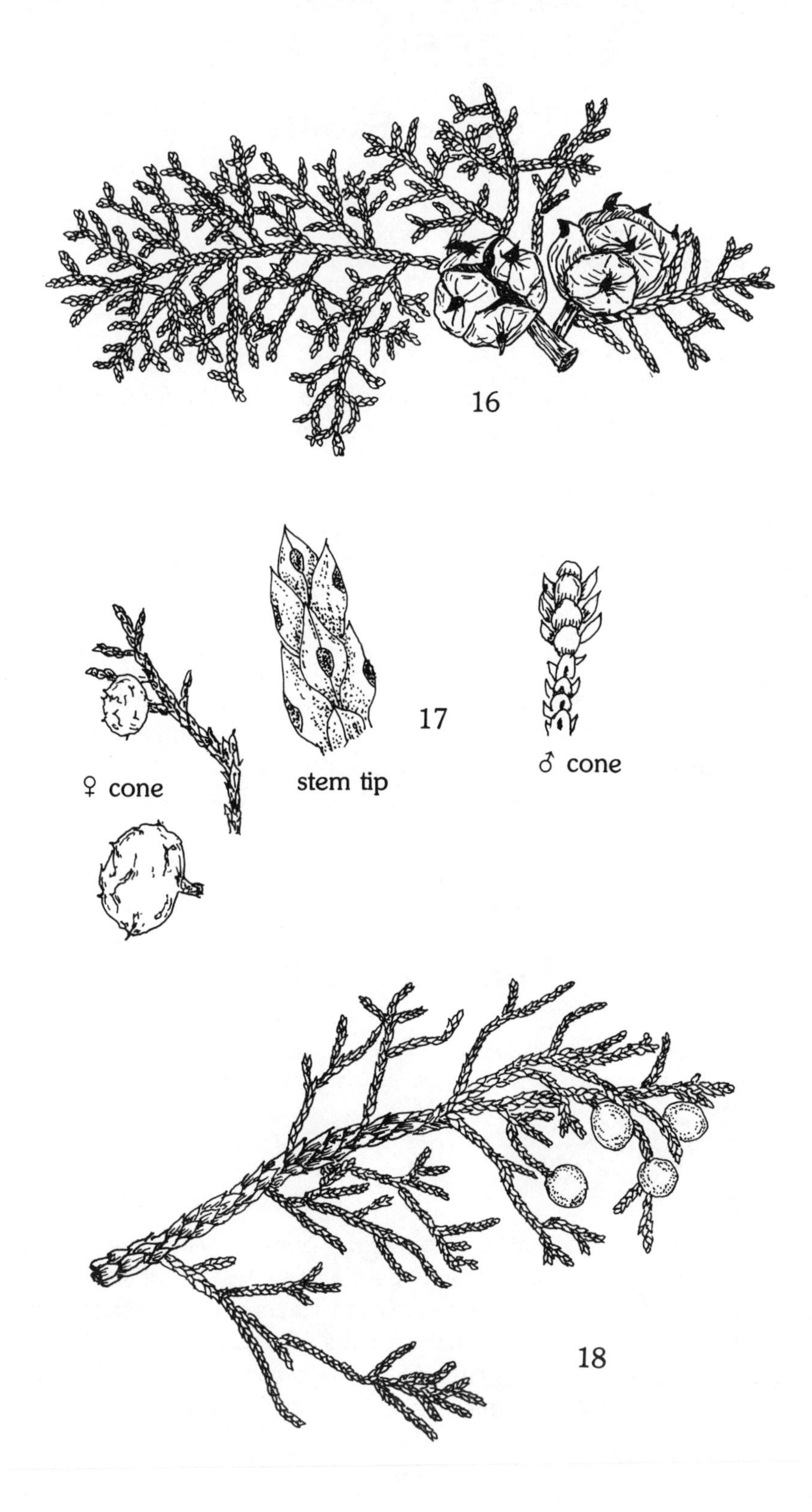
16
17
♀ cone
stem tip
♂ cone
18

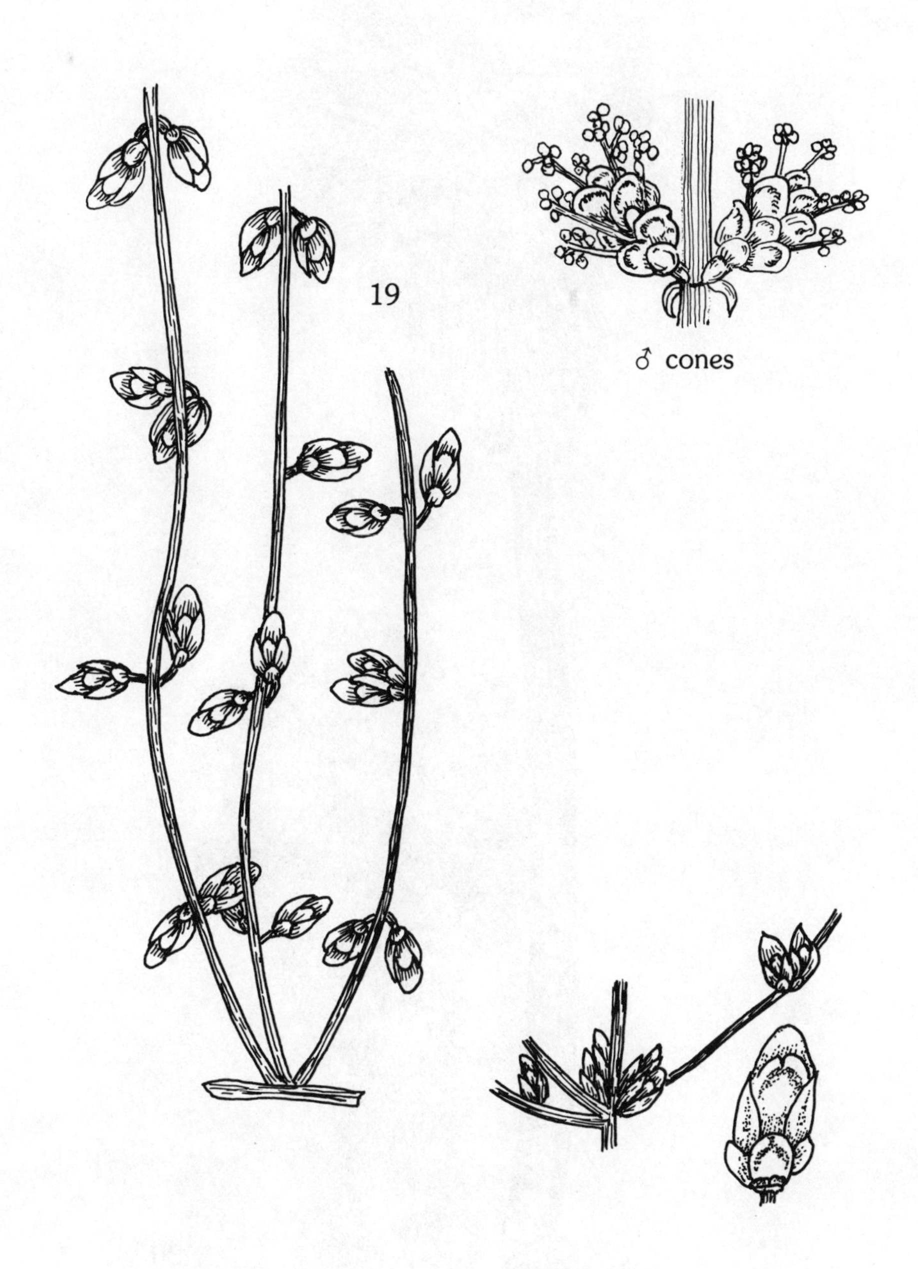
19
♂ cones

20

PALMACEAE

Palm Family

This family introduces the covered-seed plants, the Angiosperms. In this division of the plant kingdom the seeds are covered by a specialized leaf that serves as added protection for the embryo. Among these covered seeds the monocotyledons (single-leafed embryos) are listed first. Monocots found in the southwestern deserts include palms, irises, and lilies, as well as the grasses and sedges. There are about 1,500 species of palms in the world, mainly tropical, but only about 15 of these are native to the United States. There is only one western native, Washingtonia filifera. *The others are native to Florida except for two in Texas and one in Mississippi and South Carolina. They are said to be "princes" of the vegetable kingdom and are certainly noble plants. For centuries, pictures, mosaics, and statues of palms and palm leaves have adorned palaces and temples. The word* palm *means "prize" or "honor," and the leaves were used as symbols of victory.*

Characteristic of the family is the placement of leaves as a tuft at the top of the stem; the leaves may be pinnate or palmate. There are no annual rings by which to tell the age of the trees, but some probably live for 200 years or more.

20. **California Palm** *Washingtonia filifera*

Also called Desert Palm and California Fan Palm, the species name *filifera* means "thread bearing." The leaf edge does have threads, which are easily gathered by Arizona hooded and Scott orioles for nest weaving. The trees are host to many little animals—among them tree frogs and canyon wrens—besides the nesting orioles. The outside pulp and the seeds were eaten by the Cahuilla Indians, who also made flour out of the seeds.

The threads are dried edges of the palm leaf. The hooded oriole shows amazing strength and persistence in pulling them off. The bird weaves them into a hanging basket, cleverly attached to the underside of the leaf, which offers marvelous protection for the hatchlings.

21
22
23

IRIDACEAE

Iris Family

The iris family members are widely distributed over the world, with best development in South Africa. Horticultural genera include the well-known Crocus, Iris, Gladiolus, Tigridia, Freesia, Neomarica, *and* Ixia. *Like the palms, the irises are monocotyledonous seed plants.*

21. **Blue-eyed Grass** *Sisyrinchium bellum*

This genus is not a cultivated plant. It grows from a bulb and grows only in alkaline seeps of the desert. The common name, Blue-eyed Grass, is very appropriate, since the bright blue flowers appear among grass-like leaves.

24
25

LILIACEAE

Lily Family

The lily family includes many tame as well as wild genera. The wild ones are so beautiful that it is a wonder they are not all tamed to grow in our gardens. Most are typical monocotyledons, with flower parts in threes and sixes, yet they are very diverse, including herbs, vines, and woody plants with various habits and structures.

22. **Wild Onion** *Allium acuminatum*

Lehr's *Catalogue* lists fourteen genera of onions but most of them do not grow in the desert. The Wild Onion grows in clumps. Its small, white flowers are on thin stalks and are arranged in an umbel on top of the stem. Two leaves grow at the base of the umbel. The plant stem, which is topped by the leaves and flower stem, grows from a bulb—the "onion."

23. **Nodding Onion** *Allium cernuum*

Except for the "nodding" habit this onion is much like the Wild Onion, but its flower stem and leaves are much closer to the bulb in their origin.

24. **Mariposa** *Calochortus flexuosus*

Six species of Mariposa are listed for Arizona. Two of these, *Calochortus kennedyi* and *Calochortus flexuosus*, are found in the desert. Both are more colorful than other Mariposas—the species *Calochortus kennedyi* is bright red and the *Calochortus flexuosus* is purple. Most of the other species have white flowers, marked at the petal base with yellow and purple. A characteristic habit of both the desert species is to climb through a nearby bush and flower at the top.

Both the common and scientific names are very appropriate. *Calochortus* means "beautiful grass," and *Mariposa* means "butterfly."

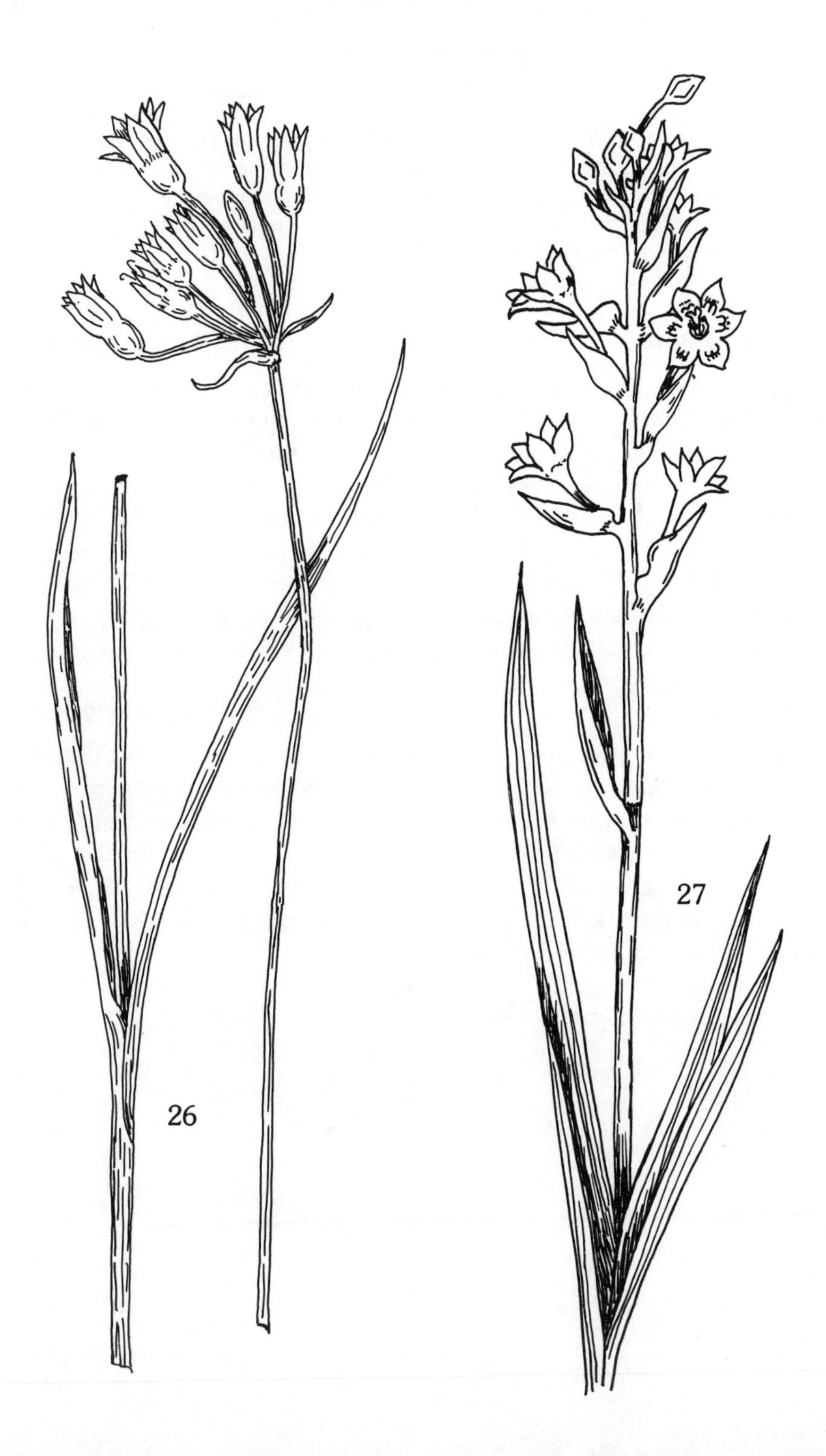
26
27

25. **Desert Lily** *Hesperocallis undulata*

This member of the lily family is in bloom from February to May. The genus name means "evening beauty" and the species name refers to the wavy margin of the leaf (see Figure 25).

The plant is usually very short-stemmed. It grows from a bulb that may be as much as two feet beneath the sandy surface of the ground.

Indians ate the bulbs, which have an onion flavor. So did the Spanish explorers, who called them *ajo*, meaning "garlic."

The flowers are white with a greenish blue streak down the middle of the dorsal surface of each petal.

26. **Blue Dicks** *Dichelostemma pulchellum*

Other common names for Blue Dicks are Wild Hyacinth, Cluster Lily, Spanish Lily, and Hog Onion. The blue-violet flowers bloom in early spring and continue into May. The bulbs are called grass nuts or gopher nuts and were eaten raw, boiled, or broiled by Indians and white settlers. The flowers can be used for salads. Blue Dicks grow on rocky hillsides and plains where Creosote Bushes flourish.

27. **White Camas** *Zygadenus elegans*

Another common name given this plant is Wand Lily.

All parts of the plant are poisonous and should not even be tasted. The true Camas is edible and can easily be distinguished from White Camas by flower color, which is blue instead of white. The Wand Lily is not quite so poisonous as other zygadenes. Another desert camas, not pictured here, is only mildly poisonous.

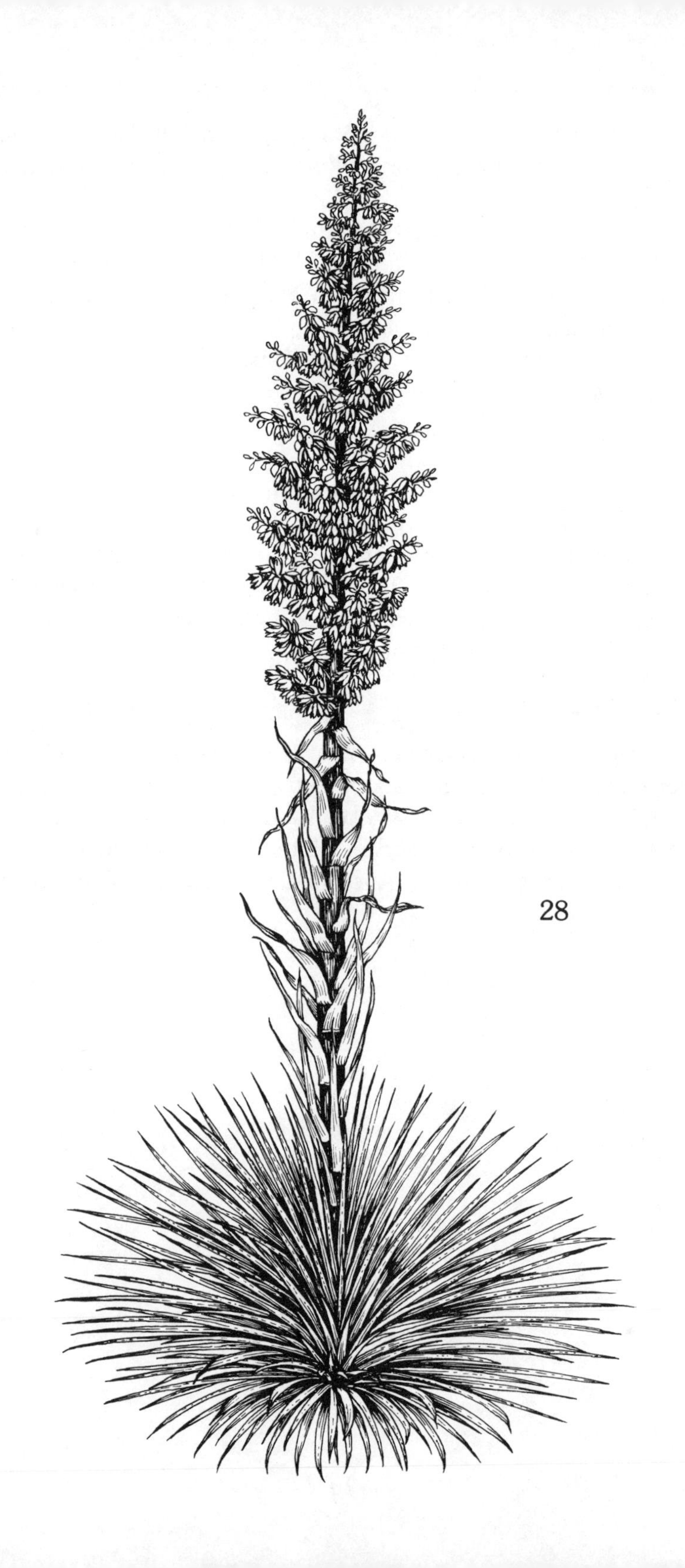

28

AGAVACEAE

Agave Family

This family is sometimes called the century-plant family. Many species have a rosette of basal leaves that are fibrous and sharp at the tips. The flowers are on strong stems and may be panicles, racemes, or spikes. Flower parts are in threes with the exception of the stamens, which are six.

28. **Our Lord's Candle** *Yucca whipplei*

Other common names include Whipple Yucca, Spanish Bayonet, and Soap Weed.

Our Lord's Candle is most abundant on the western edge of the Mohave Desert. Three other species that grow in the desert are the Fleshy Fruited Yucca, of eastern Mohave; the Joshua Tree, which occurs all over the desert; and the Mohave Yucca or Spanish Dagger, widespread but growing best in the southern part of the desert.

Much has been written about all the yuccas. *Yucca glauca* has an especially interesting reproductive arrangement involving a small moth that accomplishes the pollination process.

Of the southwestern species, the Fleshy Fruited and the Joshua Tree seem to have furnished the most food. The bulbs were eaten by Indians. They also ate the green pods raw or roasted. Dried ground fruits were stored for winter. This plant was used in soap-making and basketry. Cloth and sandals were made from the fibers.

Most interesting are the ecological relationships between the Joshua Tree and various animals. A butterfly called the Navaho yucca borer and a yucca-boring beetle produce larvae that feed on above-ground and below-ground plant parts. Wood rats and lizards are associated with Joshua Trees. The night lizard *Xantusia vigilis* could not survive without it. This lizard lives on termites, ants, and larvae found under the bark.

At least two dozen desert birds nest in tree yuccas. Among these are the Scott oriole, a screech owl, the western bluebird, flicker, cactus woodpecker, ash-throated flycatcher, cactus wren, and titmouse.

The Mohave Yucca, or Spanish Dagger—the commonest yucca of the desert—produces midsummer fruits that were used by the Indians. The fruits have a high percentage of sugar, and pack rats chew off the bitter covering to get to it.

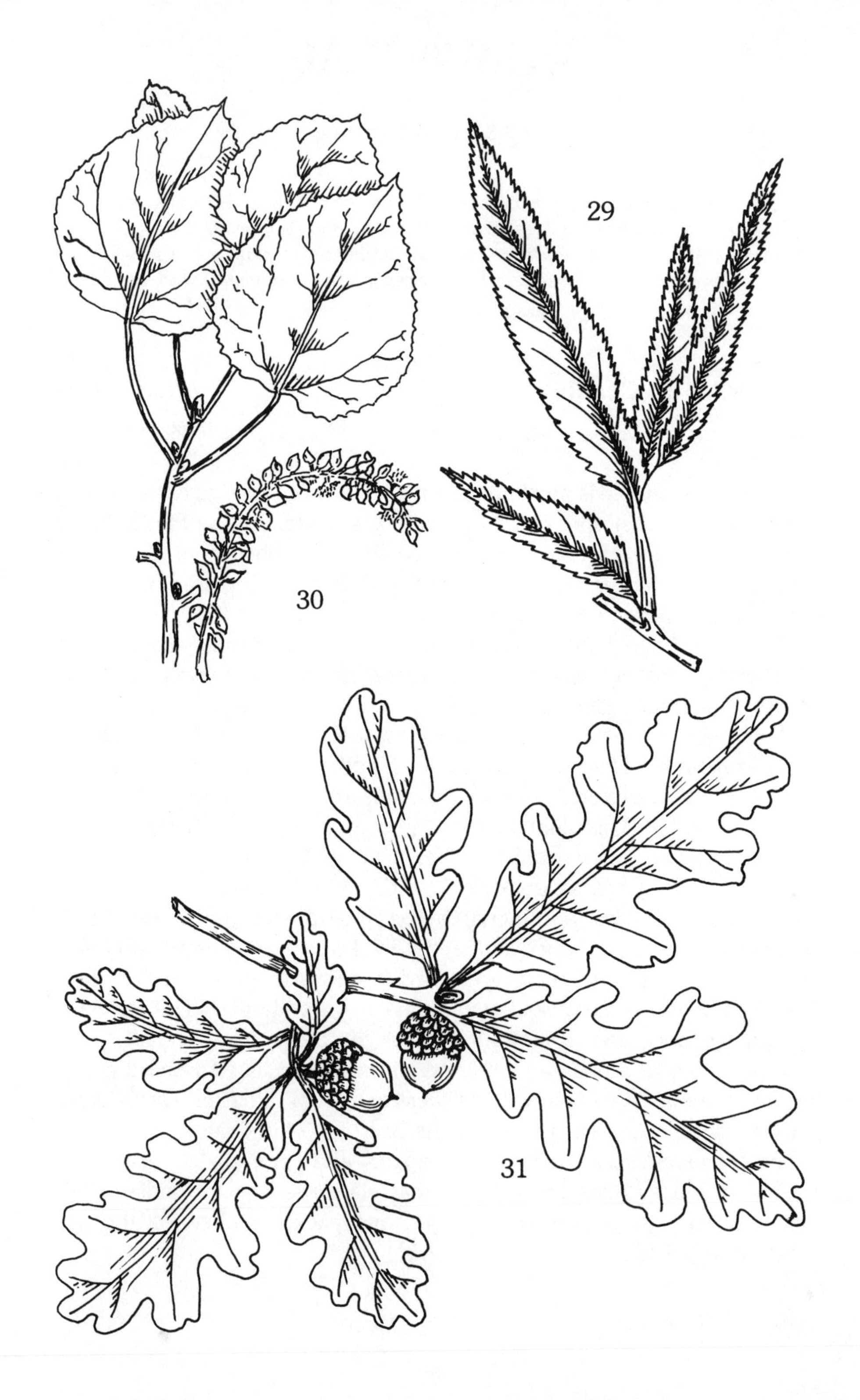
29
30
31

SALICACEAE

Willow Family

The willow family introduces the last large group of seed plants, the dicotyledons. In this group are all the plants with seed embryos developing two seed leaves called cotyledons.

Members of the willow family are trees or shrubs with simple, alternate, stipulate leaves. They are nearly always dioecious, with flowers in catkins.

29. **Narrow-Leaf Cottonwood** *Populus angustifolia*

The cottonwoods, the largest trees of the desert, are sometimes the only shade tree in desert oases. A grove of them is a welcome sight on a hot day in the desert.

The bark is smooth and cream colored above the dark furrows and ridges of the base. Some think the orange-yellow color of the leaves in autumn is more beautiful than that of aspen leaves.

30. **Quaking Aspen** *Populus tremuloides*

The reason for the trembling or quaking of the aspen is that the leaf stem is flattened at right angles to the leaf blade. This allows the leaf blade to turn at the very lightest breeze, so it seems as if the whole tree flutters most of the time. The slender, white-barked trees develop beautiful groves, and the small, rounded leaves turn a lovely golden-yellow in the autumn.

34
33
32

FAGACEAE

Beech Family

Plants of the beech family are usually monoecious, with staminate flowers in catkins. They are trees or shrubs with simple, alternate leaves. Besides the beeches, chestnuts and oaks belong to this family.

31. **Gambel Oak** *Quercus gambelii*

The Gambel Oak is one of eighteen species of oaks listed in Lehr's *Catalogue*. This oak grows in foothill areas, and hence at the edges of the deserts. It is quite variable in leaf shape and trunk height but is always small for an oak.

VISCACEAE

Mistletoe Family

The mistletoes are mostly half-parasites on trees or shrubs. They have no roots but are attached by haustoria to the host plant. They have chlorophyll, so they do make some of their own food. Almost all mistletoes are tropical plants.

32. **Mistletoe** *Arceuthobium vaginatum*

In smooth greenish or yellowish brown clumps, this parasite saps the strength of the host plant until it kills it. The genus name means "living on junipers," but this species mainly parasitizes firs. Each species usually has its own evergreen host. The host for *A. vaginatum* is Ponderosa Pine; the one for *A. americanum* is Lodgepole Pine; the one for *A. douglasii* is Douglas Fir. *A. abietinum* parasitizes White Fir.

33. **Desert Mistletoe** *Phoradendron californicum*

Desert Mistletoe hangs in great festoons in the tops of leguminous trees, looking at a distance like a brownish swarm of bees. Separated sexes are in the stem joints. The male flowers are astonishingly fragrant, smelling like apple blossoms. The fruits are pink berries and are eaten by quail, thrashers, robins, bluebirds and phainopeplas. They are a source of water for these birds during the dry winter. The Pima Indians used the berries as food. All over the desert this mistletoe can be found parasitizing Palo Verde, Ironwood, Mesquite, and Creosote Bush.

SANTALACEAE

Sandalwood Family

The sandalwoods are herbs, shrubs, or trees that are usually parasites on the roots of other plants. The use of fragrant sandalwood in the making of inlaid boxes, fans, and other articles dates as early as the fifth century B.C. The fragrance is still used in India and China for Buddhist funerals and other religious rites.

34. **Bastard Toadflax** *Comandra pallida*

The common name Bastard Toadflax means that the plant is a sort of imitation of the toadflax *Linaria canadensis.* It is the only member of the sandalwood family found in our range and is parasitic on other plants, just as the mistletoes are.

POLYGONACEAE

Buckwheat Family

The flowers of this family are in spikes or heads and are always small. The family contains some flowers with parts in threes or sixes. This is not characteristic of dicotyledons, which usually have flower parts in fours or fives.

35. **Bunched-leaf Buckwheat** *Eriogonum fasciculatum* var. *polifolium*

This is a shrubby buckwheat with many small, bunched leaves and without stalks. The flowers are white or pink. It grows in canyons and on dry slopes on the coast of Southern California as well as in Arizona. It is a good source of nectar for bees.

36. **MacDougal Buckwheat** *Eriogonum microthecum macdougalii*

The MacDougal Buckwheat is a shrubby plant. The underside of its leaves is covered by white wooliness (tomentum). It is a borderline plant between desert and evergreen-covered mountains.

Another *Eriogonum* species, *E. umbellatum*, closely resembles the MacDougal Buckwheat but has yellow flowers. It is widely distributed throughout the Rockies.

37. **Desert Trumpet** *Eriogonum inflatum*

The "trumpet" of this species is easily recognized in the field. The inflated stem is hollow. The cavities are used by a wasp (*Onyerus*) to store food for its larvae, which hatch from eggs laid on sand grains the wasp drops through the holes bored in the upper part of the inflation. After laying eggs the wasp drops in more sand grains for cover.

35
36

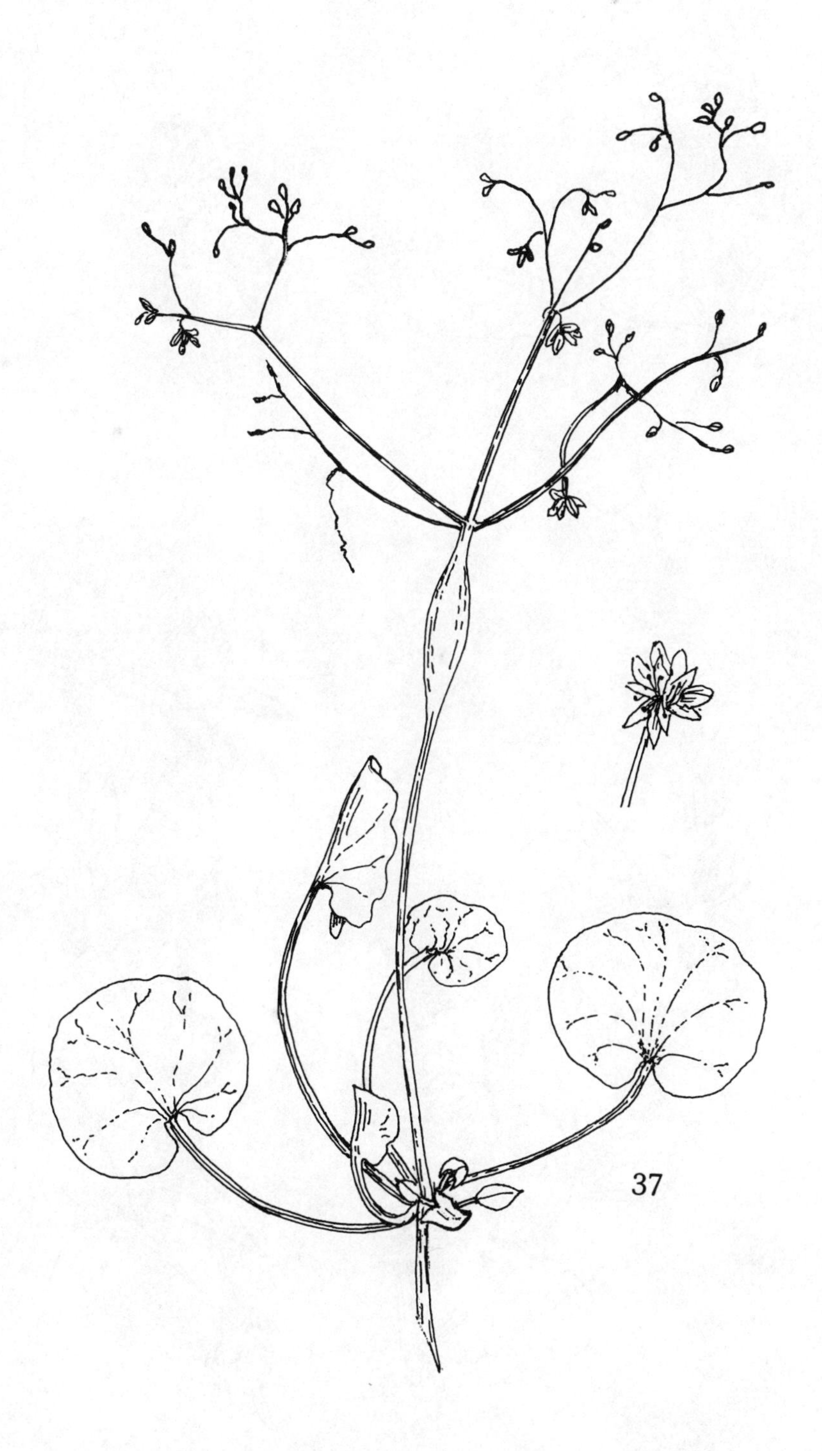

37

39
38
40

CHENOPODIACEAE

Pigweed Family

This large family of plants has only one sex to a flower—either stamens or pistils—and the flowers are inconspicuous. Many species are weeds, bearing pollen that causes hayfever. These weeds grow in alkaline soil and generally taste salty or bitter. One of the pigweeds, commonly called Lamb's Quarter, makes excellent spring greens and is usually eaten together with with Poke, Wild Lettuce, and Curly Dock.

38. **Wingscale** *Atriplex canescens*

This pigweed is a shrubby plant. Its leaves are covered with small silvery scales, which give the leaves a grayish appearance. The "wing" part of the common name refers to the four wings of the fruit, and the "scale" part refers to the leafy covering of the fruit. Wingscale is also called Four-Winged Salt Bush and is a nutritious food plant for browsing animals, such as the sheep of Arizona's caliche deserts. The desert Indians ground the seeds into meal. The Zuñi Indians mixed ground roots and flowers with saliva and used the product to heal ant bites.

39. **Desert Holly** *Atriplex hymenelytra*

Desert Holly makes a gorgeous showing not only in spring when it is in flower but also later when the leaves turn pink. In late spring the female plants are covered with large, round, green bracts. The leaves become silvery and the plant is gathered and sold for Christmas decorations, as are mistletoe and other types of holly.

40. **Strawberry Blite** *Chenopodium capitatum*

Strawberry Blite is also known as Swanpaint. The plant is too pretty to be called just a weed, but it is so considered. All parts of the plant are interesting. The leaves are smooth and bright, shaped like an elongated and serrate triangle. The base of the leaf is hastate, which means shaped like an arrowhead, with the lobes pointing outward at a wide angle. Strawberry Blite is not as much of a desert plant as its close relatives Wingscale and Desert Holly. It grows best in richer and more moist soils. The fruits form dark red, berry-like clusters on the stems. The fruits are sometimes eaten, either raw or cooked, and the whole plant can be cooked like spinach.

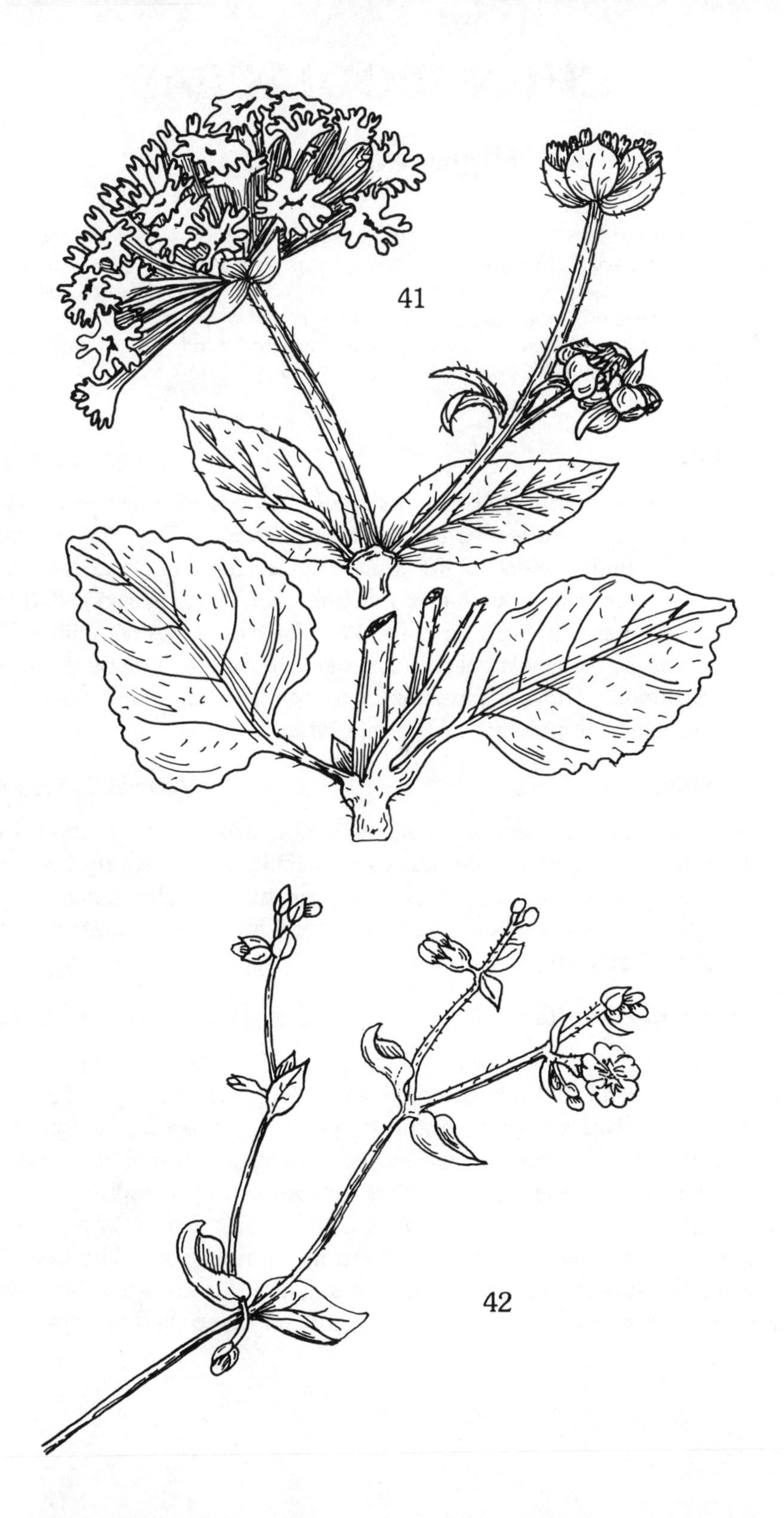
41
42

NYCTAGINACEAE

Four-o'clock Family

The flowers of the four-o'clock family have no petals, but the sepals are so brightly colored that they are often mistaken for petals by the casual observer. The sepals are joined to form a four- or five-lobed perianth. Stamens number from one to seven. A single flower or several flowers may be associated with bracts, which in many species are joined to form a cup-like involucre. The leaves are paired and the fruit is one seeded.

41. **Sweet Sand Verbena** *Abronia fragrans*

Sand Verbenas are common plants of the desert, growing all over patches of sandy soil and intermingling with other spring flowers to make the desert bloom. Some of the trailing branches measure two feet, and the fragrant flowers spread their pink to purple clusters thickly along them. Some species bloom both spring and fall.

Sweet Sand Verbena has white to lavender flowers. Its stems are covered with sticky hairs.

42. **Bigelow Four-o'clock** *Mirabilis bigelovii*

Bigelow Four-o'clock is a sprawling plant with sticky hairs on the stems and broad leaves. The flowers range from white to lavender. The fruit is egg-shaped. Besides *M. bigelovii*, there are seven other species of four-o'clock listed in Lehr's *Catalogue*. The Wishbone Bush Four-o'clock differs very little from Bigelow's except that its leaves are more pointed. The remaining six four-o'clocks have even less prominent characteristics. Only a skilled taxonomist can distinguish one from another.

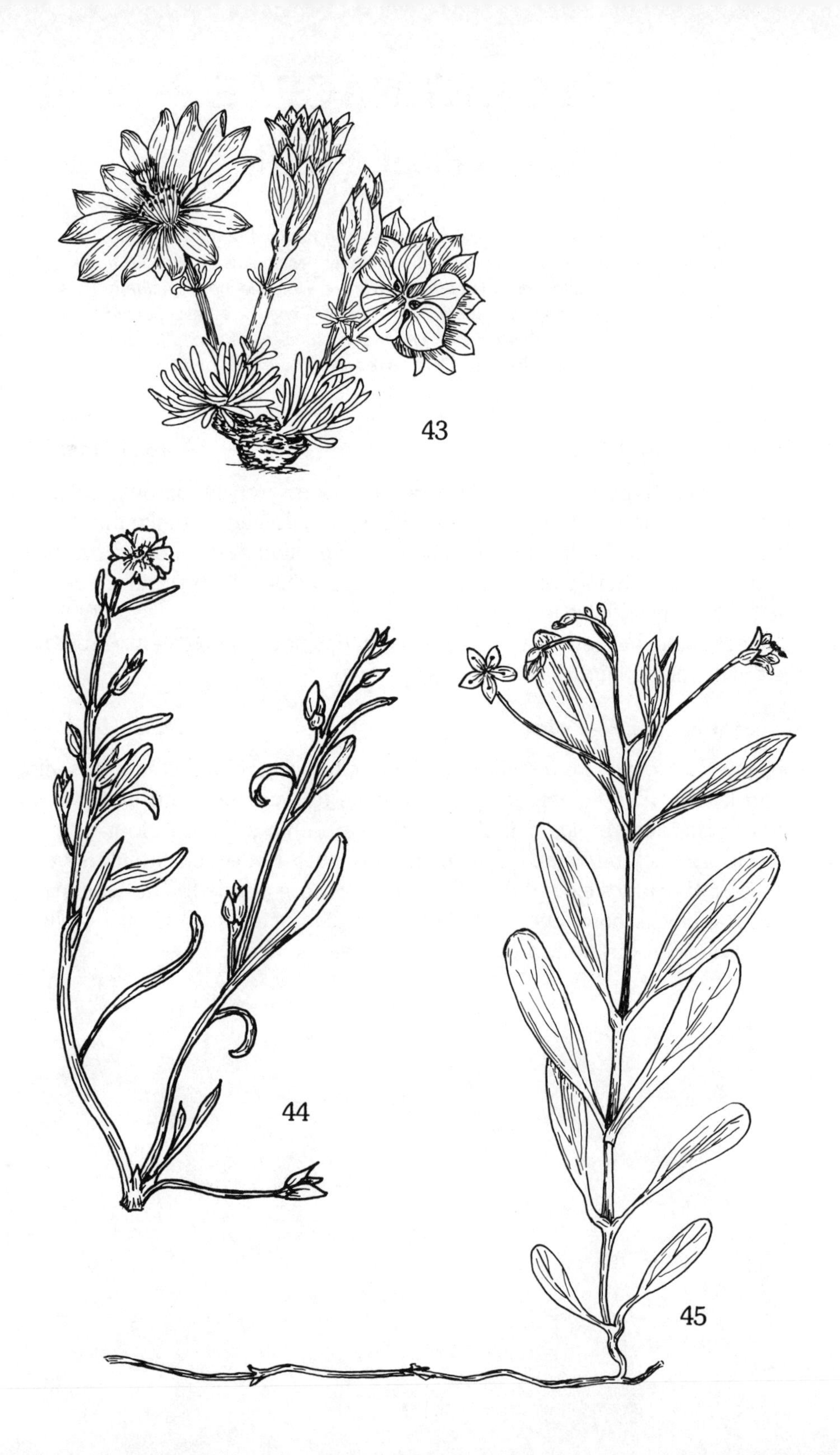
43
44
45

PORTULACACEAE

Purslane Family

The chief characteristics of the portulacas are that they have slender, juicy leaves, five or six sepals, generally five-petaled flowers, and from one to many stamens. The highly colored flowers are usually small. They open only in bright light or sunshine.

43. **Bitter Root** *Lewisia rediviva*

The genus name *Lewisia* refers to Captain Meriwether Lewis, a leader of the Lewis and Clark expedition to the Northwest. It is the state flower of Montana, a lovely and appropriate choice.

The roots really are bitter but were ground into meal, usually put into soup, and eaten by the Indians.

44. **Rock Purslane** *Calandrinia ciliata*

Rock Purslane also has the common name Red Maids on account of the brilliant color of the flowers. It is a fairly tall plant, usually over a foot high. Like so many other desert plants it grows on alkaline hills and in washes. It blooms from February to May and may be used for greens. The leaves and stems have a slightly salty taste.

45. **Indian Lettuce** *Montia chamissoi*

The species name *chamissoi* comes from the name of a German botanist and novelist, Adalbert Chamisso. This portulaca is not properly a desert plant but may be found in oases where there is sufficient moisture for its growth.

46. **Miner's Lettuce** *Montia perfoliata*

The growing, blooming, and fruiting period of Miner's Lettuce covers five months—February to June. As the common name indicates, this plant did provide salad for early settlers as well as Indians. Like Indian Lettuce it is not very abundant in the desert, preferring the more moist spots.

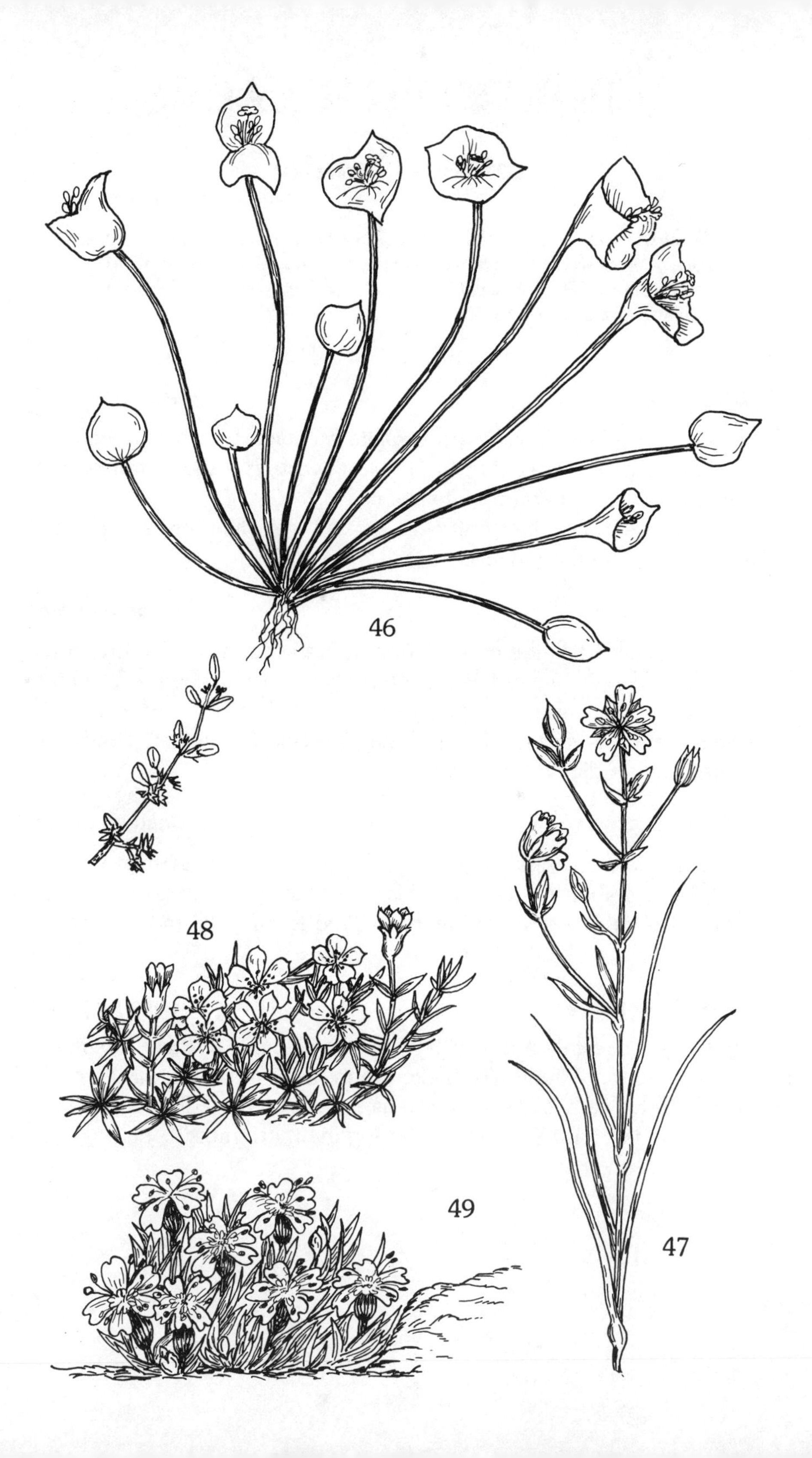
46
48
49
47

CARYOPHYLLACEAE

Pink Family

The pinks are either annuals or perennials with opposite entire leaves and perfect, regular flowers. The fruit is a capsule. The family is represented among the cultivated plants by pinks and carnations, found in many gardens.

47. **Fendler Sandwort** *Arenaria fendleri*

Sandworts are well adapted to desert living, since they have the types of plant parts that withstand drought conditions. So many plants in the southwest have the species name *fendleri* that it is appropriate to mention the German man to whom it refers. Augustus Fendler came to Houston, Texas, in 1839 to work as a market gardener. Many plants he collected in the Southwest he sent to Asa Gray, Harvard's famous botanist. Dr. Gray deposited the plants in the Gray Herbarium at Cambridge, naming several of the new species for Fendler.

48. **Cushion Sandwort** *Arenaria obtusiloba*

This sandwort is an inhabitant of the coldest regions along the Rocky Mountains. It has the interesting habit of forming cushions, which are covered with lovely white flowers. It is a close relative of the desert sandworts.

49. **Catchfly** *Silene acaulis*

This Catchfly is also a cushion plant, much like *A. obtusiloba*, and grows in similar places. The name Catchfly comes from the fly-catching, sticky surface of the stems. The species name *acaulis* means "stemless"—it is very short stemmed. The reader may choose between two suggested meanings for the genus name *Silene*. One author says it is for Silenus, a Greek god of forests. Another author says the word means "saliva," for the sticky stem fluid that enables it to catch flies.

50
51

RANUNCULACEAE

Crowfoot Family

Members of the crowfoot family are not well represented among desert flora although there are many that live in the moister areas of Arizona. Typical examples of the plants of this family are the common wild buttercups, the beautiful garden flower Delphinium, *and the tame and wild larkspurs.* Desert Wildflowers *by Edmund C. Jaeger lists only three species of this family. These are Parish Larkspur* (Delphinium parishii), *Desert Windflower* (Anemone tuberosa), *and Mouse Tail* (Myosurus cupulatus).

50. **Desert Windflower** *Anemone tuberosa*

Anemone means "wind," and the plant is called Windflower for the way the petals flutter in the breezes. The species name *tuberosa* refers to the tuberous root.

51. **Parish Larkspur** *Delphinium parishii*

The genus name *Delphinium* is derived from the Greek word for "dolphin." The nectar-bearing part of the flower is supposed to look like a dolphin. The sky-blue flowers bloom thoughout the spring flowering period. The Parish Larkspur, the only desert larkspur, is very widely distributed and very plentiful. In the book *Flowers of the Southwest Deserts* Natt N. Dodge writes that the Hopi Indians ground its flowers to make blue meal.

52

BERBERIDACEAE

Barberry Family

Members of this family are shrubs with racemes of yellow flowers. The yellow, fragrant flowers have six sepals and six petals which is unusual for a dicotyledonous plant. Flowers have ten stamens and one pistil. The fruit is a berry. A yellow dye can be made from the roots.

52. **Creeping Hollygrape** *Berberis repens*

Hollygrape is a short shrub. Pinnately compound leaves have five to seven holly-like leaflets. The flowers are bright yellow. The dark blue berries make delicious jelly.

53. **Currant-of-Texas** *Berberis trifoliata*

The Currant-of-Texas has three leaflets to a leaf, as the species name suggests. The leaflets are sharp-pointed but do not look like holly leaves the way Creeping Hollygrape leaves do.

54
53

PAPAVERACEAE

Poppy Family

Members of this family have sepals that are usually deciduous when the bud opens. The petals are so tightly packed within the bud that they emerge crinkly. The stamens are many but there is only one pistil in each flower. Desert Poppies, Prickly Poppies, California Poppies, and Cream Cups belong to this family.

54. **Prickly Poppy** *Argemone platyceras*

Prickly Poppy is also called Thistle Poppy. Its leaves and stems are covered with coarse prickles. The white flowers are large, the petals are thin and wrinkled. The bitter yellow sap of this plant congeals at the end of a cut stem, which makes water absorption impossible. But if one wishes to use the flowers in a bouquet the seal can be dissolved in boiling water or the stem can be held for an instant over a flame. The flowers will then remain fresh when put in water. The sap of the Prickly Poppy has been used to treat skin diseases.

55. **Desert Gold Poppy** *Eschscholtzia glyptosperma*

The Desert Gold Poppy is a close relative of the California Poppy, the state flower of California. They share popularity with each other and many people make pilgrimages every spring after heavy winter rains have occurred to see the extensive desert areas covered by them.

There are three species of *Eschscholtzia* listed in Lehr's *Catalogue.* Besides Desert Gold Poppy there are Little Gold Poppy and Mexican Gold Poppy. All three are desert plants. The Mexican Gold Poppy is not figured in this work.

56. **Little Gold Poppy** *Eschscholtzia minutiflora*

The Little Gold Poppy is most common in the southern part of the Great Basin. As the name suggests, the flower is smaller than the Desert Gold Poppy.

57. **Cream Cups** *Platystemon californicus*

These members of the poppy family have cream-colored flowers instead of yellow or white. The plants are about a foot tall, with slender leaves, and are hairy throughout.

55

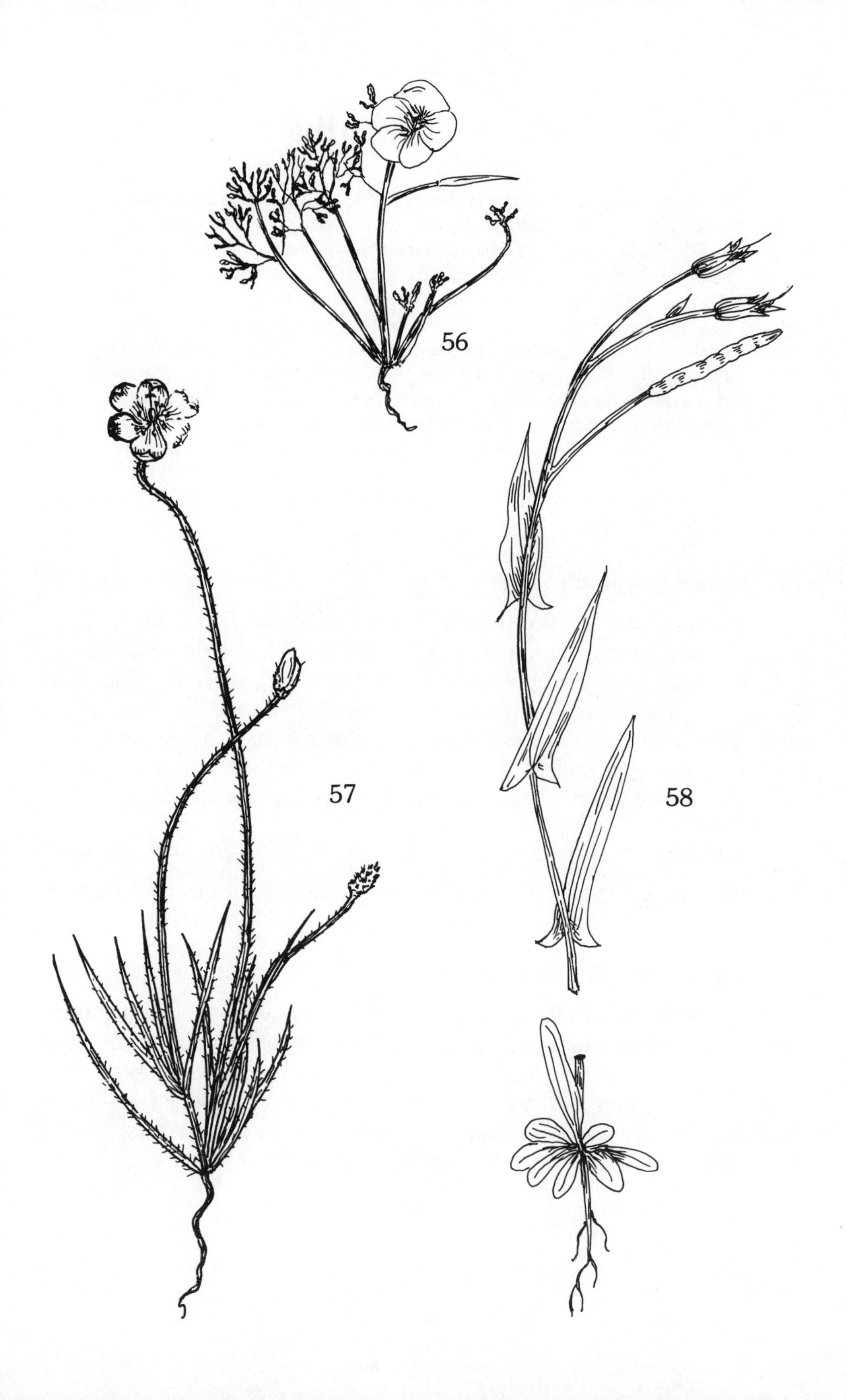
56
57
58

CRUCIFERAE

Mustard Family

There are many wild mustards and many flower-garden mustards too. Among them are Wallflower, Alyssum, and Candytuft. The common weeds Pepper Grass and Shepherd's Purse also belong to the family. Both the Latin and English names are appropriate for the members of this family. Cruciferae means "cross-bearer," and the four petals of the flowers spread horizontally to form a cross. Most of the plants in this family have a very distinct taste. Besides these characteristic features, the mustards have other peculiarities. The single ovary develops into a pod that retains a thin partition of its halves after they have dropped off and have dispersed the seeds. Also, two of the six stamens are shorter than the others. The edible mustards are well represented in vegetable gardens by radishes, horse radish, cabbage, turnips, and mustard. Watercress, another mustard, grows in clear, spring-fed streams.

58. **Drummond Rock Cress** *Arabis drummondii*

All of the mustards in the genus *Arabis* can be called Rock Cress. They differ very little from one another. Most are smooth stemmed but there are hairy ones also. Pods must be examined for accurate identification. Most of the Rock Cresses have auriculate leaves that clasp the stem at the base. Drummond Rock Cress shows this characteristic as well as having the broad, long, flat pods of the genus. The genus name, of course, refers to Arabia, where in one district this plant is found in a rocky desert.

59. **Mustard** *Athysanus pusillus*

This mustard is a short plant, only a few inches tall. It has ovate leaves near the base. The flowers are very small. The pod is spherical.

60. **Gordon Bladder Pod** *Lesquerella gordonii*

Lesquereux, for whom the genus *Lesquerella* was named, was an American botanist of the nineteenth century. He was educated abroad but was brought to America in mid-century by the famous Louis Agassiz. This bright yellow flower is responsible for the springtime color of extensive desert areas. The narrow basal leaves are tapering toward their attachment. On each side of the pod partition there are four to ten seeds.

59
60
61

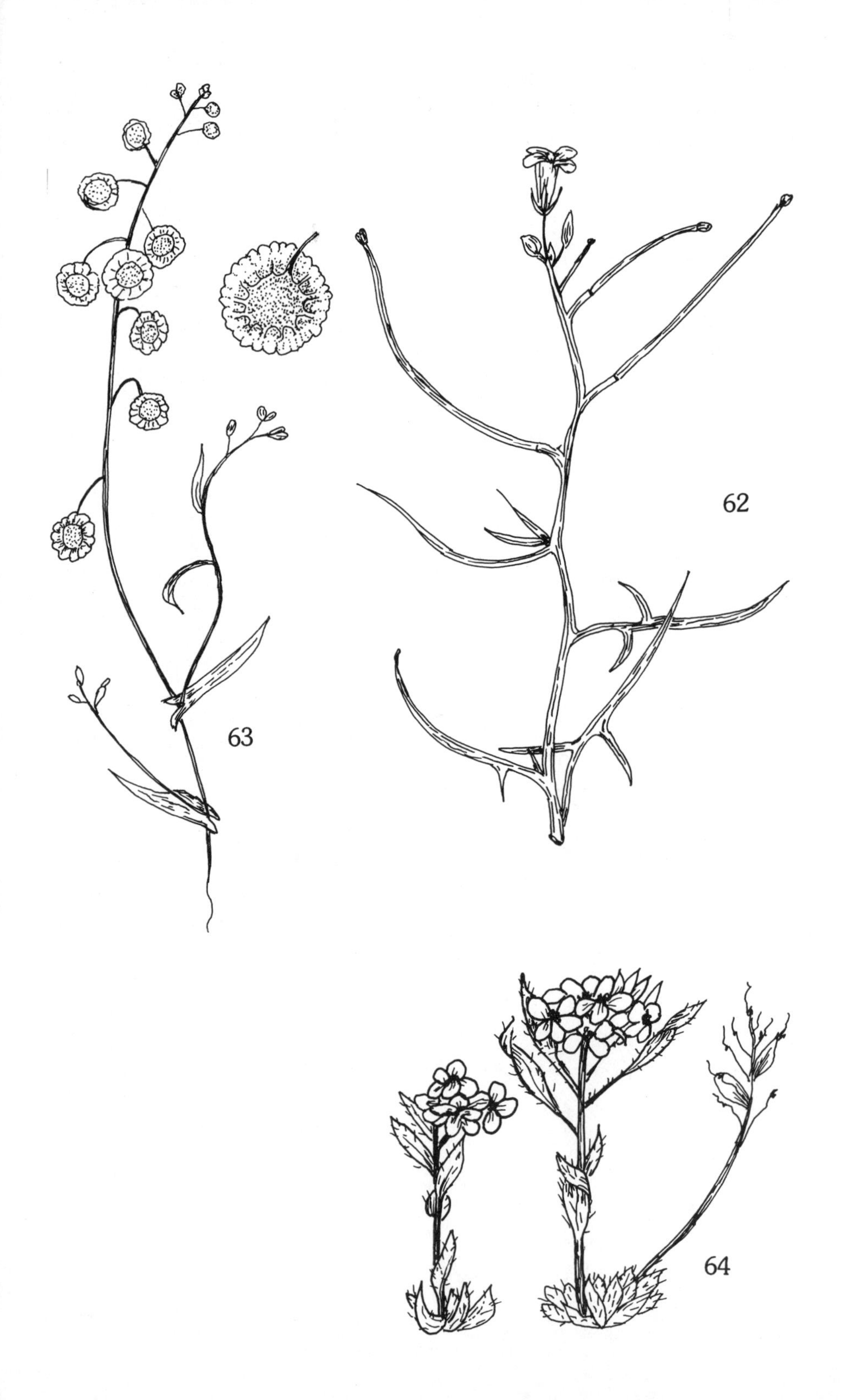
63
62
64

61. **Bladder Pod** *Lesquerella purpurea*

All the *Lesquerellas* are called Bladder Pod. This one could be called Purple Bladder Pod because it is the only one that has purple flowers, as the species name indicates.

62. **London Rocket** *Sisymbrium irio*

London Rocket is an invader from Europe. It has established itself throughout the irrigated areas of Arizona, among crops of alfalfa and grains, in orchards and pastures, and along roadsides. It also inhabits waste places. The plants flourish in winter and early spring but die when the hot, dry, summer weather comes. The little, yellow flowers are in clusters at the tips of stems. As the stems elongate more flowers appear and the long narrow pods mature from older flowers below them.

63. **Lace Pod** *Thysanocarpus laciniatus*

The genus name *Thysanocarpus* means fringe fruit—a lacy fringe, according to the species name. Another species having the same kind of pod is called Fringe Pod. The racemose flower stalk dangles its little lacy flowers on a curved stem. The flowers bloom during May and April in desert washes and canyons.

64. **Golden Draba** *Draba cuneifolia*

A clump of Golden Draba consists of several stems arising from a basal rosette of spatulate leaves. Stems and leaves are thickly covered with hairs. The flowers are yellow.

65. **Desert Plume** *Stanleya pinnata*

Desert Plume gets its genus name from Edward Stanley, Earl of Derby, an ornithologist rather than a botanist, who was president of the Linnean Society in the eighteenth century. *Pinnata* means "feathered," the leaf of Desert Plume being pinnate. It is said that the Indians used the plant for greens, discarding the first water of boiling because it made them sick. Their sickness may have been due to the presence of selenium that needed to be boiled out of the leaves, which absorb this poisonous element from the soil. The plant is considered an indicator of selenium in the soil and is certainly poisonous to livestock.

65

CAPPARIDACEAE

Caper Family

The caper family is chiefly tropical. The flowers are either regular or irregular (bilaterally symmetrical). The petals and sepals are atop the ovary, hypogynous. There are four petals, four sepals, and four or more stamens—numbers also characteristic of these plant parts in the mustards. The fruit is a capsule.

Capers used in cooking are the pickled flower buds of Capparis spinosa, *a European caper.*

The Hopi Indians are reported to have used young plants as potherbs.

66. **Bee Plant** *Cleome serrulata*

This handsome plant can grow to be three feet tall. The numerous rosy purple flowers cluster at the tops of stems. The flowers provide good bee pasture since the nectar is very plentiful. The plant is also called Skunk-weed.

67. **Stink Weed** *Atamisquea emarginata*

The Stink Weed owes its common name to its bad-smelling leaves. As with Bee Plant, it is also called Skunkweed. *Atamisquea* is a shrubby plant growing to be four feet high on the average. It is one of the few plants that enlivens the desert by blooming throughout the year.

66
67

SAXIFRAGACEAE

Saxifrage Family

Currants and gooseberries are sometimes put into a family of their own, the Grossulariaceae, but they are so closely related to saxifrages that they are included in the Saxifragaceae in some books. They belong to the genus Ribes *and are shrubs, usually spiny. The yellow flowers form racemes in the axils of leaves. The fruits are good to eat. Some of the wild species are even more tasty than tame varieties. Animals like them too. Indians mixed them with pemmican, which is basically buffalo meat. The blister rust fungus on pines has to live on some species of gooseberries during part of its life cycle, so the spread of this rust is controlled by destroying the gooseberries in the pine area. Besides the plants that live in the desert there are several species that live in other areas of Arizona. Altogether there are eleven species of* Ribes *listed in* Lehr's Catalogue. *The Sticky Currant* (Ribes viscossissimum) *lives high in the mountains. The Colorado Currant* (Ribes coloradense) *is found in the subalpine forests.*

68. **Golden Currant** *Ribes aureum*

The Golden Currant has no spines. Its smooth foliage turns red in autumn and brightens the foothill canyons in which it grows. The edible berries are black or red. It is also called Clove Bush on account of its spicy odor.

69. **Squaw Currant** *Ribes cereum*

Unlike Golden Currant, Squaw Currant has prickly stems. It grows on sunny montane slopes and dry foothills. The berries are rather tasteless and so not much used as food.

70. **White-stemmed Gooseberry** *Ribes inerme*

Like Squaw Currant, this Gooseberry is prickly. It lives in more moist places than either currant. Its purplish tart berries make good jelly. *Inerme* is not a suitable species name because it means "unarmed" but the stems of this plant have both prickles and spines.

71. **Gooseberry** *Ribes montigenum*

As the species name suggests, this plant grows on rocky slopes at the edges of the high deserts.

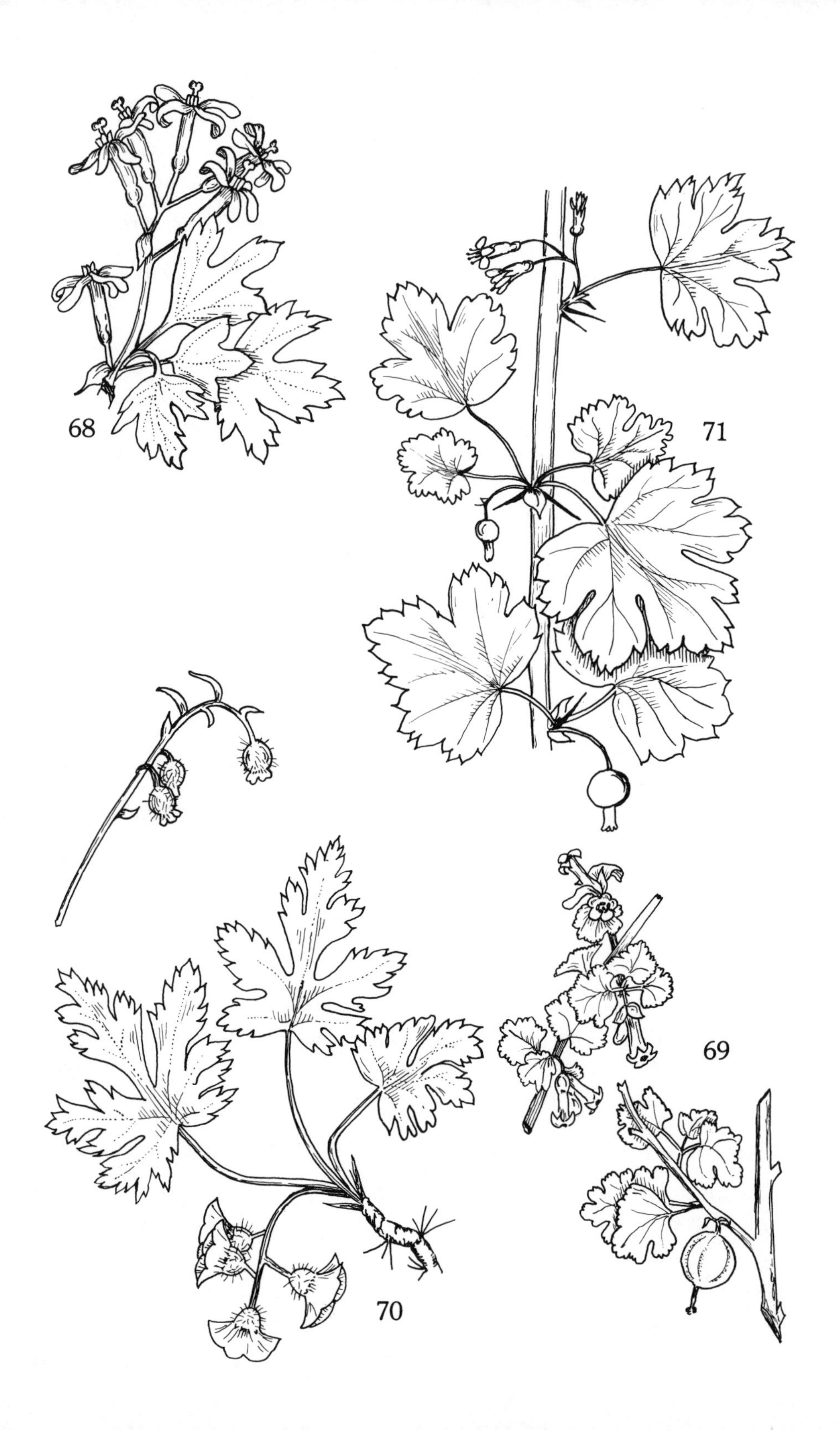
68
71
69
70

CRASSULACEAE

Orpine Family

The orpines contain many cultivated ornamentals such as Bryophyllum, Kalanchoe, Crassula, and Echeveria. *Both tame and wild ones are succulents. They are annual or perennial, with simple leaves and perfect flowers.*

72. **Rock Echeveria** *Dudleya saxosa*

Dudleya saxosa, commonly called the Live-Forever, is the cultivated Echeveria, easy to grow, and a very handsome addition to anybody's garden. It has the convenient property of being able to live in poor, sandy soil. Its succulent leaves can withstand drought.

CROSSOSOMATACEAE

Crossosoma Family

In the western deserts, the crossosoma family has but one genus, Crossosoma. *Members of the family are smooth, irregularly branching shrubs with alternate leaves and gray bark. The white flowers are at the tips of lateral branches. There are five petals, five sepals, fifteen to numerous stamens, one to six pistils. The fruit is a follicle. The plants grow in canyons and washes and on cliffs and hillsides.*

73. **Ragged Rock Flower** *Crossosoma bigelovii*

The one genus of the Crossosomataceae has two species that live in the western deserts. Both are species *Crossosoma bigelovii* but one is *Crossosoma bigelovii* var. *glaucum*. Both species are branched shrubs and differ from each other in that the variety has fewer spines and small leaves.

Crossosoma bigelovii, the Ragged Rock Flower, bears one of the most beautiful flowers of the western deserts. Arizona shows it at its very best in the canyons of the western part of the state. It blooms in March. It represents, along with the species with variety, a very unusual family with long geological history. *C. bigelovii* is widely dispersed; it appears on Catalina and other islands off the California coast. This broad distribution indicates that at one time the plant was widespread.

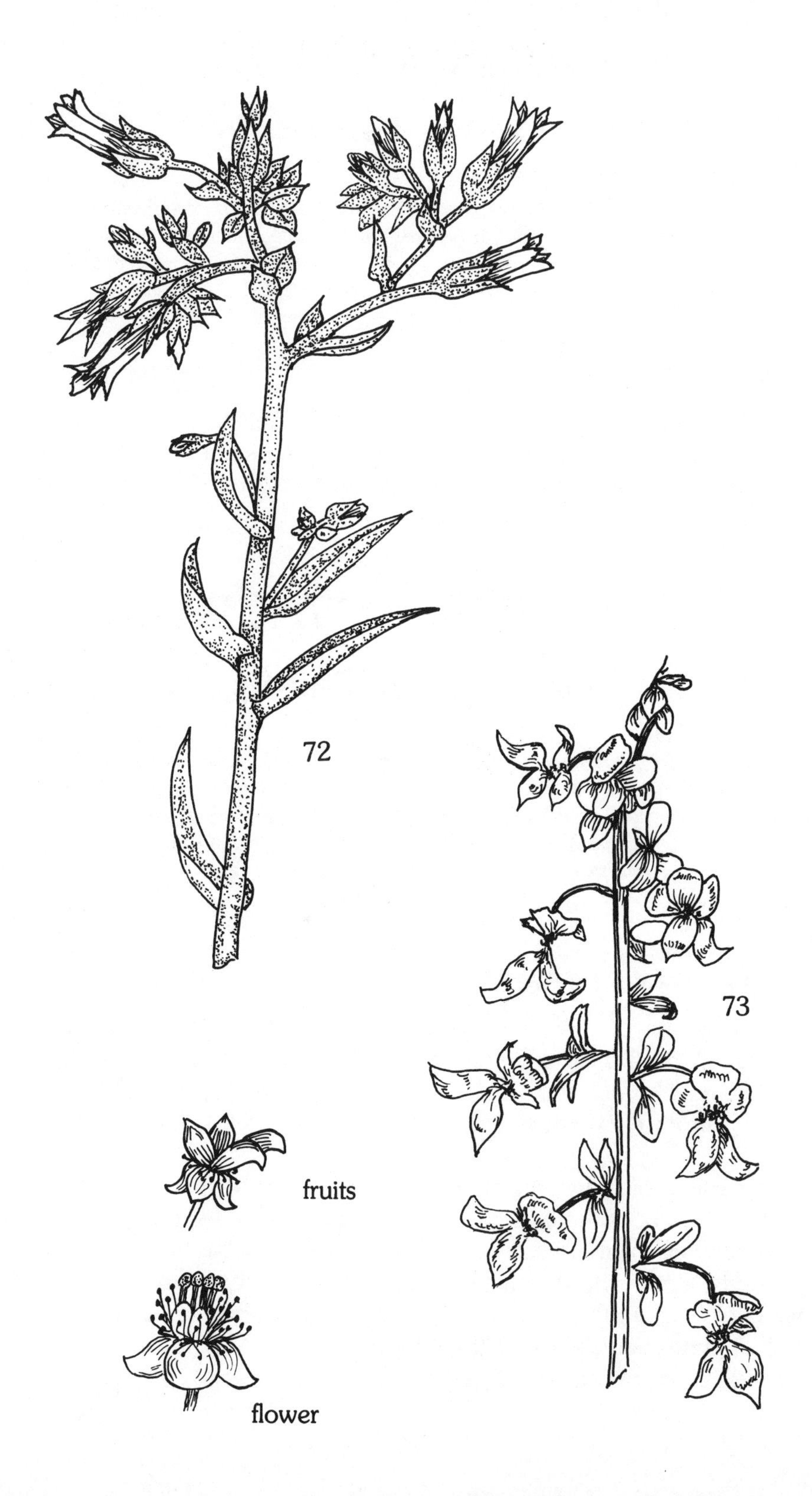
72
73
fruits
flower

ROSACEAE

Rose Family

The plants of the very large rose family include widely different species and genera. Comprising trees, shrubs, and herbs, the members can have simple or compound leaves. The branching is mostly alternate; the leaves are stipulate. The flowers are usually large and ornamental. Figures of four genera are shown in this work. Many edible fruits are produced by members of the rose family. Apples, plums, raspberries, and pears are examples. These are not only "people" food; browsing animals eat them along with foliage and twigs.

74. **Alder-Leaf Mahogany** *Cercocarpus montanus*

As the common name suggests, the leaves are shaped like alder leaves and show whitish undersides. Sometimes the trunk of the tree is twisted. The fruits have long, feathery tails that are as much as six centimeters long.

75. **Apache Plume** *Fallugia paradoxa*

Apache Plume is a bushy plant about a meter high. It has white bark and dissected leaves. The white flowers are from two to three centimeters across. They cover the plant in May and June. Each flower has several pistils with long, hairy styles. When the fruit develops the styles grow longer, making plumose tails upon the achenes. The tails are from two to four centimeters long. Apache Plume is so named because of the fancied resemblance of the reddish tail clusters to the war headdress of the Apache Indians. The genus name comes from Fallugius, a botanist churchman of the late seventeenth century.

Indians used the wood to make arrow shafts and brooms. An edible evergreen, it is a good winter range plant.

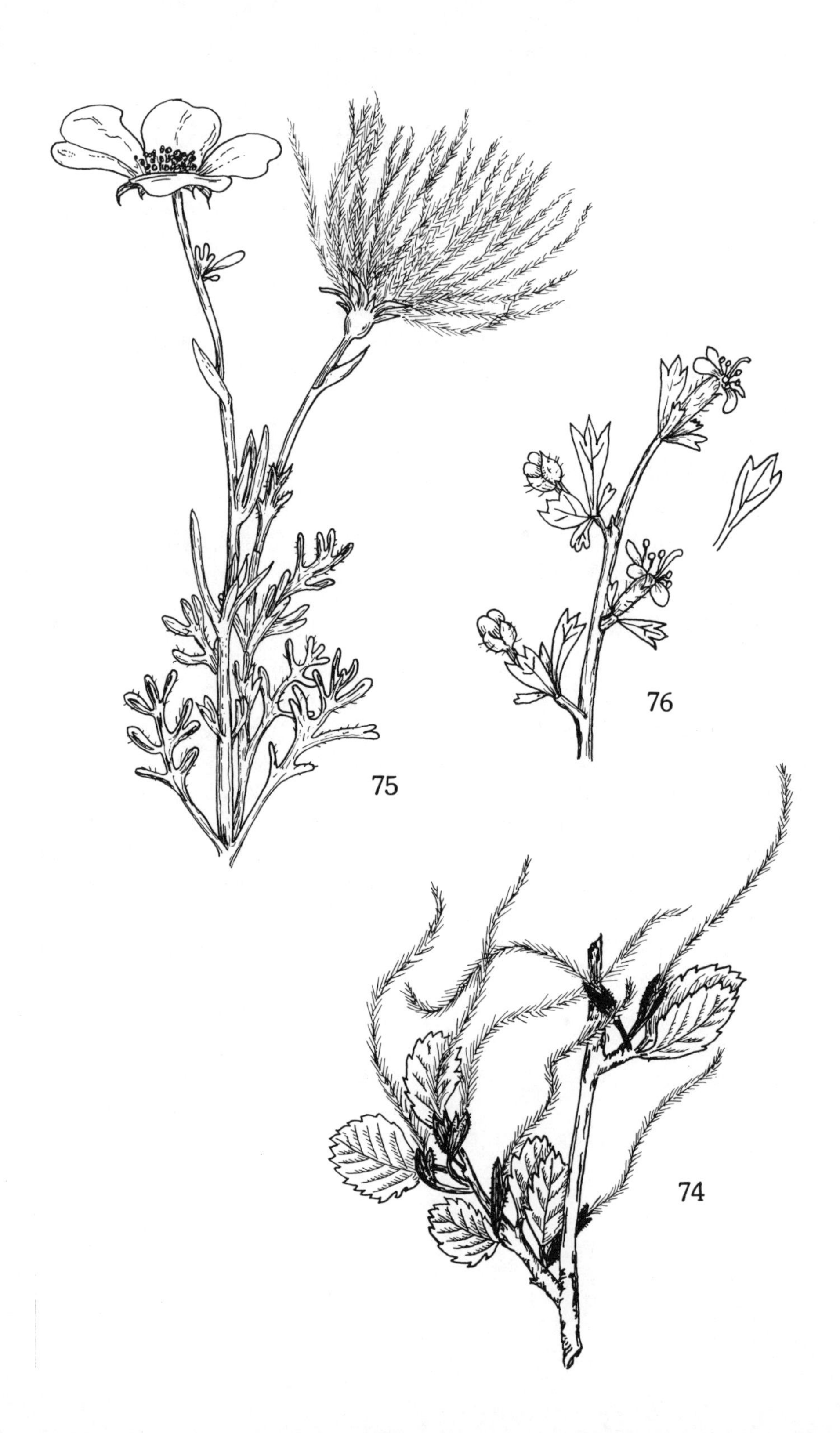
75
76
74

76. **Antelope Brush** *Purshia tridentata*

Antelope Brush can be considered a desert plant although it grows mostly in the Piñon-Juniper areas bordering the deserts. It is widely distributed and is foraged by cattle and deer throughout the year. The three-toothed leaves are very distinctive. The flowers look a great deal like gooseberry flowers but are a much paler yellow. The flower has only one pistil, which ripens into a large, brownish achene.

77. **Sulfur Cinquefoil** *Potentilla recta*

Flowers of the large genus *Potentilla* are easily recognized. In all species five bracts alternate with five sepals and most species have yellow petals. The presence of these bracts is enough to distinguish potentillas from the buttercups, with which they might otherwise be confused.

78. **Beauty Cinquefoil** *Potentilla pulcherrima*

Beauty Cinquefoil grows on the desert border and at higher altitude than most other cinquefoils do. Figure 77 shows a five-leaflet leaf but Beauty Cinquefoil may have as many as eleven leaflets. This species has been described as having palmate leaves because, in some cases, leaflets are so close together with midribs so short as to resemble palmate leaves. However, many of the leaves are definitely pinnate. The upper side of the leaf is dark green and the undersurface is white with wooly hairs. The leaves are toothed.

79. **Shrubby Cinquefoil** *Potentilla fruticosa*

Potentilla means "powerful" and refers to the medicinal value of the plant. Most species are not very medicinal though, being only a little astringent. The common name, Cinquefoil, means "five leaf" and was applied to a European species with five leaflets. The name is not appropriate for the whole genus as most of the cinquefoils have more than that many leaflets to a leaf. The small shrubs have blossoms like little yellow roses. Petal color increases in intensity depending on the plant's location, from palest the low altitude desert margin to most vivid in the alpine heights.

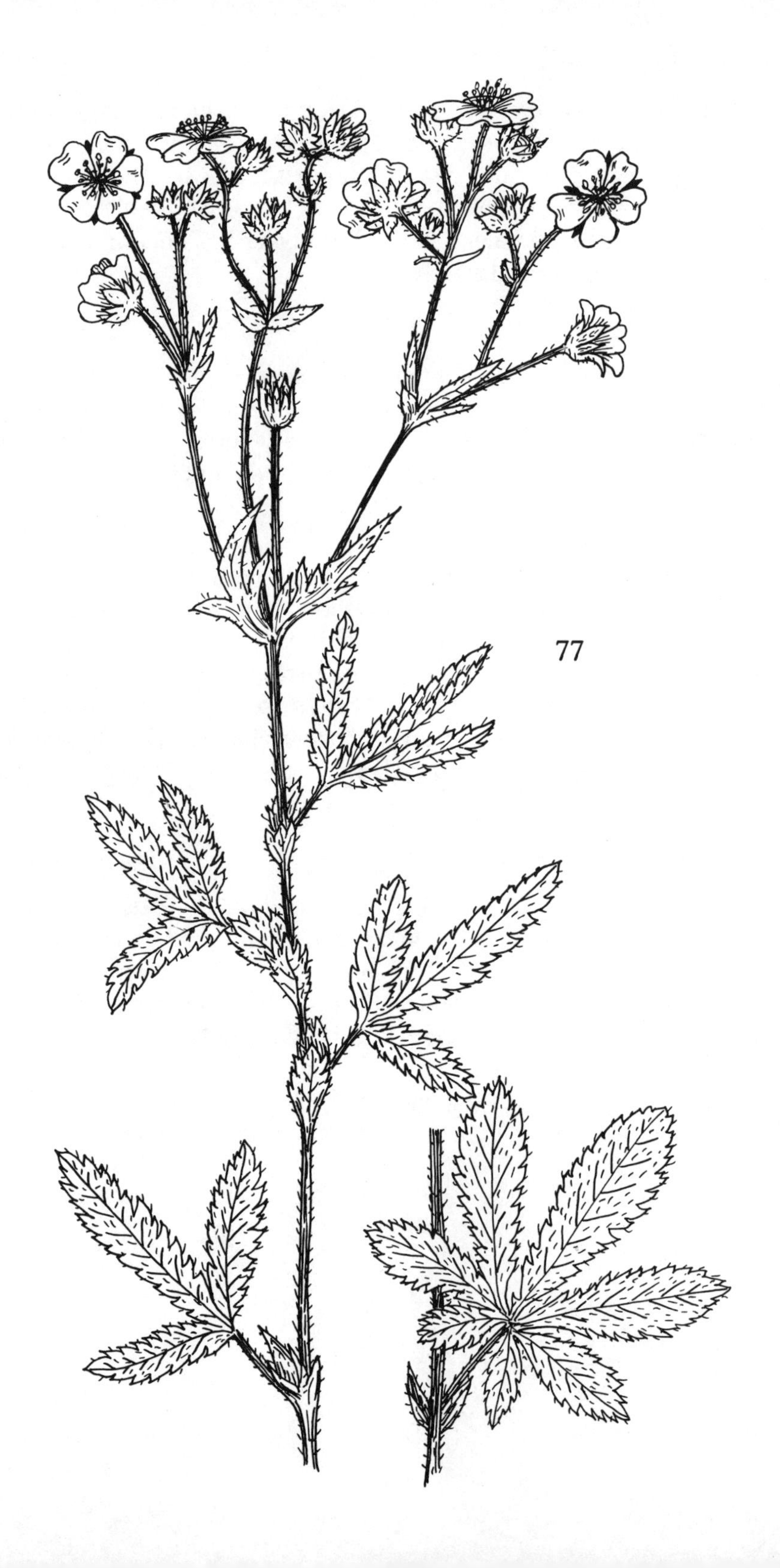

77

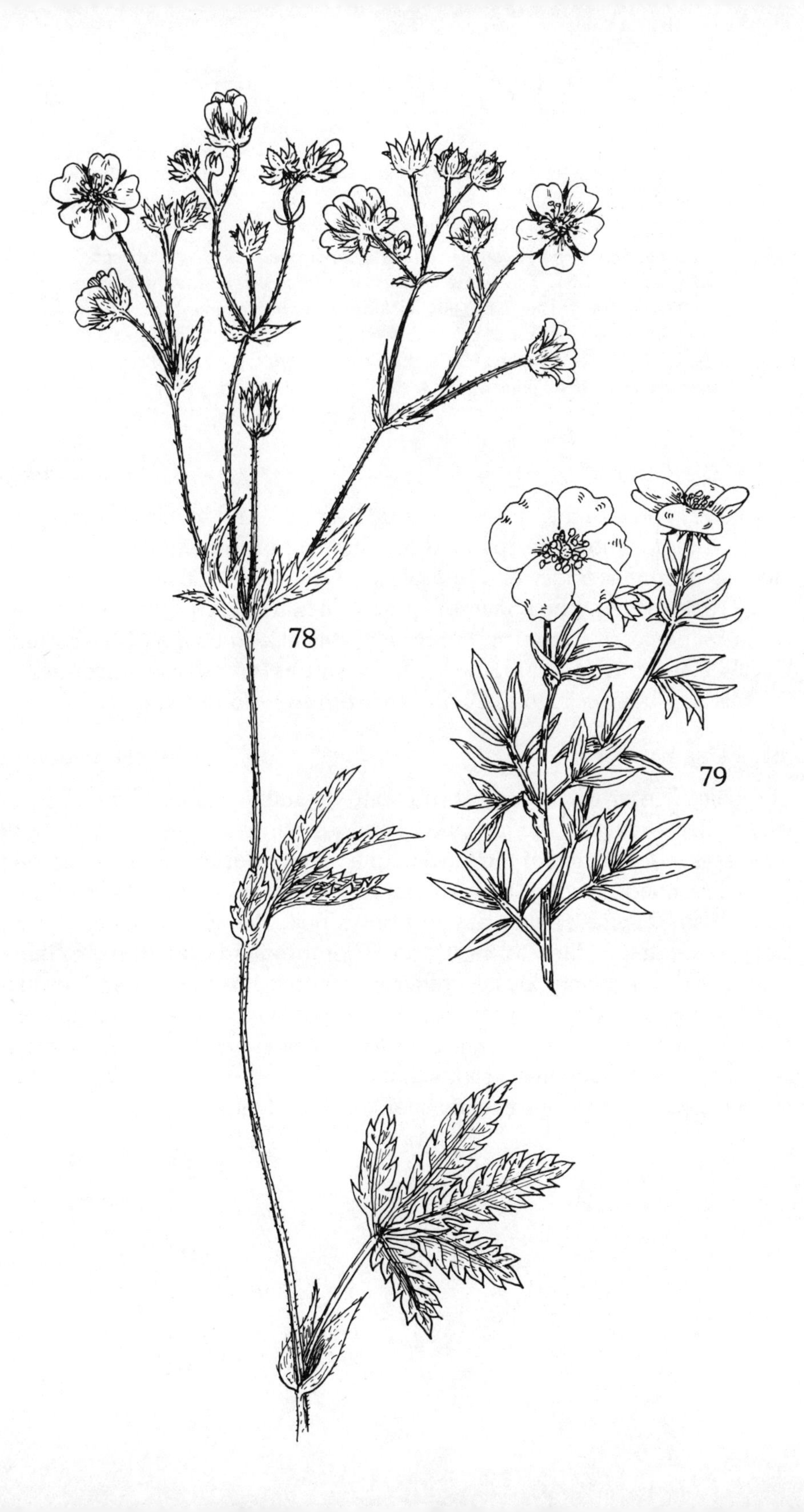
78
79

LEGUMINOSAE

Pea Family

The members of this family can be distinguished by their distinctive, irregular corollas. The name for this type is papilionaceous, meaning "butterfly-like." The five petals include an upper banner, two wings, and two lower petals united into a keel. There are ten stamens and one pistil. The pistil develops into a pod, called a legume, which is several seeded and splits along two lines, the length of the pod.

80. **Cat's-Claw** *Acacia greggii*

The genus name of this species means "thorny." The species is named for Josiah Gregg, whose life spanned the first half of the nineteenth century. He was a frontier trader and author and was called "doctor" by his contemporaries because he knew some medical and surgical facts. The plant's common name also refers to the thorns. It is also known as Tear-Blanket, Devil's Claw, and Wait-a-Moment. These shrubs form dense, impenetrable thickets and bear yellow, fuzzy flowers from April to October.

81. **Fairy Duster** *Calliandra eriophylla*

The Fairy Duster is a woody shrub with "beautiful stamens" and "wooly leaves," according to the genus and species names. The common name expresses the similarity of the flowers to a feather duster—a miniature one. Book descriptions list the flower color as varying from white through pink to crimson. Figure 81 was drawn from a beautiful scarlet-flowered plant along the entrance lane to the Boyce Thompson Arboretum near Globe, Arizona. Besides Fairy Duster, other common names are False Mesquite and Mesquitilla. The plant has small mesquite-like, twice pinnately compound leaves. The leaves are said to be eaten by deer and livestock. Jaeger's *Desert Wildflowers* states that "the leaves are very nutritious, and the prospector's donkeys eagerly seek out the plants."

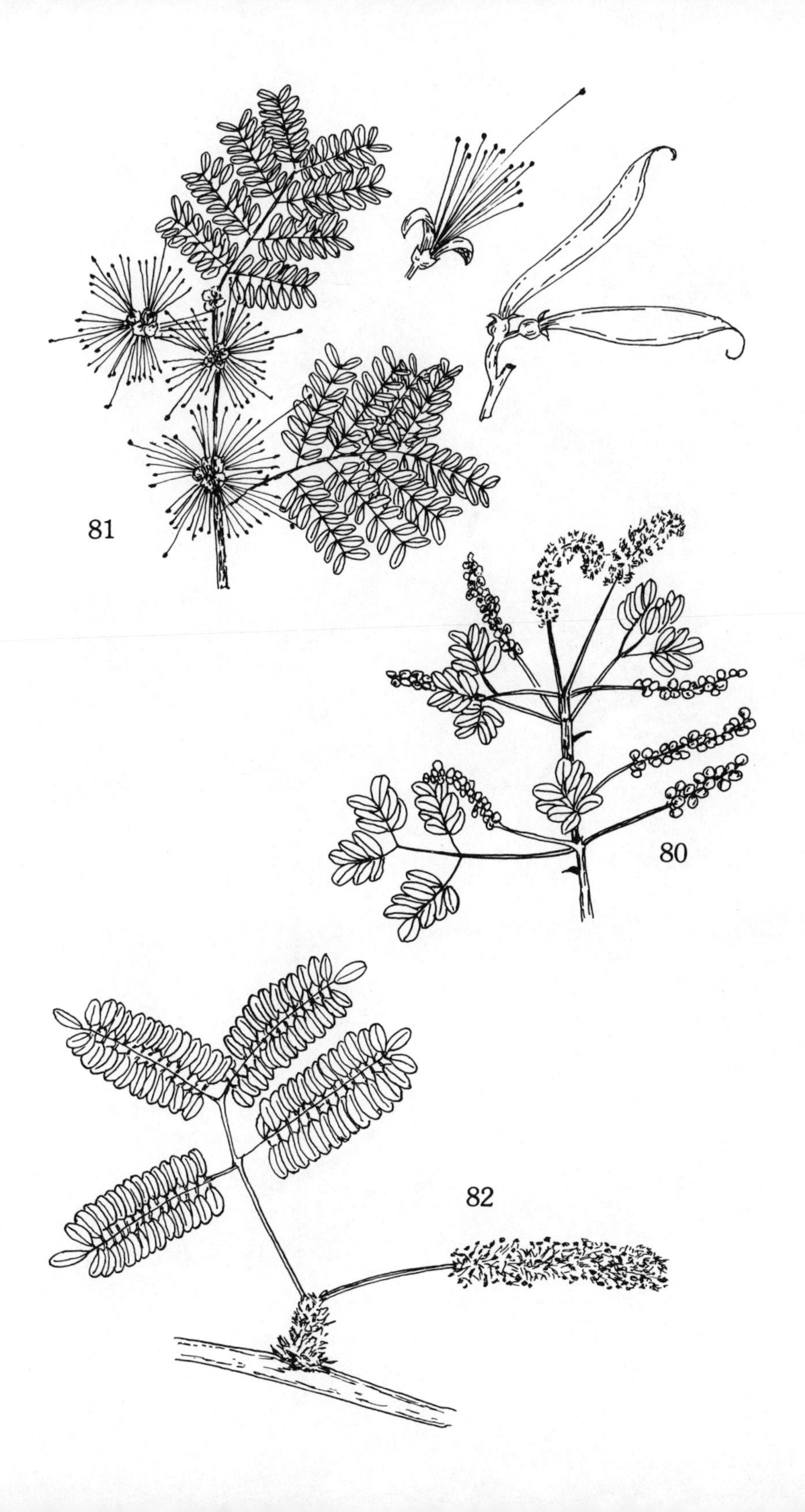
81
80
82

84
83

82. **Honey Mesquite** *Prosopis juliflora*

Very beautiful when in bloom in the spring, Honey Mesquite is also an unusually useful plant. It is host for mistletoe and ends by being killed by this parasite. The larva of the mesquite girdler, a little gray beetle, kills the trees by burrowing under the bark. A kind of weevil, lives inside the pods and eats the beans. Another beetle pulverizes the dry wood. Indians of the Cahuilla tribe formerly ground the pods, weevils and all, and baked the meal in sand heated by the sun. The cake so made contained a nutritious sugar. A drink was made out of the cooked bean juice. The Indians rubbed, pounded and pulled the bark to make diapers for the babies and skirts for the women. (No doubt it was the women who did this chore.)

Sand dunes are formed around the plants, covering all but their tips, which continue to grow—keeping ahead of burial by the blowing sand. In the hillocks so formed rodents make their tunnels and nests.

The nectar-bearing flowers attract a variety of insects, including honeybees.

Mesquite is the rival of Ironwood as a fuel source. It is the deep growing roots that are used, so one has to dig for the wood. Smoke from the burning wood has a fragrant odor, and the glowing coals of a dying fire last a long time. This wood has relatively recently been discovered by backyard barbecue gourmet cooks throughout the United States and, therefore, is of great commercial value. The roots, which are said to grow to a depth of sixty feet to reach moisture, are indicators of water sources.

Mesquite is also used as a cement to mend pottery. A black dye can be extracted from its tissues.

83. **Desert Cassia** *Cassia armata*

Desert Cassia is an early-blooming plant. Its greenish-yellow, sweet-smelling flowers appear in April and last through May. These are the only months of the year that Desert Cassia has leaves and fruits. The leaves are few and are pinnate like other leguminous leaves. The midribs are quite unusual, being almost as wide as the leaves.

85

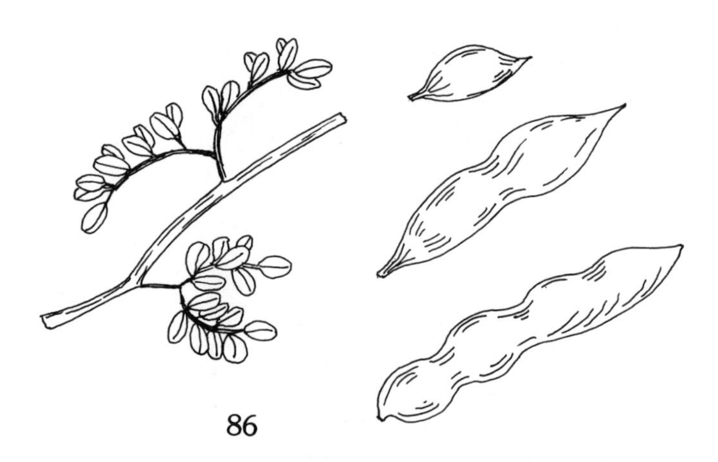
86

84. Coves Cassia *Cassia covesii*

Coves Cassia is not like Desert Cassia. It is covered thickly by white hairs, and its flowers are in the leaf axils instead of terminal. A distinguishing characteristic is the split seed pods, which remain on the plant all year. This species is much rarer than *Cassia armata*.

85. Blue Palo Verde *Cercidium floridum*

Palo verde means "green stick," but the species *floridum* has a bluish green stem. The genus name *Cercidium* is derived from the name of a weaver's instrument, which the pod resembles. The Palo Verde lives in the hottest, dryest portions of the desert. It is extremely drought resistant.

86. Foothill Palo Verde *Cercidium microphyllum*

The yellowish green bark of the Foothill Palo Verde distinguishes it from the blue-green-barked *Cercidium floridum*. The flowers furnish nectar for many kinds of insects. Both Foothill and Blue Palo Verde develop legume fruit that is not eaten by browsing animals until other food is gone.

The wood is not a good fuel because it burns too fast and the smoke odor is unpleasant.

87. Mexican Palo Verde *Parkinsonia aculeata*

The Mexican Palo Verde is considered a shrub, but it grows to eight or more meters tall and could also be called a small tree. It has pairs of spines at the leaf nodes and also at the tips of stems. The leaf stems are from six to sixteen centimeters long, with tiny alternate leaflets. The fruit is a legume sharply pointed at the tip. This shrub is native to the Arizona desert but is widely cultivated throughout the West.

88. Indigo Bush *Parosela schottii*

The choice of the genus name is interesting. *Parosela* is an anagram of *Psoralea* also a member of the pea family. *Psoralea* means "scurfy." The scurf consists of warty points and glandular dots all over the plants. *Parosela* plants have the scurf as red, blister-like glands on the seed pods. The plant is very ornamental when the deep indigo-blue flowers are in bloom.

87
88
89

90
92
91

89. **Silk Dalea** *Dalea mollis*

Dalea mollis is covered with silky hairs. The plant has a pleasant odor when crushed. The flowers are pinkish white. There are about 200 species of the genus *Dalea*; they are most abundant in the southwestern deserts of the United States as well as in Mexico.

90. **Ground Plum** *Astragalus crassicarpus* var. *cavus*

Astragalus is one of the largest genera of plants. Many species are found west of the Mississippi. Even trained botanists find it difficult to distinguish the species from each other. *Astragalus* is the name of one of the curved bones of the ankle. These bones were used as dice, so the plural *astragali* means dice. The fruit of the genus is supposed to look like the bone. The species name *crassicarpa* means "thick-walled fruit."

Milk Vetch and Locoweed are common names for all members of this genus. The Locoweeds of this genus are distinguished from the Locoweeds of the genus *Oxytropis* by the rounded keel of the flower instead of the sharply pointed keel of in the oxytropes.

The Locoweeds are poisonous to livestock. The poison is selenium, which is present in the "badland" soils in which these plants grow.

91. **Sweet Vetch** *Hedysarum boreale*

Hedysarum boreale, the Sweet Vetch, has beautiful racemes of rose or purple flowers. Its roots are edible.

92. **Desert Rock Pea** *Lotus rigidus*

The generic name *Lotus* comes from a Greek word *lo*, meaning "to cover." This has obscure reference to the fruit, which was said to make people who tasted it forget their home. The species name *rigidus* obviously means "stiff" or "woody."

93. **Silvery Lupine** *Lupinus argenteus*

Leaves of all lupines are palmate with five to nine leaflets. The leaves are almost always hairy. The flowers are usually blue and in Texas the lupines are called Blue Bonnets. The seeds and pods contain alkaloids poisonous to livestock, especially sheep.

94. **Shockley Lupine** *Lupinus shockleyi*

Flowers of the Shockley Lupine are purplish blue. The inflorescence is a raceme with only one flower in bloom at a time. The fruits have pustules on their surfaces, which make them look beaded. When dry the beads look like scales.

95. **Arizona Lupine** *Lupinus sparsiflorus* var. *arizonicus*

The species name *sparsiflorus* means "few flowered." The flowers are reddish blue with some yellow on the banner. The leaf is said to be shaped like the spokes of a wheel. The name Lupine comes from the Latin word for "wolf" the implication here is that the plant was considered to rob the soil of fertility. In fact, because of their ability to fix nitrogen, these plants improve the soil rather than impoverish it.

96. **Royal Desert Lupine** *Lupinus odoratus*

When newly opened the flowers of *Lupinus odoratus* are pink, but they turn to royal purple. As the species name suggests, the flowers are fragrant.

97. **Prairie Clover** *Petalostemum purpureum*

The inflorescence of Prairie Clover is a tight terminal spike of little purple flowers. The three to five leaflets are usually folded and have small, glandular dots on their lower surfaces. Figure 97 shows a plant with small leaves clustered in the axils of the larger leaves. The name *Petalostemum* refers to the peculiar fusion of petal with stamen.

98. **Desert Ironwood** *Olneya tesota*

Olneya tesota is known as Desert Ironwood as well as Locoweed. Tesota, from Spanish, means "stiff" or "firm." The implication is that this tree makes excellent firewood, though the smoke from it has an unpleasant odor. It contains the poisonous alkaloid that its closely related leguminous plants have. Seeds are peanut-flavored and are relished by the Indians, who also used the wood to make arrow points and tool handles. Mistletoe infests the trees, stimulating growth by the tree of irregular, ugly swellings. Locations where this Ironwood is native are selected by lemon, orange, and grapefruit growers as sites for their crops.

95
94

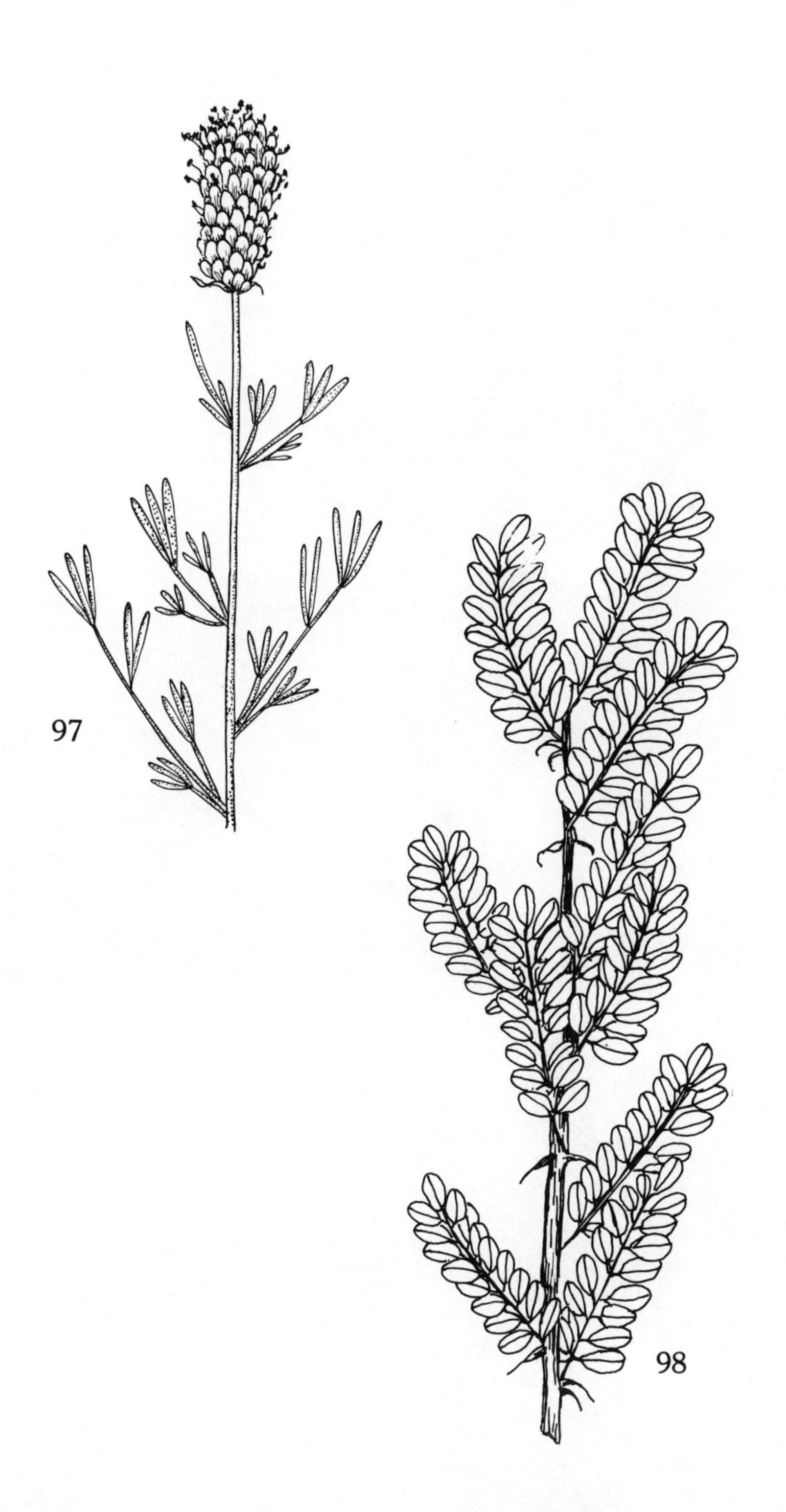
97
98

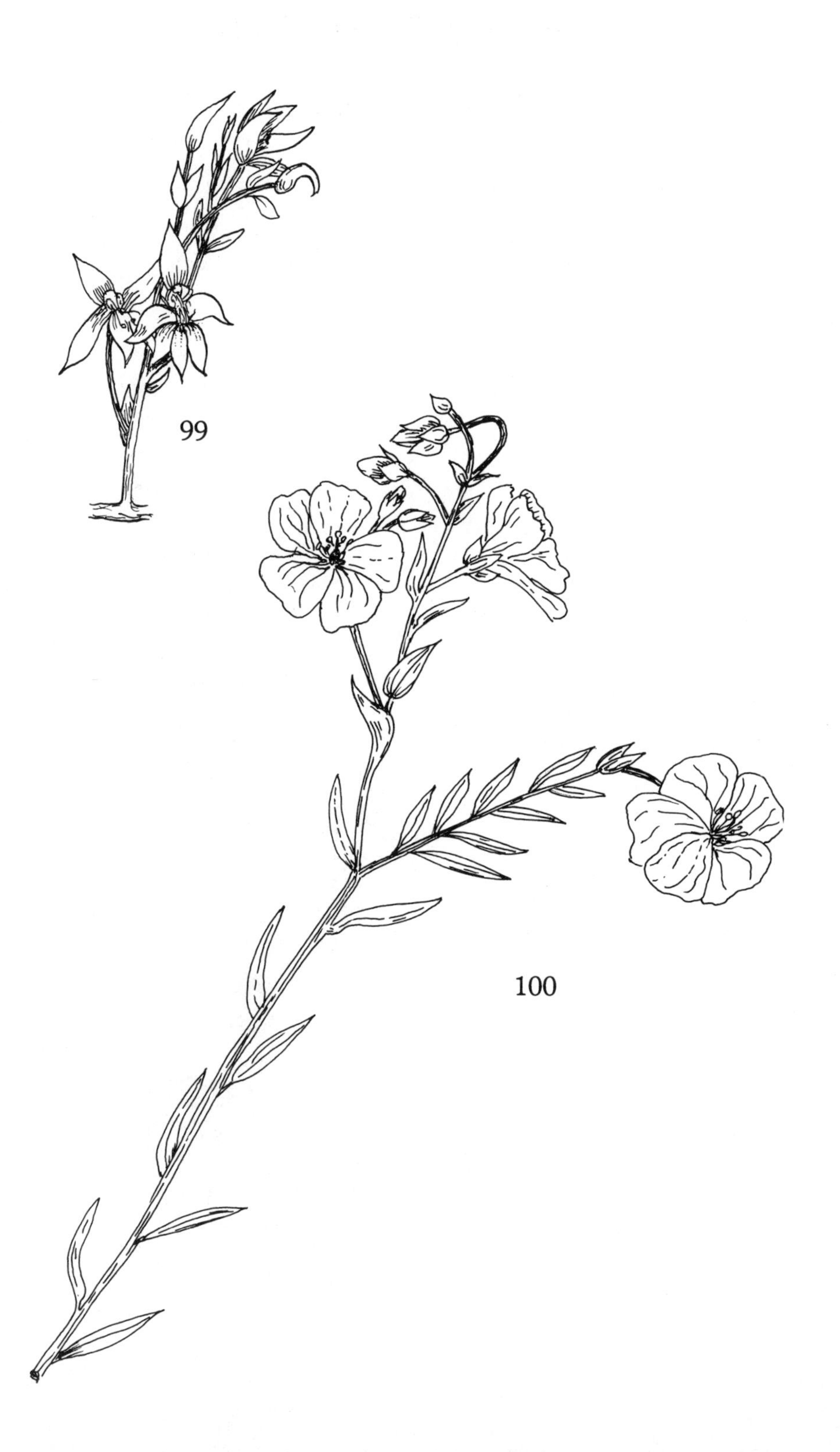
99
100

KRAMERIACEAE

Ratany Family

This is a small family of trees or shrubs that are parasitic or semiparasitic on the roots of other plants. Flowers grow in racemes or panicles. Three of the five petals are at the top of the flower and larger than the lower two. Usually stamens will alternate with the petals, especially the upper three.

99. **White Ratany** *Krameria grayi*

The genus name comes from the men who identified the plant—John George Kramer and William Henry Kramer, father and son, Austrian botanists. The *Kramerias* are shrubs parasitic on roots of other woody plants. The red flowers smell sweet. The name White Ratany refers to the soft wooly hairs on the leaves. Pima Indians used the plants to treat sores. The plants have been used to produce dyes. One species from Peru is used to color wool and skins, another to color port wine.

LINACEAE

Flax Family

All the members of the flax family that grow in the United States belong to the genus Linum. *This genus was introduced from Europe, where for centuries it has been cultivated for its useful fibers. Not many of the flax species growing in North America produce fibers that can be made into thread, twine, fishing lines, carpet materials, canvas, and duck. The seeds of some species are used to make linseed oil and for birdseed. Seeds are also used to make cakes for livestock.*

The flowers have five sepals, five petals, and five stamens. The flower color is either blue or yellow. A yellow-flowered species that grows in Arizona has been reported to be poisonous to horses and sheep. The poison is said to be one of the cyanogens.

100. **Blue Flax** *Linum lewisii*

There are six species of *Linum* listed in Lehr's *Catalogue*. Of these *Linum lewisii* is only a borderline plant of the high desert. Its delicate, pale blue petals veined in dark blue are not suited for desert living. This blue flax was named *lewisii* in honor of Meriwether Lewis of the celebrated Lewis and Clark exploration. It is well distributed all over the Southwest.

ZYGOPHYLLACEAE

Caltrop Family

Plants of the caltrop family are herbs or shrubs with stipulate leaves that are palmate, or pinnate and are in either opposite or alternate arrangement. The flower parts are in fives, with stamens usually twice as many as the petals and sepals.

101. **Creosote Bush** *Larrea tridentata*

There are eleven genera of the caltrop family listed in Lehr's *Catalogue*. Jaeger's *Desert Wildflowers* lists only two of these as desert living. Creosote Bush is not only the most widespread member of the family in the desert regions of the Southwest but is the most conspicuous and most widespread of all desert plants. The Mexicans call the plant "little bad smeller." Its strong odor, between carbolic acid and creosote, smells a bit sweet when the rains come. Creosote Bush smoke gives a pleasant taste to foods cooked over the wood.

The five-parted flowers are yellow, and the capsule fruit is five celled. When this ball-like fruit "decorates" the plant it is as attactive as when it is in flower. The leaf nodes have resinous warts. The leaves are opposite, stemless, and have two leaflets, which make them look like little butterflies perched on the stems.

The plants are habitats for a variety of insects. One is a midge that makes leafy galls about the size of hickory nuts on the stems. A moth larva makes a silk case ornamented with pieces of leaves. When the eggs hatch, the larvae make their own bags and live in them until they become moths. A lac insect that lives on the Creosote Bush makes a resinous exudate that the Indians used to attach arrowheads, mend pottery, and waterproof baskets.

The plant also furnishes a yellowish dye used by the Indians for painting their skins and dyeing fabrics.

Medicinal uses of Creosote Bush are myriad. The Indians used it to cure rheumatism and to heal wounds and burns. Taken internally it was supposed to cure tuberculosis and intestinal troubles.

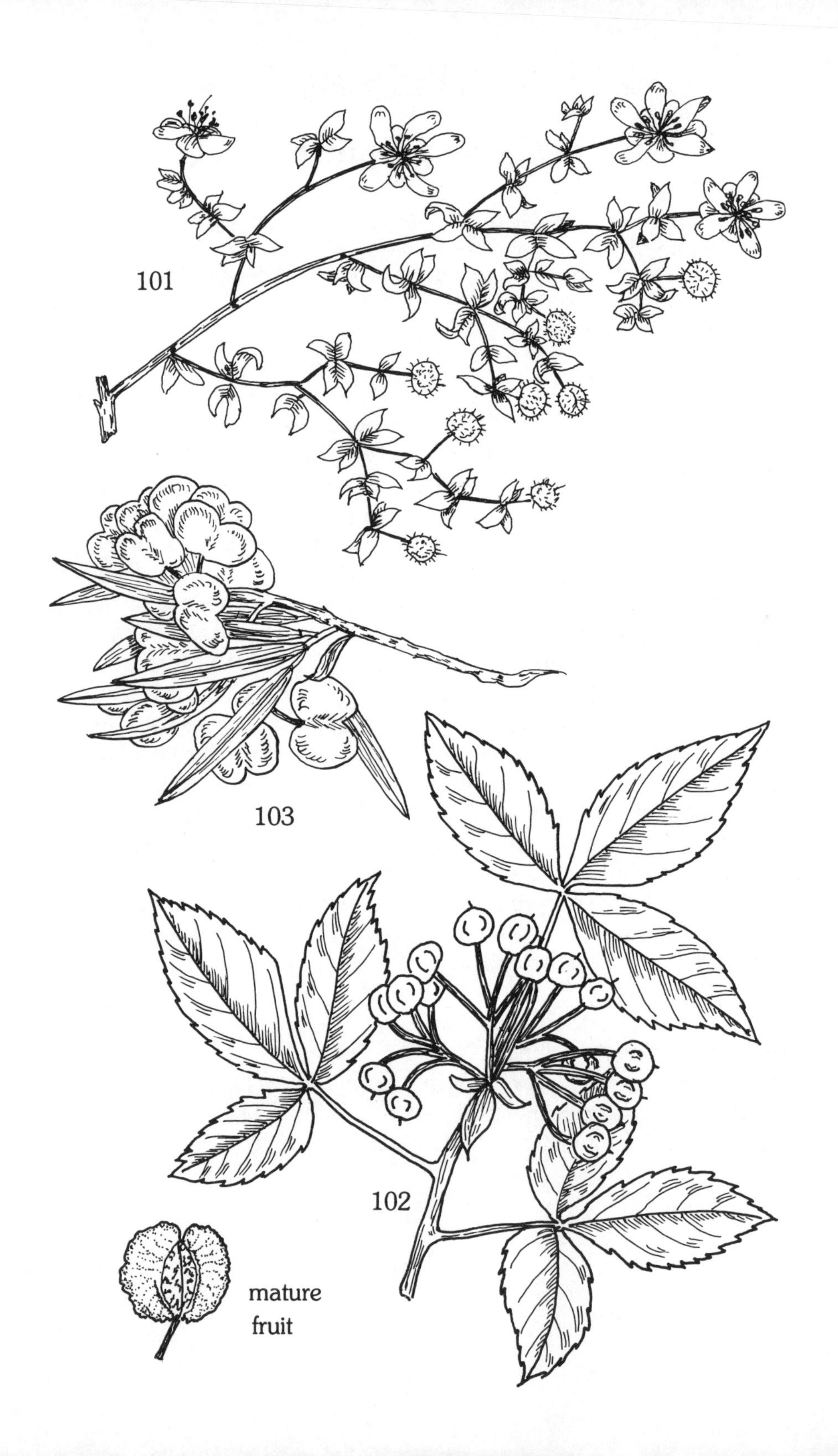
101
103
102
mature
fruit

RUTACEAE

Rue Family

The rue family comprises mostly trees and shrubs. The plants are strongly scented. They have simple or palmately compound leaves. The petals and sepals are in fours or fives. There are usually as many, or twice as many, stamens. From an economic standpoint the oranges, grapefruit, and lemons are the most important members of the family.

102. **Hop Tree** *Ptelea trifoliata*

There is only one species of the genus *Ptelea* in the Lehr *Catalogue*, but there are six subspecies and varieties listed. Some of the species of *Ptelea* are used in brewing. Ground hops are used for this purpose. Mixed with yeast the powder is also used in making excellent bread. The Hop Tree is easy to identify in the field by its trifoliate leaves and its clusters of round, winged fruits. This is the type of winged fruit called the samara. *Samara* is a Latin word that means "seed of the elm." The type of inflorescence is the cyme (see Plate F of the Appendix).

103. **Hop Tree** *Ptelea trifoliata* ssp. *angustifolia*

Hop Tree subspecies *angustifolia* differs very little from *Ptelea trifoliata.* It has narrower leaflets and larger fruits with thicker wings. Figure 103 shows these modifications.

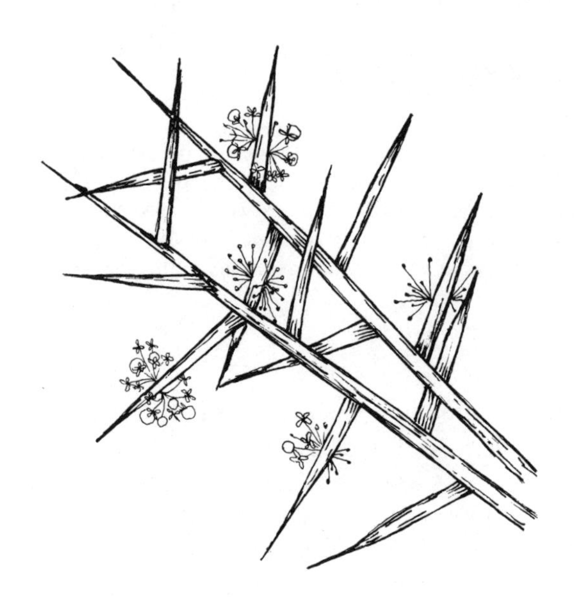

104

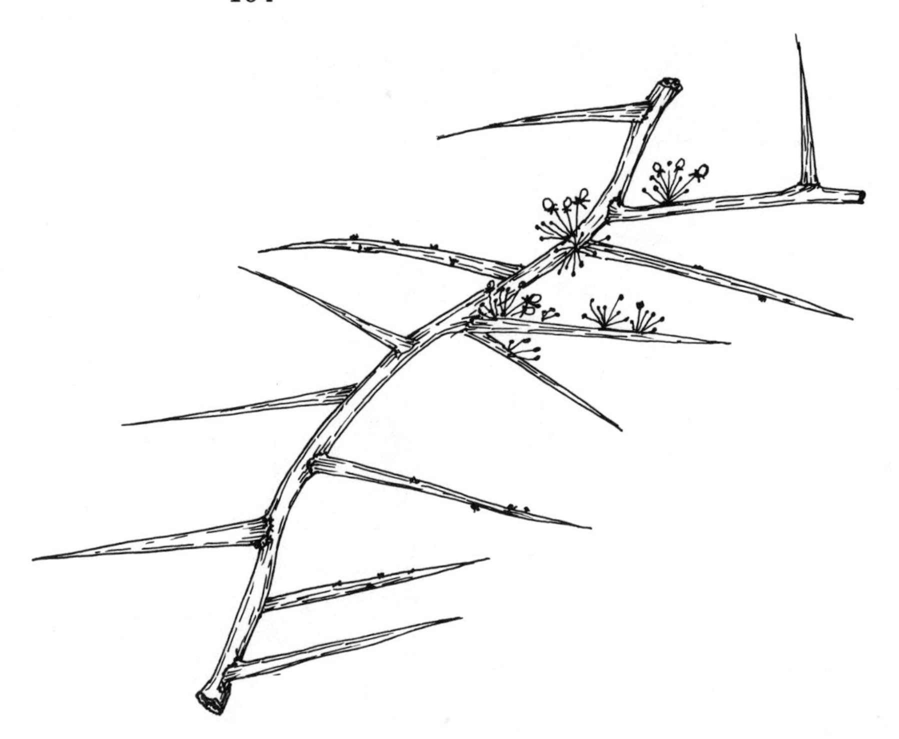

KOBERLINIACEAE

Junco Family

The junco family should be rush-like plants, since junco means "rush," but the juncos are very unlike rushes. Instead of being grass-like, they are thorny shrubs with leaves reduced to small scales.

104. **Junco, All Thorn** *Koeberlinia spinosa*

This spiny junco is also called Crown of Thorns, Crucifixion Thorn, and Corona de Cristo. It certainly must help control erosion by repelling livestock. It is considered a range pest on account of its large thorns. The well-armed shrub blooms in March.

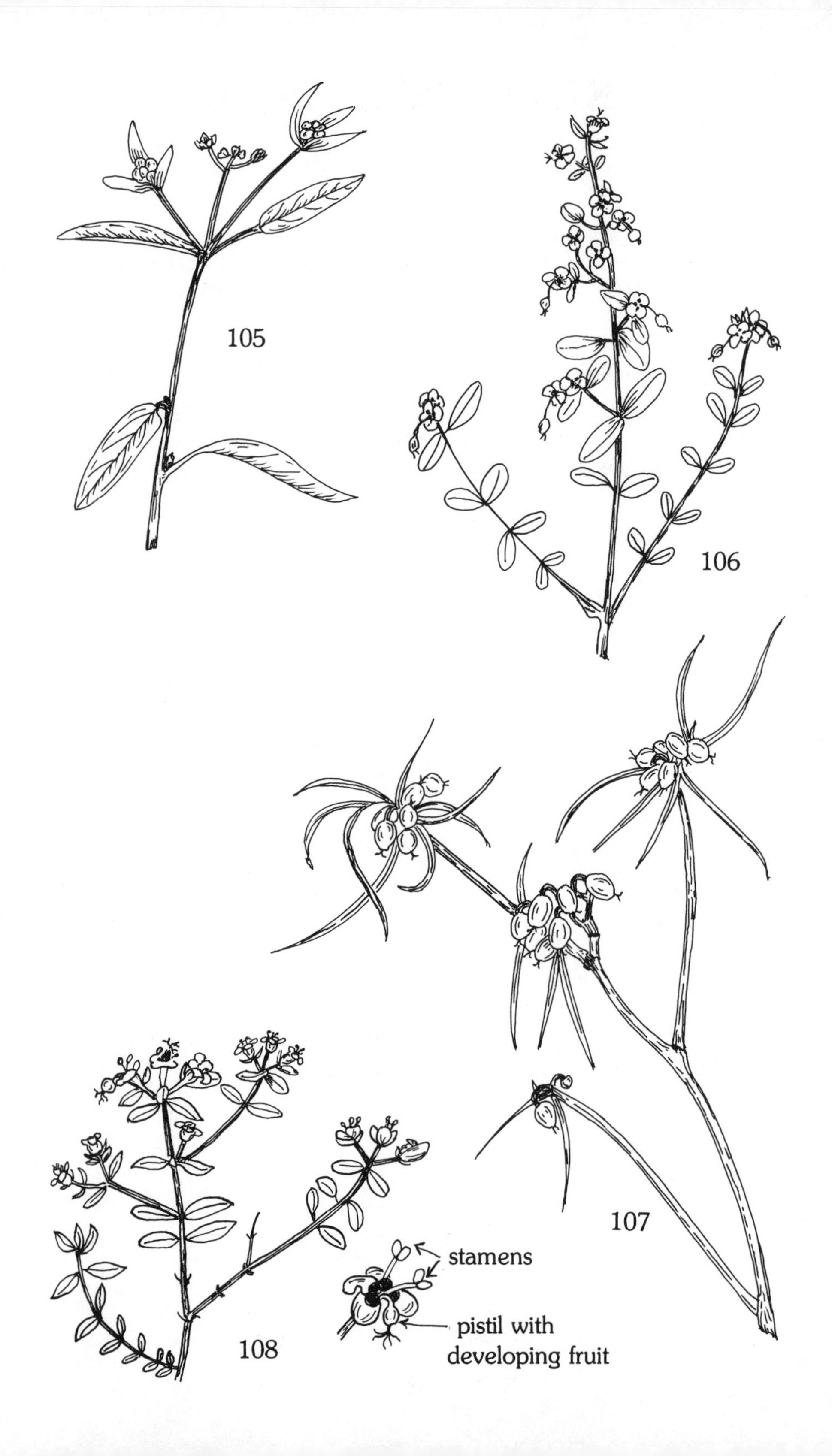
105
106
107
108
stamens
pistil with
developing fruit

EUPHORBIACEAE

Spurge Family

Genera of this family may be either trees, shrubs, or herbs. It is a large family of plants, usually having milky juice, which is often poisonous. Castor beans belong to this family. Oil extracted from castor beans is used medicinally, particularly as a purgative. Some of the spurges furnish rubber. Important foods of the tropical countries belonging to the family are Cassava and Tapioca. The very popular cultivated plant, Poinsettia, *is also a family member. The flowers are unisexual. There is only one stamen in the staminate flower. An odd arrangement is that the staminate flowers occur in a cluster around the one pistillate flower. This makes the inflorescence look like a perfect flower.*

105. **Desert Croton** *Croton californicus* var. *mohavensis*

Croton means "tick," and the plant got its name from the tick-like seed of its relative, the castor bean. The Spanish name is El Barbasco. This refers to a poison in the plant that is used to induce narcosis in fish. The odor of the plant is, however, not unpleasant. Hot packs can be made from it to lessen rheumatic pain. In late summer the stems of the drying plant curl inward and make a little brush. Figure 105 shows a single stem.

106. **Spurge** *Euphorbia brachycera*

Euphorbus, for whom this spurge genus was named, was physician to King Juba II of Numidia and Mauritania, who ruled in the first century B.C. Euphorbus was a writer of historical and geographical works. His contribution to botany was his work *De Euphorbia herba.*

Euphorbias are widespread among the deserts and may have existed in some locations where the salty seas receded. Lava beds make particularly fine soils for the growth of spurges.

Some species of the genus *Euphorbia* are called "sand mats" on account of the way they flatten themselves on the sandy soils. The Indians thought sand mats were good snakebite remedies when crushed and applied as poultices.

107. **Desert Poinsettia** *Euphorbia eriantha*

Desert Poinsettia does not look like the cultivated Poinsettia—its involucral leaves are greenish bronze instead of scarlet. It can be identified in the field by its white downy flowers and very narrow leaves.

108. **Small-seeded Sand Mat** *Euphorbia polycarpa*

Euphorbia polycarpa is a good example of this genus. The Small-seeded Sand Mat forms a mat about six inches across. The "blooms" of this species, which are not really flowers but flower clusters, are white with dark red centers. The cluster has one female flower and several male ones.

BUXACEAE

Box Family

The box family's members are sometimes classified with the spurge family. They are perennial herbs, trees, or shrubs usually with grayish green leaves. Stamens and pistils are in separate flowers on the same plant or on different plants. The flowers are small and greenish, without petals and sometimes without sepals.

109. **Goat Nut, Coffee Berry** *Simmondsia chinensis*

The Goat Nut is a one- to two-meter-tall shrub. It is a characteristic plant of canyons up to 4,300 feet altitude but grows especially well in the alluvial soils at canyon mouths. Because it is evergreen, it is eaten throughout the year by deer and other browsing animals. The oily nuts are eaten by goats and ground squirrels. Products made from the oil are becoming more and more developed as the problems of raising the plant commercially are solved. For a long time it has been used as a hair and body oil and shampoo ingredient. The oil is nondigestible by humans and the tannin in it makes it taste bitter. The oil is actually a liquid wax and is variously used as a substitute for beeswax in electrical insulation, varnishes, and phonograph records. The seeds can be specially treated to make a coffee substitute, as the common name Coffee Berry suggests. Other common names are Jojoba, Deer Nut, and Wild Hazel.

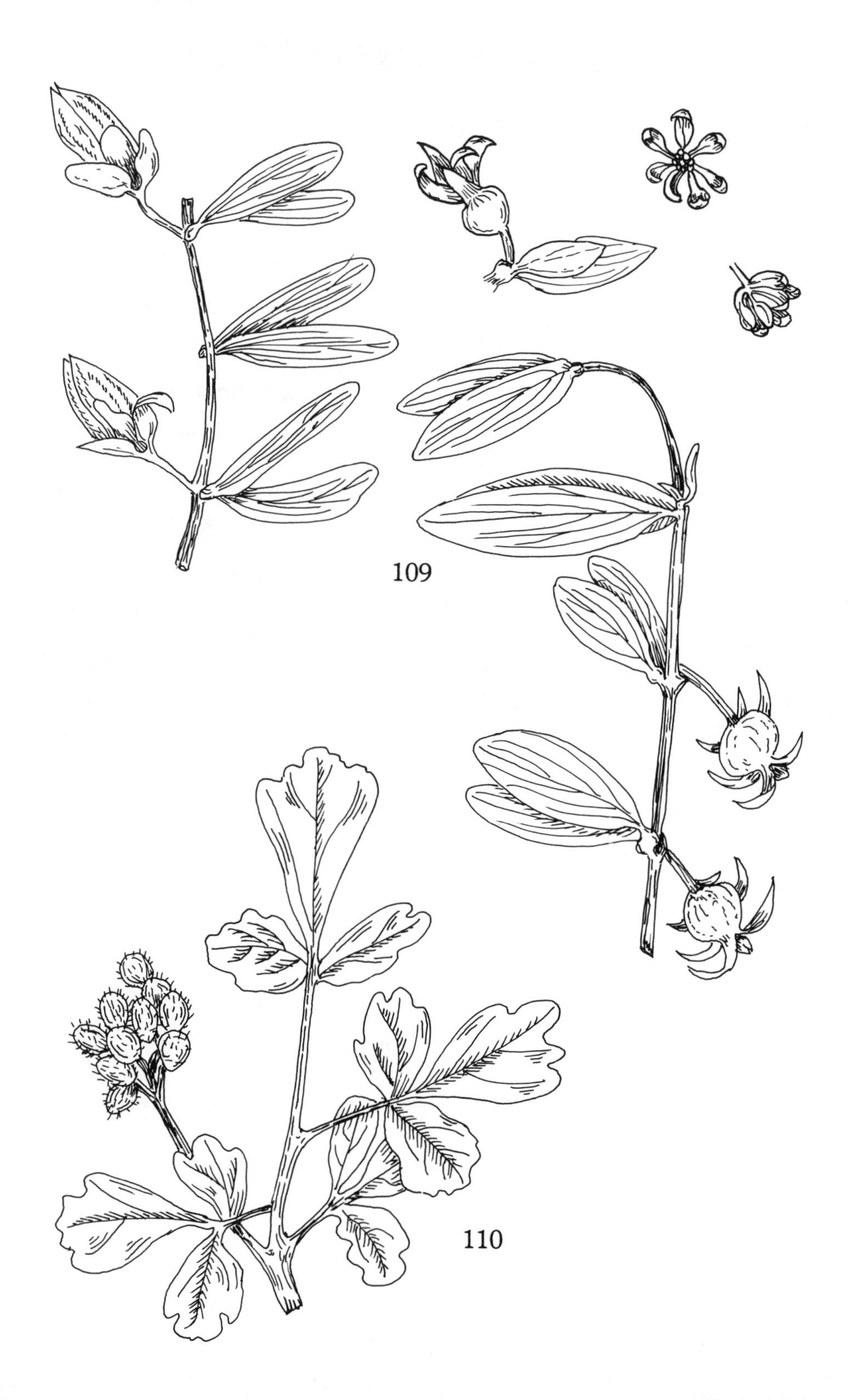
109
110

ANACARDIACEAE

Sumac Family

The sumacs are shrubs with resinous and pungent juice. Some species are poisonous. Poison Ivy (Poison Oak) is an example of a sumac with poisonous juice. The poison is urushiol, which causes swellings and eruptions of the skin. The milky juice is poisonous to swallow. Leaves of the sumacs are trilobed or pinnate. The flowers are axillary or terminal panicles. The fruit is a drupe.

110. **Desert Squaw Bush** *Rhus trilobata*

Squaw Bush has the three-lobed leaves, panicled flowers, and drupe fruit characteristic of the family. The juice is not poisonous and a delicious "lemonade" can be made from the fruits. Indians used the limber stems for basketmaking and the juice for tanning leather.

Pliny and Dioscorides said of *Rhus trilobata* that honey and vinegar mixed with the leaves relieved gangrene and canker. Also this liquid helped roughness of the tongue and throat. It was said that tea made from the green leaves would turn the hair black. The plant was used to keep out clothes moths. The Indians treated smallpox with a lotion made from the berries.

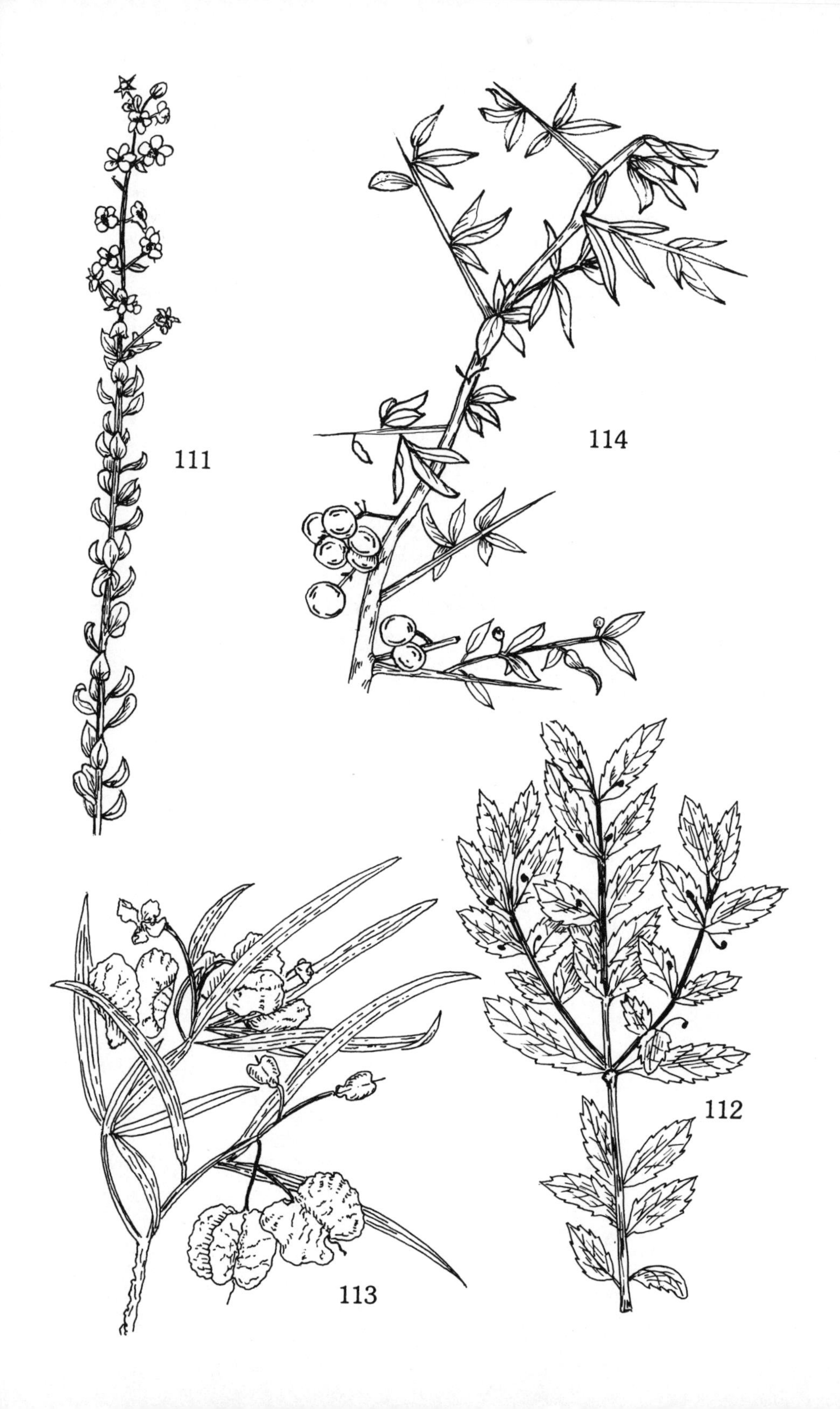
111
114
113
112

CELASTRACEAE

Bittersweet Family

The bittersweets are a dicotyledonous family of trees, shrubs, and woody vines. The leaves are simple, alternate, or opposite. The flowers are small, axillary or terminal, and may be solitary or clustered.

111. **Bittersweet** *Mortonia scabrella* var. *utahensis*

Mortonia scabrella var. *utahensis* is a many-branched shrub with thick leaves. It was named for Samuel G. Morton, a professor of anatomy at Pennsylvania Medical College. Dr. Morton assembled a world-famous collection of twenty thousand skulls.

112. **Mountain-Lover** *Pachystima myrsinites*

Mountain-Lover, also called Myrtle Boxleaf or Oregon Boxwood, is a small evergreen shrub. The axillary flowers are very small. It makes a low-growing ground cover and is eaten by deer.

SAPINDACEAE

Soapberry Family

The soapberries are shrubs and small trees with simple or pinnately compound leaves, small flowers, and one-seeded fruits. The family name Sapindaceae is from sapo indicus, *meaning "Indian soap," referring to the soapy character of the berries.*

113. **Hop Bush** *Dodonaea viscosa* var. *angustifolia*

Three genera of the soapberries are listed in Lehr's *Catalogue*: Balloon Vine *(Cardiospermum)*, Hop Bush *(Dodonaea)*, and Soapberry *(Sapindus)*. *Dodonaea* is the only genus represented in this work. The species name *viscosa* indicates the characteristic that distinguishes the genus from the other genera of soapberries: the leaves, when young, are covered with a sticky juice. The leaves of the Hop Bush are slender and about five centimeters long. The fruits are winged like those of the Hop Tree, *Ptelea*.

RHAMNACEAE

Buckthorn Family

The buckthorn family includes trees, shrubs, and woody vines of tropical and temperate zones. The leaves are alternate or opposite, the flowers small. The fruit is a drupe or a two- or four-parted capsule with one ovule to a cell. Several medicinal plants belong in this family. One of these produces cascara sagrada, *a potent laxative. The Indian Jujube, or Chinese Date, belongs to this family.*

114. **Gray-leaved Abrojo** *Condalia lycioides* var. *canescens*

Gray-leaved Abrojo makes dense thickets on mesas, slopes, and plains of the western deserts. Many of the buckthorns furnish good browsing, but Abrojo is not eaten by domestic animals and deer. Birds like it, however, and find shelter in its thick growth.

Juice of the roots was used by the Pima Indians to treat sore eyes. The juice was also used as a soap substitute.

VITACEAE

Grape Family

Members of the grape family are, of course, all vines, with twining stems or tendrils—familiar plants to everybody. The cultivated grapes are the most valuable commercially for juices, jellies, and preserves, but some of the wild species are delicious also. The wild ones are excellent bird food.

115. **Thicket Creeper** *Parthenocissus inserta*

Parthenocissus inserta is commonly called Virginia Creeper. The leaves are palmately compound with five to seven leaflets. The berry clusters are very decorative, as is also the autumn foliage, but the berries are not fleshy enough to be good food.

116. **Canyon Grape** *Vitis arizonica*

The berries of Canyon Grape make good juice and jelly. The Indians eat them, both fresh and dried, and birds eat them, too. The vines along draws and canyons check soil erosion.

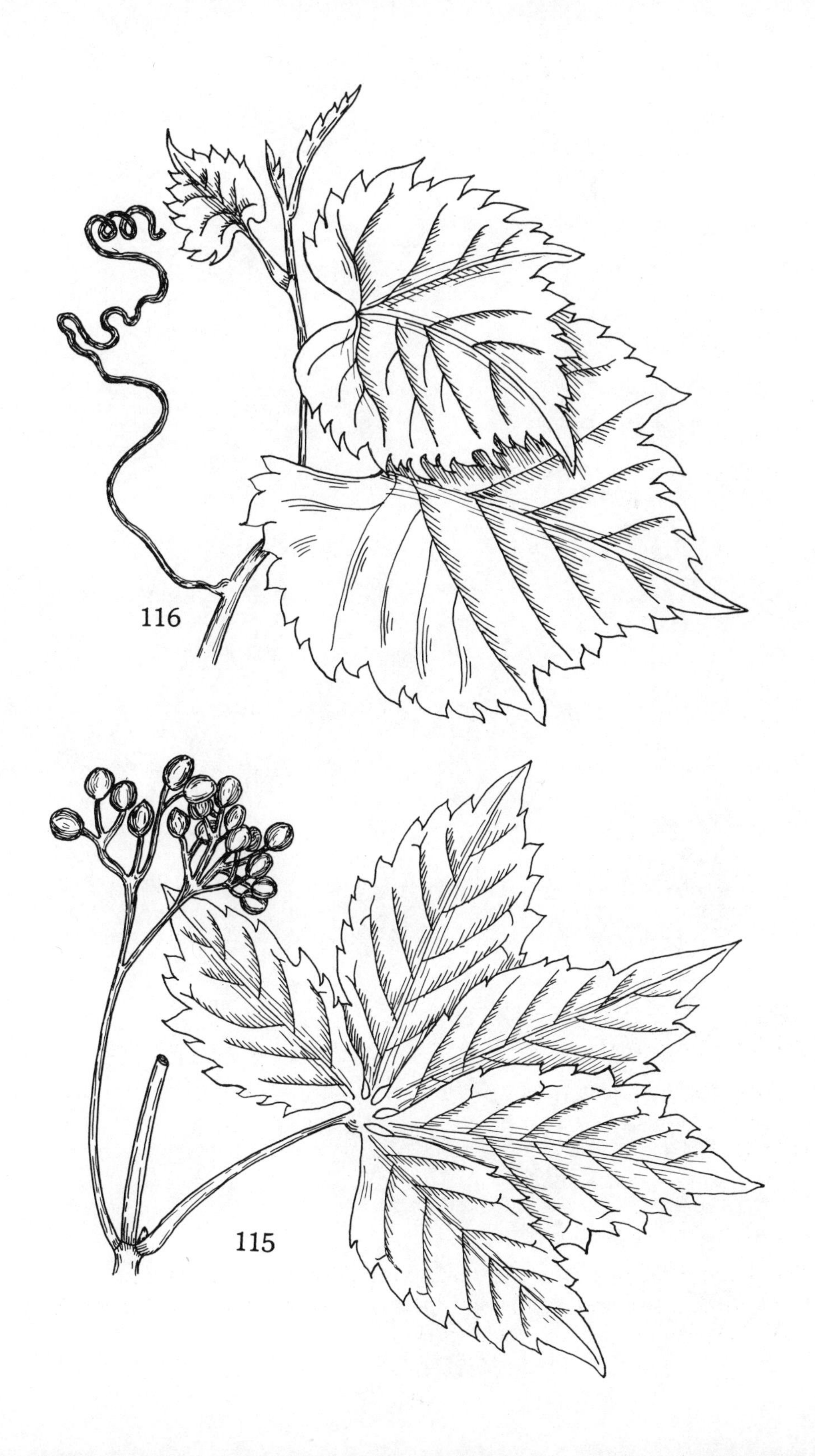
116
115

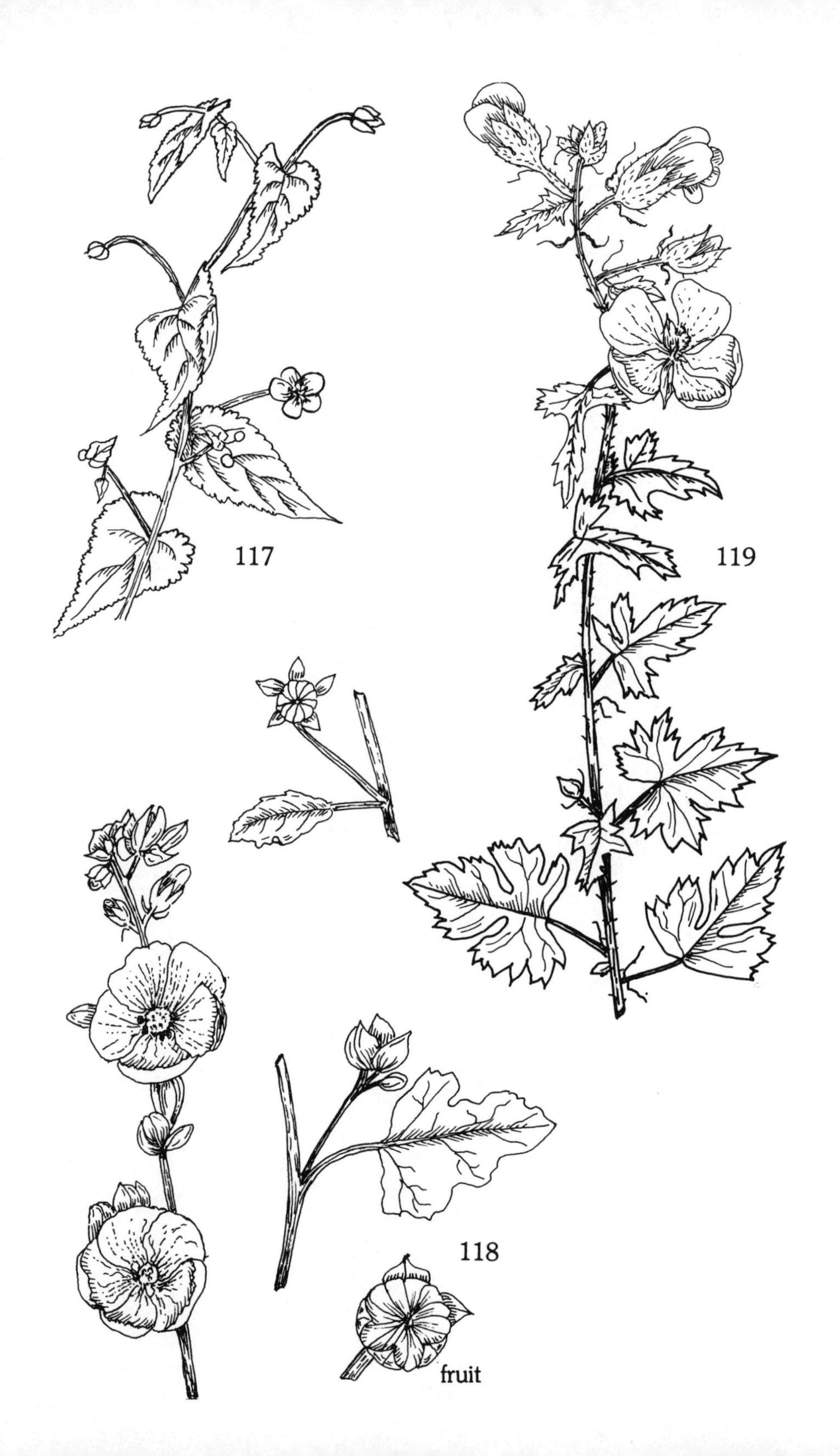
117
119
118
fruit

MALVACEAE

Mallow Family

There are about one thousand species of mallows and they grow all over the world except in the coldest zones. They are among our most easily identifiable plants because of the unique habit of their stamens, which encircle the pistils with their coalesced filaments. The family includes many cultivated, economic, and ornamental plants.

Cotton is one such plant. It not only furnishes the familiar fiber but also oil and meal. An explosive, guncotton, is made by extracting the fibers with nitric and sulphuric acids. One of the mallows, okra, is a popular food. It is especially good in soups.

Large-flowered species, such as hollyhocks, hibiscus, and althea, are familiar garden flowers.

117. **Indian Mallow** *Abutilon californicum*

The genus *Abutilon* comprises about 150 species that live in tropical and warm temperate zones of both hemispheres. They are shrubs or herbs and are usually covered with fine soft hairs. Their leaves are broad and lobed. The flowers are predominantly yellow.

Indian Mallow is a shrubby plant, between one and two meters high. The leaf blades are covered thickly with star-like hairs. The fruit segments have short, stout tips.

The Southwest has several other *Abutilons* not figured in this book, but they are pictured in color in volume 4, *The Southwestern States*, of Harold William Rickett's series *Wild Flowers of the United States.*

118. **Desert Mallow** *Sphaeralcea ambigua*

All the *Sphaeralceas* have brightly colored flowers. Desert Mallow flowers range from the color of grenadine to peach red. The size of this plant makes it either a tall herb or a short shrub. The genus name *Sphaeralcea* means "globe marshmallow"—the fruit is spherical.

119. **Mohave Desert Mallow** *Sphaeralcea pulchella*

The species name of this mallow means "little beauty," and the apricot-colored flower is very handsome. Its brown stems and green leaves are coated with fine white hairs.

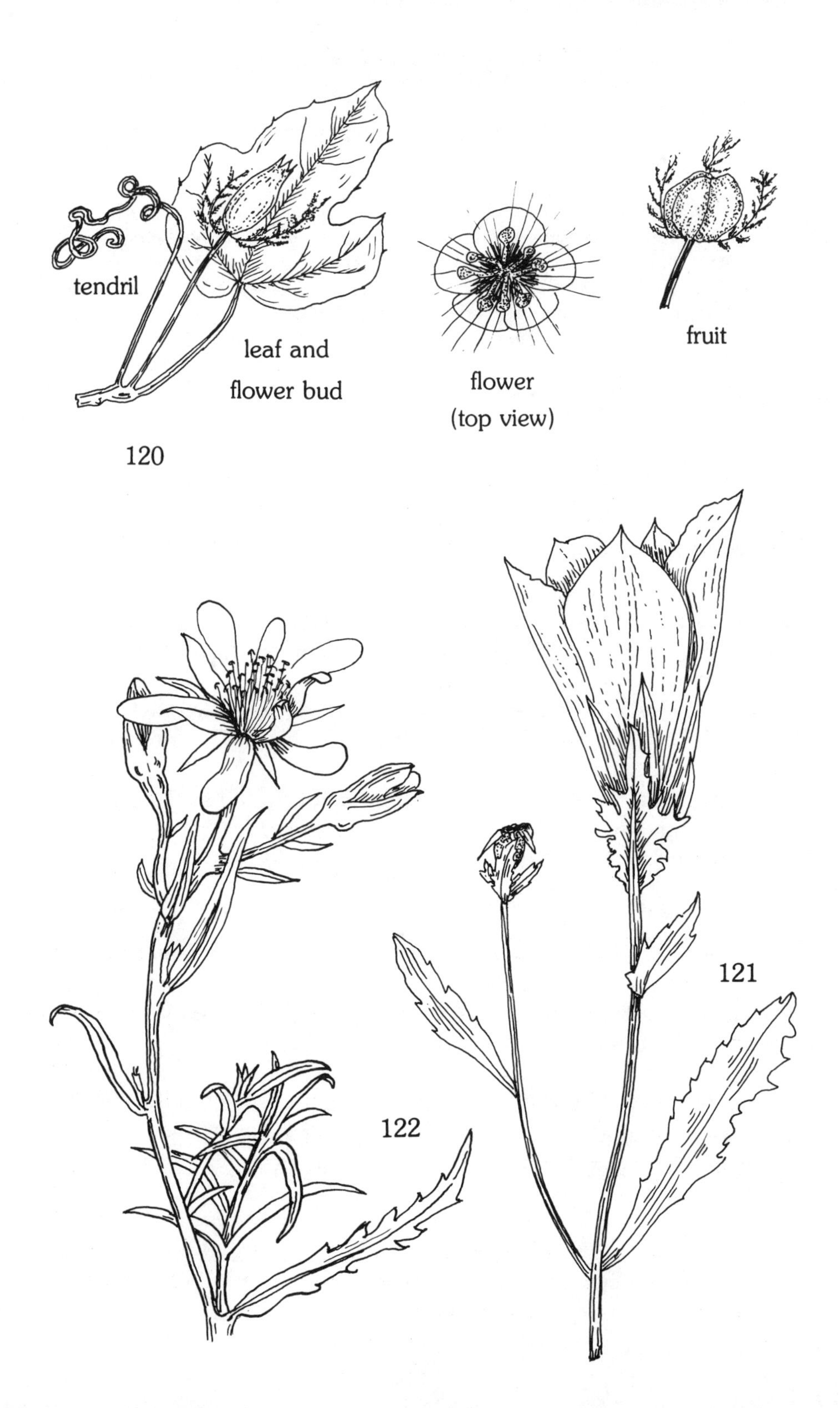
tendril
leaf and
flower bud
flower
(top view)
fruit
120
121
122

PASSIFLORACEAE

Passionflower Family

The plants of this family are vines climbing by tendrils. The priests among the early explorers saw in the structures of the flowers an image of the crucifixion—Christ's passion.

The leaves are palmately three lobed or three cleft. The fruit is a round berry.

120. **White Passionflower** *Passiflora foetida*

Another common name for the White Passionflower is Corona de Cristo, meaning "Crown of Christ." Inside the circles of five sepals and five petals there are two or three circles of beautiful fringe, thought to resemble the crown of thorns. The three-knobbed styles of the pistil were the nails, and the stamens were the five wounds. The ten sepals were the apostles—minus Peter and Judas.

LOASACEAE

Loasa Family

The members of this family are either herbs or shrubs, either erect or climbing. They usually have sticky, bristly, barbed, hooked, or stinging hairs. The leaves are opposite. The flowers are large and showy. Many members of the family are used as ornamentals.

121. **Sand Blazing-Star** *Mentzelia involucrata*

The name Blazing-Star is given to many different kinds of plants. The *Mentzelias* do have star-shaped flowers, but the cream color is not exactly a "blazing" one. Another common name is perhaps more appropriate: Stickleaf, on account of the viscid hairs on the leaves. The species name of this plant refers to the two sharp-pointed bracts that form the involucre below the flower (shown in Figure 122). This Blazing-Star is found in washes and on canyon sides.

122. **Blazing-Star** *Mentzelia pumila*

The species name of this Blazing-Star, *pumila*, means "dwarf." The plant is slightly smaller than species *involucrata* but the characteristic bracts are much narrower. The stems are whitish and twisted.

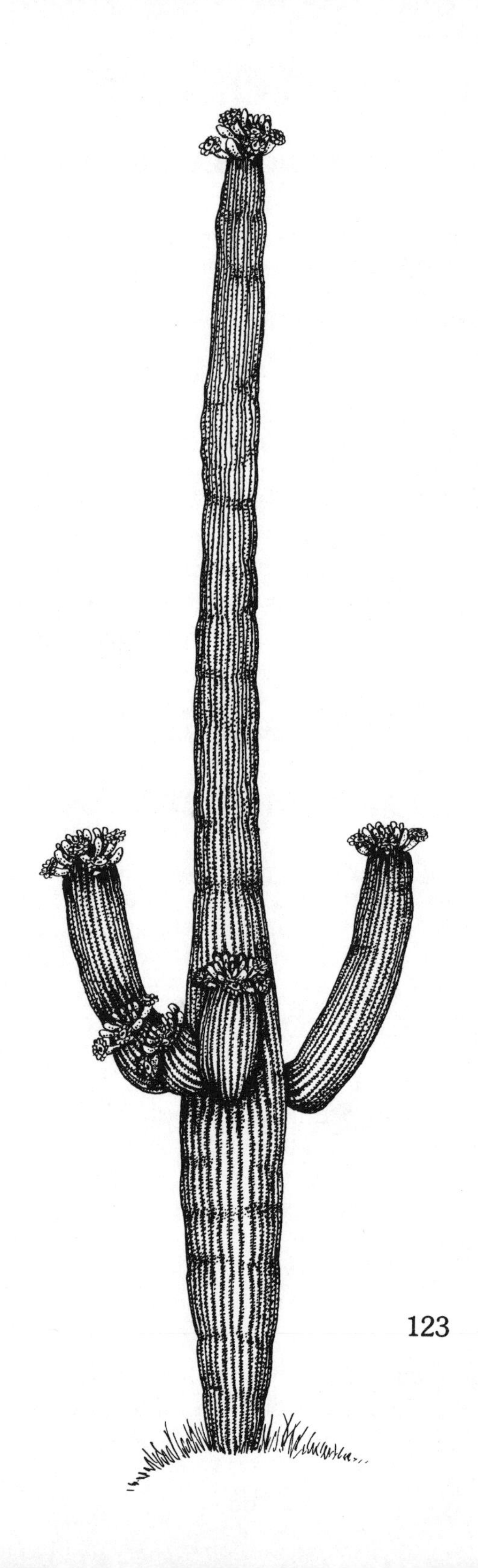

CACTACEAE

Cactus Family

The cacti are the most characteristic plants of the deserts and are easy to identify. Their many forms are spiny, their stems are succulent. Few have leaves; the outer green layers of the stems carry on the food manufacturing that leaves usually do. The small areas where the spines grow in clumps are called areoles.

The brilliantly beautiful flowers have many petals and sepals, which are generally indistinguishable from each other. There are also many stamens. There is only one pistil, a single style, and several stigmas. The fruit is a berry with many seeds. It is sweet and juicy in some species and is used for human food.

The whole plant is too spiny to be attractive to herbivorous animals. The development of spineless forms for use as cattle feed has not yet been completely successful.

123. **Saguaro** *Cereus giganteus*

The Saguaro is the state flower of Arizona and the largest species of cactus in the United States. The genus name *Cereus* means "torch" and refers to the candelabrum-like branching of some of the species. The species name *giganteus* means, of course, "very large." This cactus is said to be an indicator of the Sonoran desert. The flowers open at night, remaining so until late the next day. They attract clouds of insects. The insects attract birds. When the cucumber-like fruit ripens in June, it bursts, revealing red pulp and little black seeds. Both pulp and seeds are eaten by birds and rodents.

Because of the water-storing capacity of the Saguaro, it can produce fruit through long periods of drought. The Pima and Papago Indians could thus always depend upon it for food.

Syrup extracted from the fruit is fermented to make an alcoholic drink. The seeds are ground into an oily paste to spread, like butter, on tortillas.

Elf owls and cactus wrens live in the stems in holes bored out by woodpeckers.

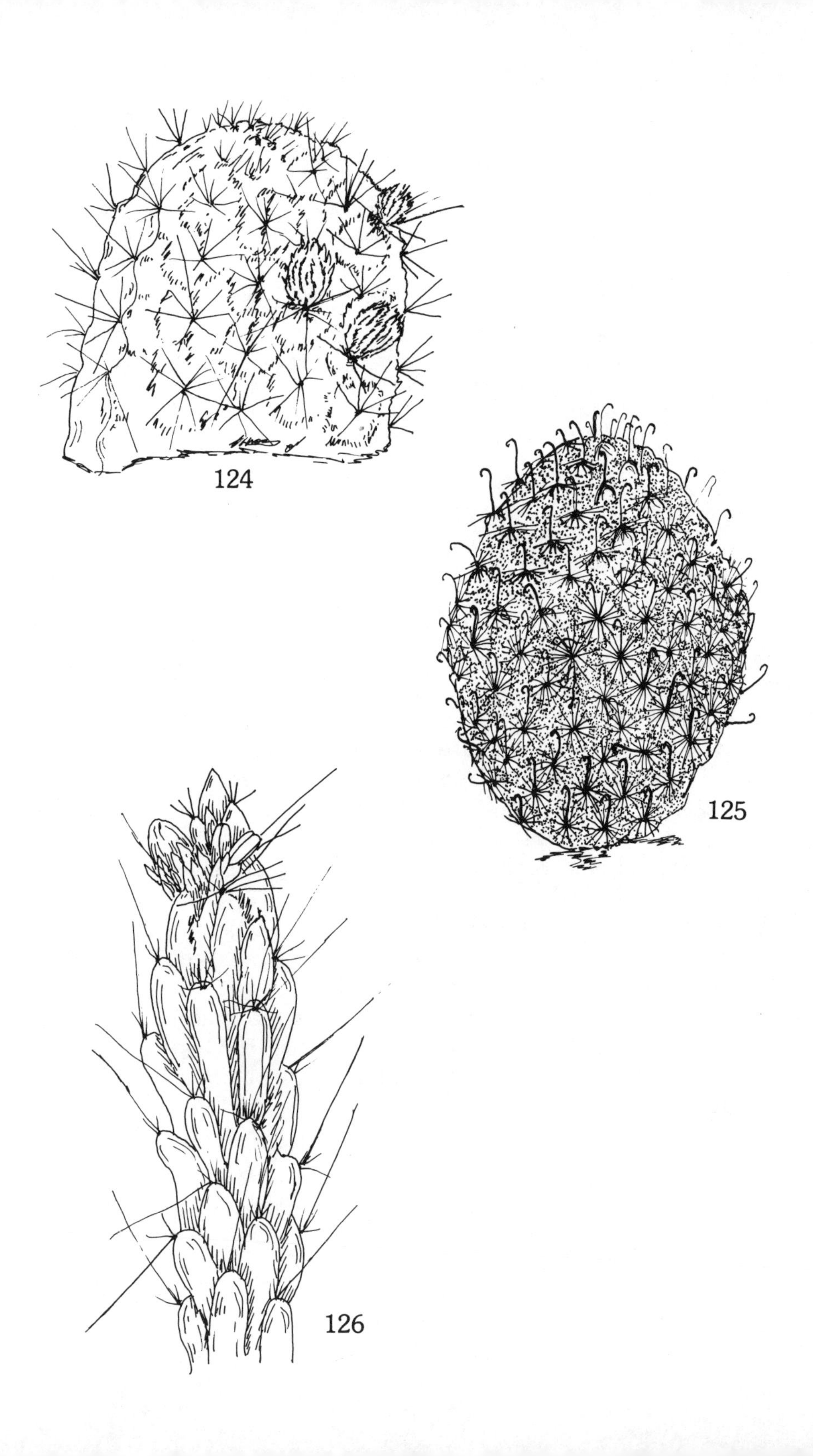
124
125
126

124. **Hedgehog Cactus** *Echinocereus fasciculatus*

The Hedgehog Cactus can be identified by examination of the number of spines on each areole. If there are two or more central spines and twelve or thirteen spines surrounding them, the cactus is *Echinocereus fasciculatus*. The Hedgehog Cactus grows in clumps. The many spreading spines almost obscure the stems. The dark red juicy fruits are edible.

125. **Fishhook Cactus** *Mammillaria microcarpa*

The *Mammillarias* are small cacti that grow in low clumps. The lavender flowers bloom toward the tops of the plants and sometimes look like a garland around it. The long spines are hooked at the tip, which make them look like fishhooks.

A common name for all *Mammillarias* is Pincushion Cactus. The common names for individual species, such as Fishhook, are given on account of some structure peculiar to each—examples are Corkseed, Nipple, and Button. The Pincushion Cacti live on dry, sandy hills throughout the Southwest.

126. **Buckhorn Cactus** *Opuntia acanthocarpa*

The reddish brown color of the Buckhorn Cactus is characteristic of those that live in the mountains of southern Arizona. If transplanted to another location, the plant turns green. There are two kinds of *Opuntia*, distinguished by type of stem. Those called chollas (pronounced "CHO-yahs") have cylindrical joints; others have flattened, rounded joints. Buckhorn Cactus is an example of the cholla type.

127. **Prickly Pear** *Opuntia phaeacantha*

The Prickly Pear is one of the cacti with flattened stems. The plant may form large clumps many feet across, or it may occur as a single plant. The species name *phaeacantha* means "brown spine," but the spines may in fact be many other colors. The flowers are yellow and the fruit is edible.

128. **Hunger Cactus** *Opuntia polyacantha*

The Hunger Cactus has yellow flowers that form on the edges of the flat joints, which may be up to fifteen centimeters long. The yellow color turns to orange when the flowers fade.

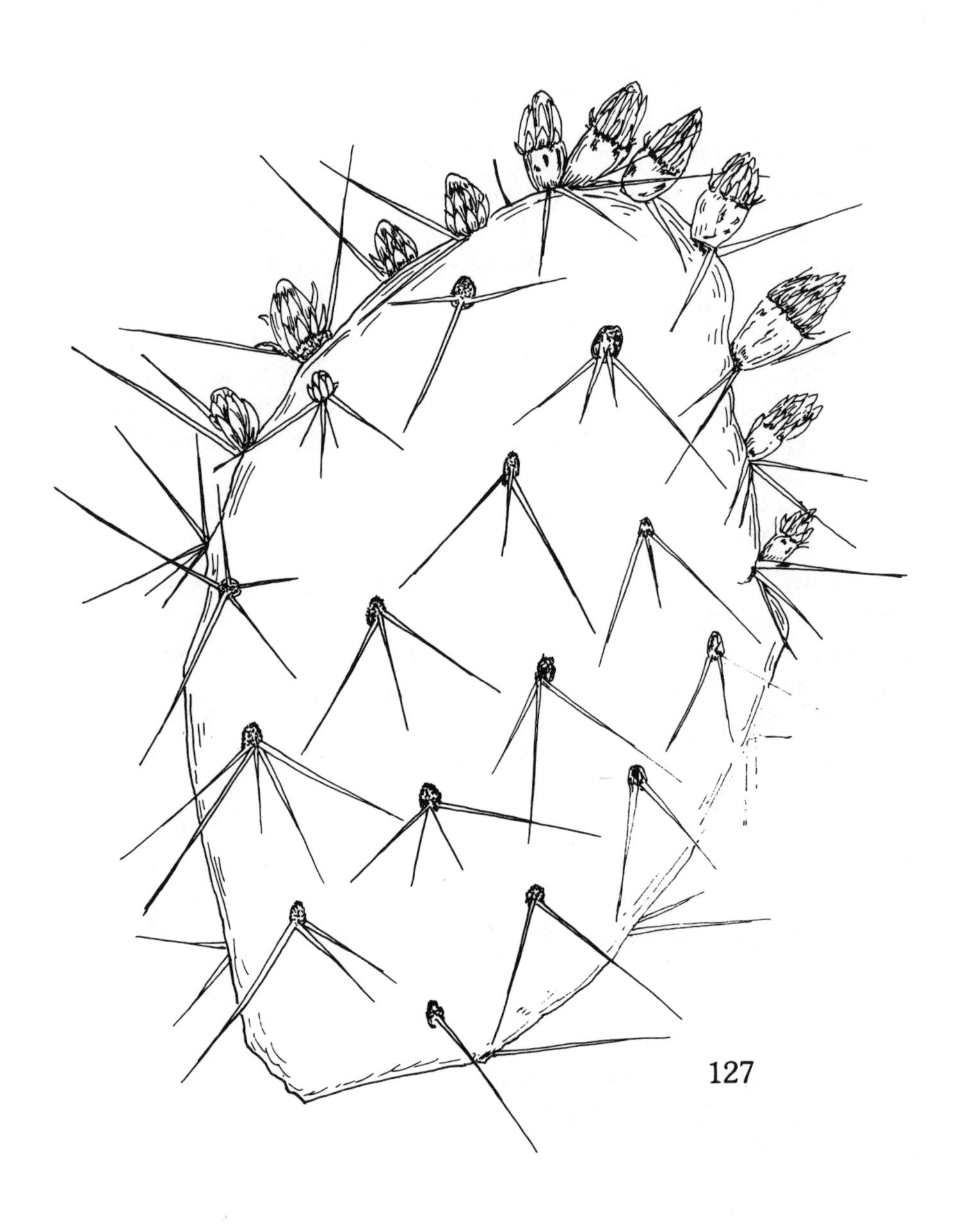

129. **Pincushion Cactus** *Pediocactus simpsonii*

Due to its shape, the Pincushion Cactus also has the name Mountain Ball Cactus. The ball is slightly flattened at its top and it ranges in size from five to fifteen centimeters. The areole-bearing tubercles are little balls arranged in spirals on the surface of the stem ball instead of in rows (as in Figure 130).

130. **Green-flowered Hedgehog Cactus** *Echinocereus viridiflorus*

The areoles of the Green-flowered Hedgehog Cactus are arranged on longitudinal ridges. The ridges may be slightly spiraled on the joint. The joints are about six centimeters high and may grow singly or in clusters. The chartreuse color of the flowers is unusual.

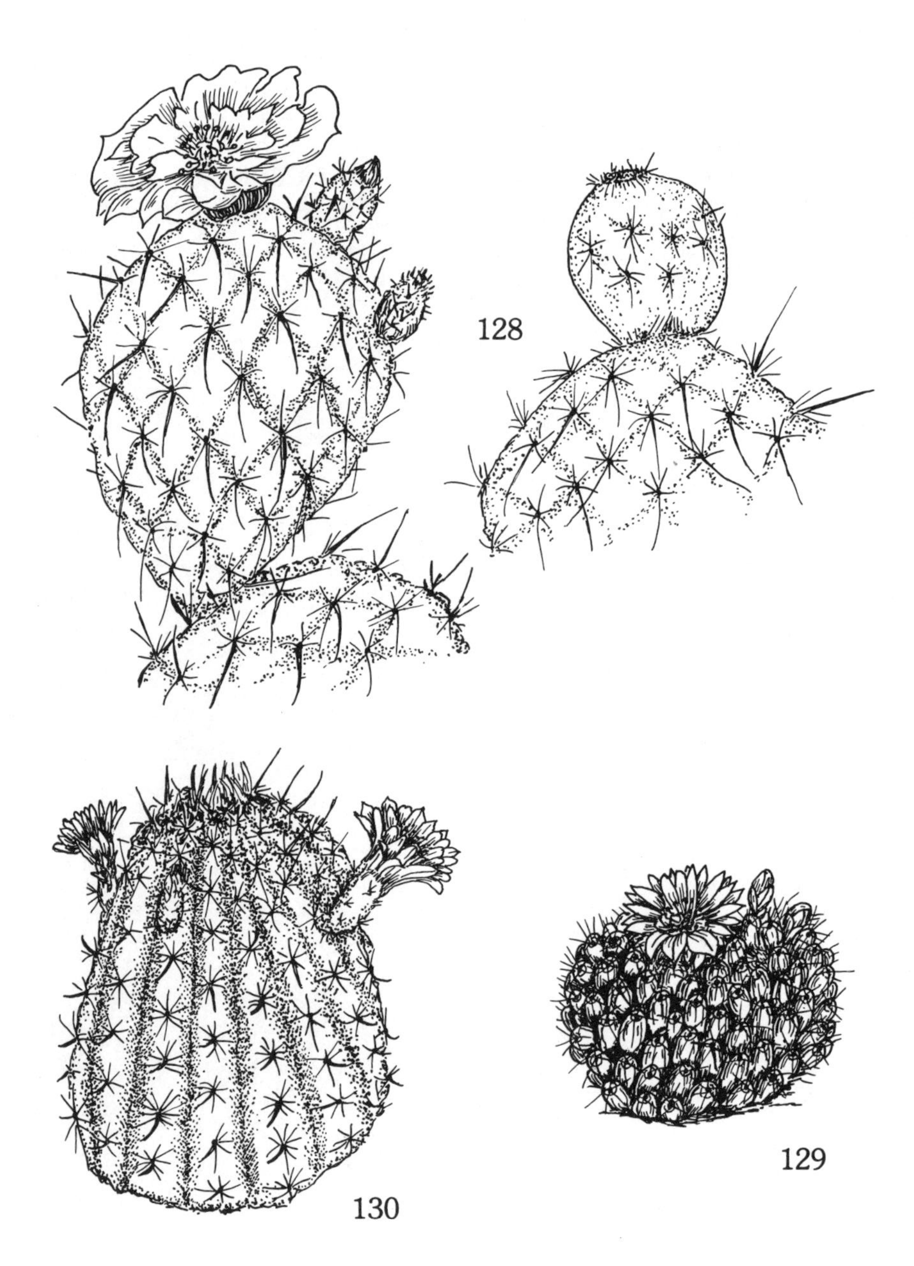
128
129
130

ONAGRACEAE

Evening Primrose Family

Many members of the evening primrose family have four sepals, four petals, and eight stamens. The stigma is four-parted or entire. The ovary is inferior, being embedded in the tip of the flower stalk. On top of the ovary a tube arises, around the rim of which are the sepals and petals. At first glance this tube might be mistaken for a flower stalk. There are exceptions to these numbers of parts since some of the family members have two or five sepals and petals.

Another family, the mustards, also has flower parts in fours, but the ovaries are superior—that is, they are above the points where the petals and sepals are attached. The Onagraceae evening primroses are not directly related to the Primulaceae primroses, despite the similarity of their names.

131. **Small-flowered Primrose** *Camissonia micrantha*

The Small-flowered Primrose is to be found in desert areas where the Creosote Bush grows. It is an annual plant with erect or sprawling stems that spread widely around the main axis. The plant is covered thickly with fine hairs. The leaves are lanceolate along the stem but narrowly elliptic in the basal rosette. That the flowers are small is expressed in the species name *micrantha*. The petals are yellow.

132. **Narrow-leaved Primrose** *Camissonia refracta*

Camissonia refracta is another species with lanceolate leaves, but they are longer than those of the Small-flowered Primrose. It is an annual that grows to a height of thirty-two centimeters. It has reddish stems, the epidermis of which peels off. The flowers are white and bloom from March to May. The fruit is a slender stemless capsule.

The Narrow-leaved Primrose grows in sandy soils and is common in the Mohave Desert.

131

132

133

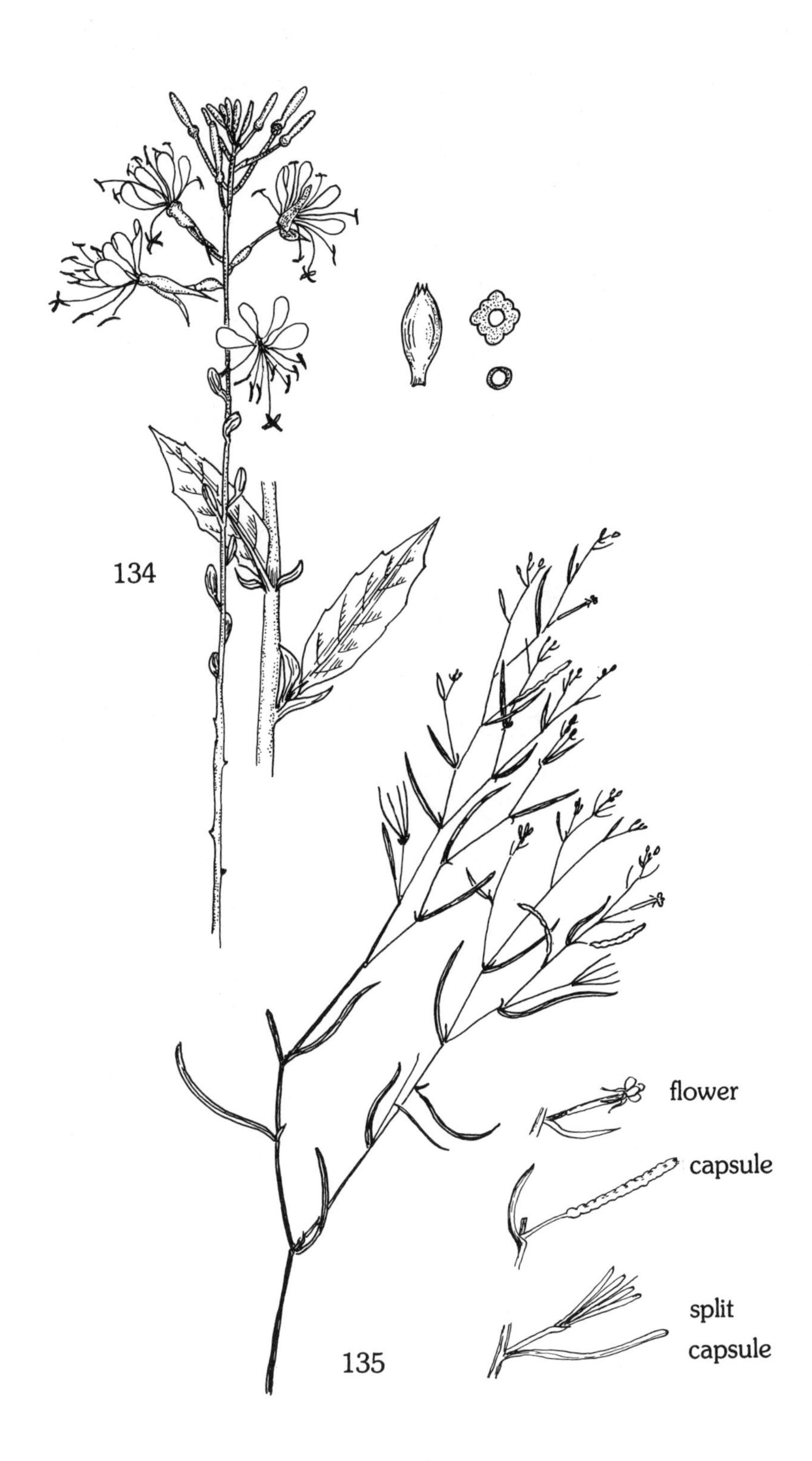
134
135
flower
capsule
split
capsule

133. **Fireweed** *Epilobium angustifolium*

Other common names for Fireweed are Great Willow-Herb, Blooming Sally, and Willow-Weed. The name Fireweed seems most appropriate because this plant invades after a fire and becomes established, thus covering the fire scars. The name is also appropriate because the red flower looks like a flame. The unbranched stems grow tall—up to two meters—and are covered by lanceolate leaves. Fireweed blooms in the summer, from June through August. It is said that baby bald eagles make their first flights from the nest when the flower begins to bloom. Fireweed is not truly a desert plant; it grows in richer, more moist soils than are usual in the desert.

The people of Europe and Asia use Fireweed as food, like asparagus or greens. The English use it as a tea adulterant. Medicinally it is used as an intestinal astringent.

134. **Scarlet Gaura** *Gaura coccinea*

Gaura is a native western plant that grows throughout the Southwest, on barren or overgrazed flats of the high desert grasslands. The stems are smooth, covered with appressed hairs, or densely hairy. The leaves are slenderly oblong to lanceolate, entire or shallowly sinuate, and thickly covered with fine hairs. The flowers are pinkish, turning red when in full bloom. The capsule is obovate to pyriform and also covered with fine hairs.

135. **Weedy Primrose** *Gayophytum ramossissimum*

Members of this genus, *Gayophytum*, fall into two groups: those with branches near the base of the plant that do not branch themselves, and those with branches that do bear branches. This is an easy way to identify the two groups, but the identification of the individual species is most difficult and requires microscopic examination. The plants are very small. They have four petals and eight stamens (the characteristic numbers for members of the evening primrose family). The white flowers are borne in the axils of the slender leaves. The fruit is a pod with two rows of seeds.

Gayophytum ramossissimum belongs to the group in which the branches fork. It may sometimes exceed twenty centimeters in height.

136

137

136. **Evening Primrose** *Oenothera caespitosa*

Oenothera could be called the type genus for the evening primrose family. Certainly it is the largest genus of the family. Lehr's *Catalogue* lists more than two dozen species.

The genus is easy to identify. Individuals have four sepals, four petals, and eight stamens. The petals may be yellow, red, pink, or white, but yellow is the dominant color. The species that are yellow have the common name Sundrops besides being called evening primroses. *Oenothera caespitosa* has white petals, aging to pink. They open in the evening, bloom all night, and are large, beautiful, and fragrant.

137. **Cut-Leaf Evening Primrose** *Oenothera coronopifolia*

This primrose is called Cut-Leaf because of its sharply toothed or divided leaves. Like *Oenothera caespitosa* it has white petals fading to pink, but the flowers are smaller.

138. **Brown-eyed Primrose** *Oenothera claviformis*

The "brown eyes" of this primrose are the brownish red spots at the bases of the white petals. The flower cluster is racemose. The leaves are pinnately compound and mostly basal. The plant is common in the dry desert sands below four thousand feet.

139. **Heart-leaved Primrose** *Oenothera cardiophylla*

The heart-shaped leaves of this primrose are covered with hairs, giving them a grayish green color. The flowers are yellow. The annual or more often perennial plants may attain a height of forty centimeters.

140. **Evening Primrose** *Oenothera pallida*

The pale flower of *Oenothera pallidula* is, in size, like the flower of the Brown-eyed Primrose *(O. claveaformis)*. Evening Primrose is also found in Arizona, southwestern Utah, and the Death Valley of California. It grows on canyon slopes of the desert areas.

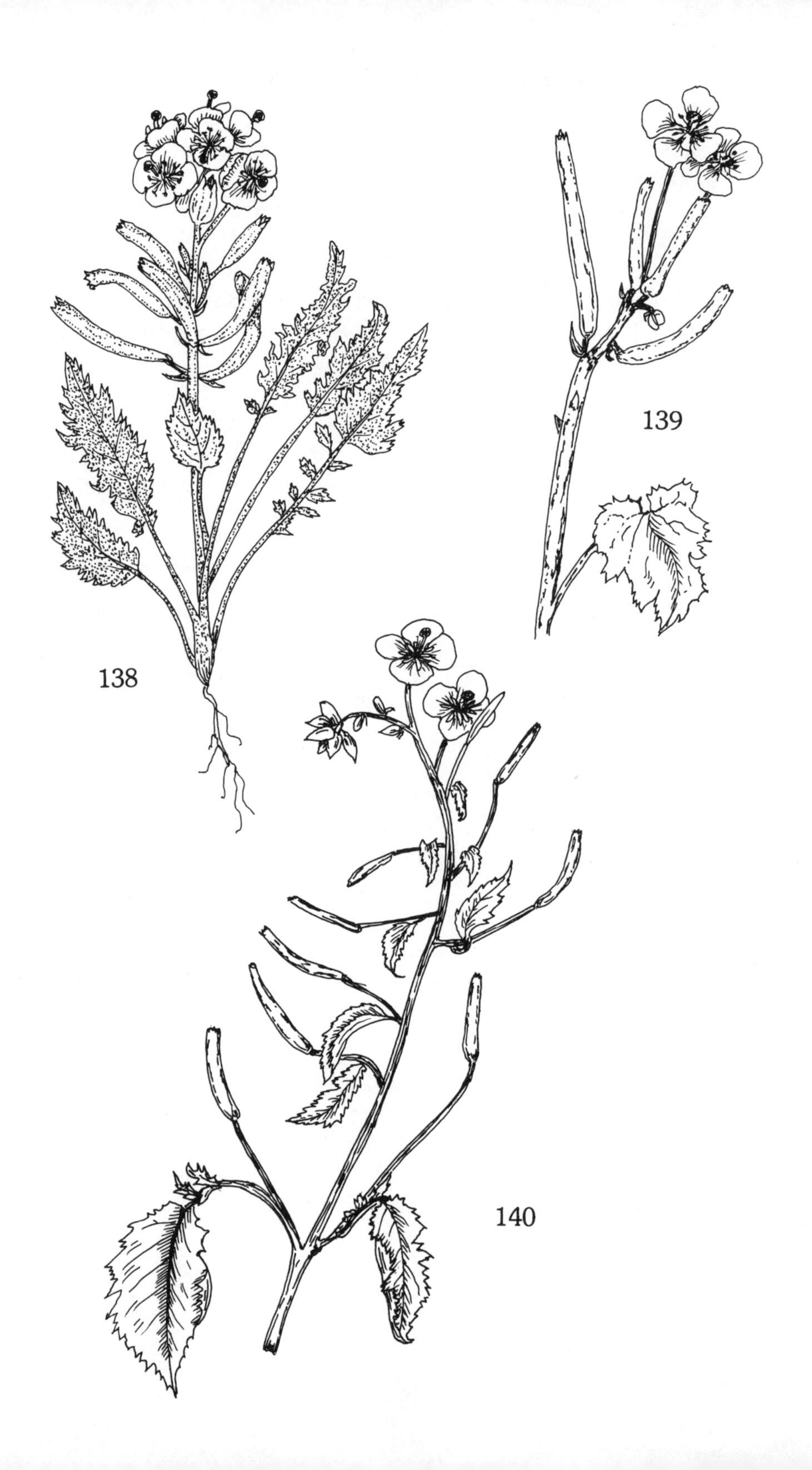
138
139
140

UMBELLIFERAE

Parsley Family

The characteristic flower arrangement of the Umbelliferae is, of course, the umbel, in which all the pedicels originate at the same point. The compound umbel has the branches again branched at the tips. Various garden vegetables (carrots, parsnips, celery, and parsley) and condiment plants (caraway, fennel, dill, anise, and coriander) belong to this family. Some of the umbellifers are poisonous—the water-hemlock and the poison-hemlock. Carrying out a death sentence, Socrates died by drinking hemlock poison.

141. **Cow Parsnip** *Heracleum lanatum*

The Cow Parsnip grows to be from one-third of a meter to over two meters tall. It has hollow stems. The large leaves are compound—three parted—with several irregular, toothed lobes. The umbels are large and flat-topped. The white flowers are larger on the edge of the umbel than toward the center. Figure 141 shows a leaf with its conspicuous basal sheath. New Mexicans call the plant Bear Weed. Other common names are Cow-Cabbage, Masterwort, and Hercules Parsnip. Domestic and wild animals eat Cow Parsnip. The plant is also used as food by Indians and Eskimos. It has medicinal uses as well.

142. **Alpine Parsley** *Oreoxis alpina*

Mats of Alpine Parsley are found on rocky slopes of the high mountain deserts. The compact umbels are yellow flowered and the leaves are finely dissected.

143. **Porter Lovage** *Ligusticum porteri*

Porter Lovage is from twenty centimeters to one and one-half meters tall. It is a plant of the high deserts. It looks a great deal like the Queen Ann's Lace of the mid-eastern and eastern United States. Spanish-speaking people call it *osha* or *chuchupate*. Its celery-flavored stems are used to make soup. It is prized for its medicinal value in cases of stomachache, colds, flu, pneumonia, tuberculosis, fevers, cuts, rheumatism, headache, snake bite, and colic—quite a catalog of remedies. Spanish settlers and Indians used the hollow stems in place of cigarettes.

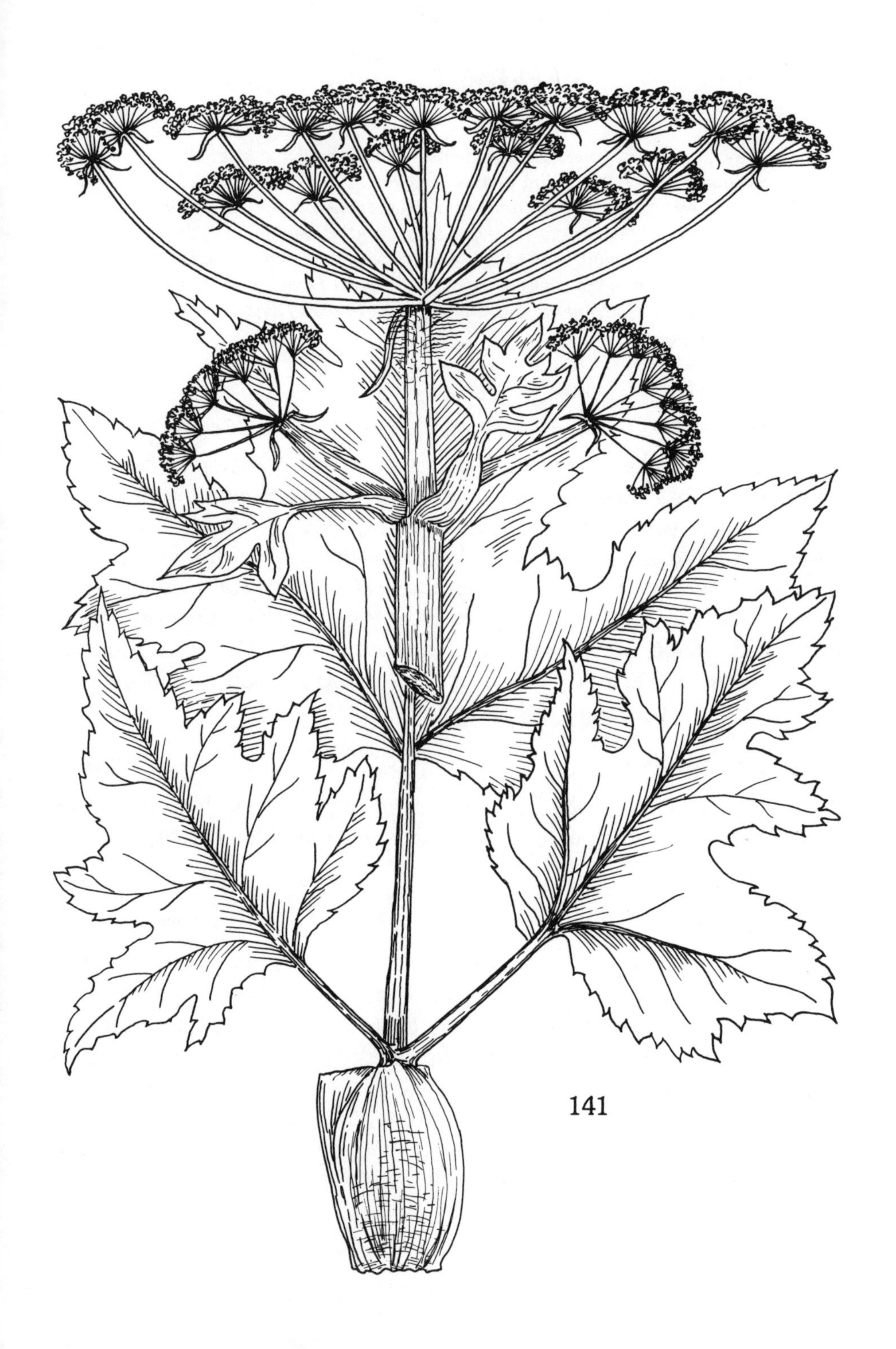
141

143
142

145
144

144. **Sweet Cicely** *Osmorhiza depauperata*

Sweet Cicely is a small plant—fifteen to sixty centimeters high. Its umbels are sparsly flowered and the fruits are about a centimeter long. The female name Cicely is from a Greek word, *seseli*, meaning "sweet-scented." The scent is like licorice. *Pimpinella*, a genus of the Umbelliferae, is the source of Anise, which has the licorice-like flavor common to the *Osmorhiza* genus.

145. **Mountain Parsley** *Pseudocymopterus montanus*

One way to distinguish Mountain Parsley from other Umbelliferae is by the presence of hairs on the stem just below the umbel. The flowers are yellow. The leaves are twice pinnate. The fruit is winged.

ERICACEAE

Heather Family

There are only a few members of the heather family that live in the southwestern deserts. They are low shrubs that have their five petals fused into a bell shape. There are ten stamens, which have the odd method of shedding their pollen through pores at the tips. The leaves are evergreen, borne single or bunched, and are either broad or needle-like.

146. **Desert Manzanita** *Arctostaphylos glauca*

This Manzanita is found in the Piñon Pine–covered area along the south-western edge of the Joshua Tree National Monument. Manzanita means "little apple," as its fruit is shaped like an apple. Another common name is "Bear-Berry," which is the translation of the genus name—*Arctos* meaning "bear," and *staphylos* meaning "bunch or cluster of grapes." The berries have a single seed, stony and elliptic, and are food for wildlife. Juice of the berries can be used to make jelly and cider. The Indians have used it medicinally for treating rheumatism, urinary disorders, and anemia.

147
146

FOUQUIERIACEAE

Ocotillo Family

The ocotillo family is very small. The members are very puzzling but interesting. Botanists have attempted to classify them with other families, but they are too different from any family to have a place anywhere but in their own unique group. There is only one genus and few species. Their desert homes are in the southwestern United States and Mexico. Fouquieria splendens *exhibits so well the family characteristics that it is practical to describe this species instead of going into the details of the whole family structure and habit.*

147. **Ocotillo** *Fouquieria splendens*

Ocotillo is the diminutive of an Aztec word meaning "pine." *Fouquieria splendens* has several common names besides Ocotillo. Others are Coachwhip, Candle Flower, Candle Weed, Flaming Sword, and Slimewood. The genus is named for a French doctor, Fouquier. The species name is descriptive of the whole plant, especially the brilliant scarlet flowers. Ocotillo competes with Saguaro in furnishing splendor to the Arizona desert. The shrub may have as many as a hundred thorny canes in one bunch.

The thorns are really the stems (petioles) of the first leaves, the blades of which soon fall. Many secondary leaves arise in the axils of the thorns after the rains, but fall during the droughts between rains. The showy clusters of flowers bloom in early spring at the tips of the canes.

One use of the canes is for firewood—the bark is full of resin and burns with great heat and heavy smoke. The flowers and seeds are edible.

OLEACEAE

Olive Family

To the olive family belong not only the edible olive but several popular ornamentals—the lilacs, privets, jasmines, many species of Syringa, *and the ashes. Leaves of the members are usually opposite, simple or pinnately compound, sometimes evergreen. Flowers have four-parted, joined corollas.*

148. **Tanglebrush** *Forestiera neomexicana*

Tanglebrush is a large, much-branched shrub. The leaves are often fascicled. The flowers are so closely bunched that a group of flowers looks like a single flower. The wood is very hard, and the Hopi Indians are said to have used it to make digging instruments.

149. **Twinberry** *Menodora scabra*

Twinberry can be found in many states—western Texas, southern Utah, northern New Mexico, California, and Arizona. The plant grows to be ten centimeters tall. The flowers are yellow. The species name *scabra* means "rough," and both the leaves and stems are rough surfaced.

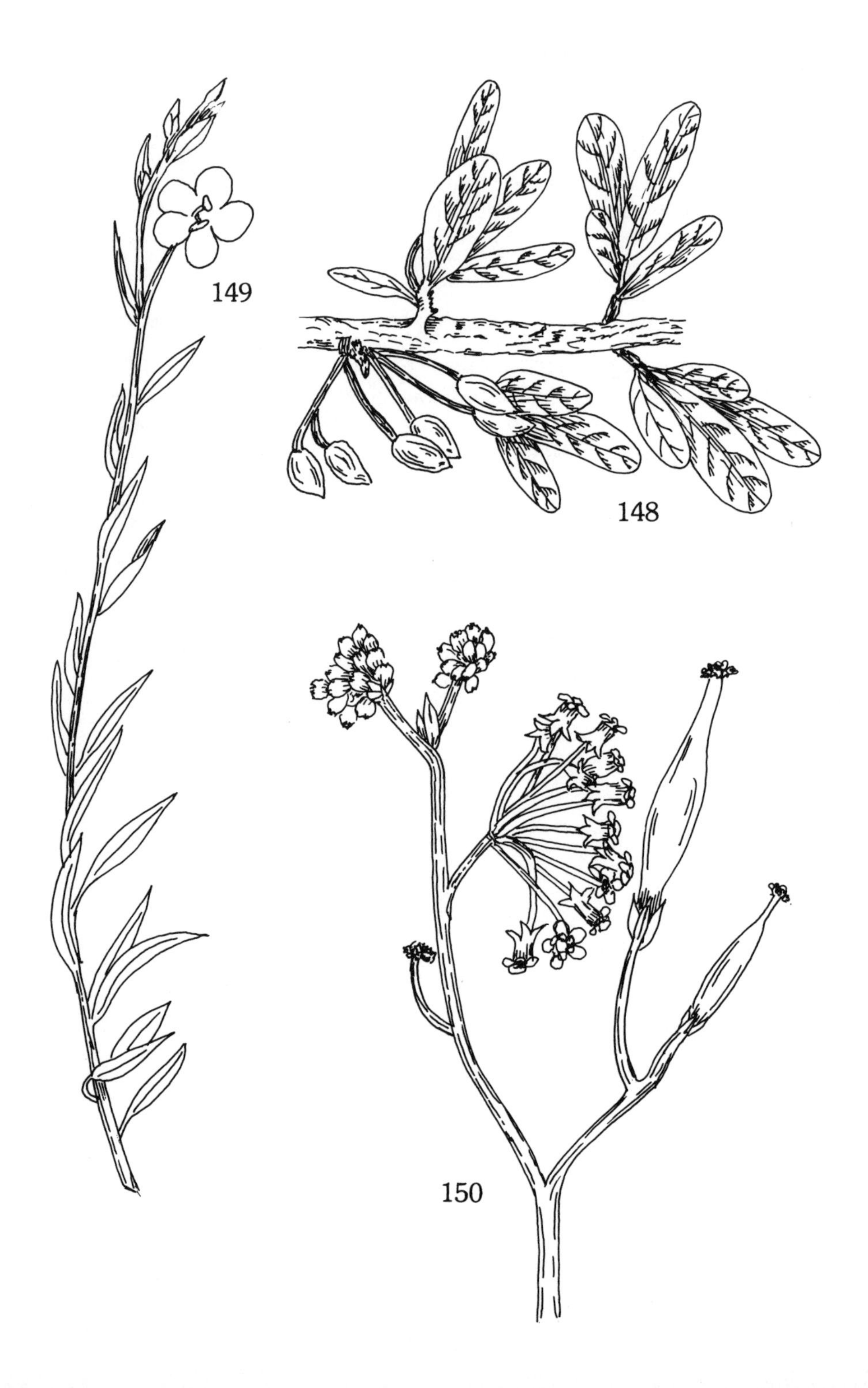
149
148
150

ASCLEPIADACEAE

Milkweed Family

There are about 2,500 species of milkweed and they are mostly tropical plants. They have milky juice, as the common name of the family suggests. The scientific family name is for the great Father of Medicine, Asclepiades. The leaves are usually simple and opposite. The flower clusters are stemmed, terminal, or axillary umbels. The peculiar flowers, characteristic only of this family, have a structure called a corona, or crown. It surrounds the pistil. The central stigma is flat and five lobed. The somewhat united encircling anthers are, in turn, encircled by five nectar-containing hoods. This combination of stigmas, anthers, and hoods makes up the corona.

The fruit consists of two follicles. Each follicle is packed with many seeds, each topped with a tuft of silky hairs. The packet of seeds looks like a small scaly fish. When the follicle splits, the seeds float away on their parachutes of expanded silk.

150. **Ajamete** *Asclepias subulata*

Ajamete is a shrubby milkweed which is found in the deserts and dry slopes of western Arizona. Rubber can be made from the milky juice (latex) of this plant. The stems are gray-green. The leaves are threadlike and often fall before the flowers bloom. The flowers are yellowish white. The juice of some *Asclepias* species has been used medicinally to heal cuts, cure warts, and treat inflammatory rheumatism. Some species are used for food. Fibers of the plant have been used for string and fishnets. The milk has been made into chewing gum.

151. **Purple Climbing Milkweed** *Funastrum heterophyllum*

The genus name *Funastrum* means "rope star." The "rope" refers to the climbing stem and the "star" refers to the flower shape. A single stem could not be called a rope, but eight or ten stems can wind themselves into a sizable rope that climbs to the tops of tall trees.

151
152

POLEMONIACEAE

Phlox Family

The members of the phlox family typically have bell-shaped, five-lobed flowers arranged in a cyme at the tip of the stem. The fruit is a capsule.

152. **Starflower** *Eriastrum diffusum*

Starflowers grow at an altitude below six thousand feet, in sandy desert soils. They bloom from March to May, and when the season is extra rainy, they may cover large areas with their whitish blue blossoms. The alternate leaves are linear or deeply trifid.

153. **Gilia** *Gilia sinuata*

The basal leaves of *Gilia sinuata* form a rosette. They are pinnately lobed and are pubescent, as are the stems. The flowers vary in color from pale violet to white.

154. **Sky Rocket** *Ipomopsis aggregata*

The common name Sky Rocket is appropriate for this plant because of its brilliant, red-mottled, trumpet-shaped flowers scattered along the stems. The leaves are pinnately divided and the segments are often redivided. In the older taxonomy books genus *Ipomopsis* is included under *Gilia*, usually as a subspecies.

155. **Nuttall Gilia** *Linanthus nuttallii*

Nuttall Gilia has two characteristics by which the plant can be identified easily. It has a cymose inflorescence that is so closely packed that it looks like a head; its leaves look like whorls at the nodes but are really opposite, and each is parted into three to seven lobes. These bushy plants are very common on sandy and gravelly soils of the desert.

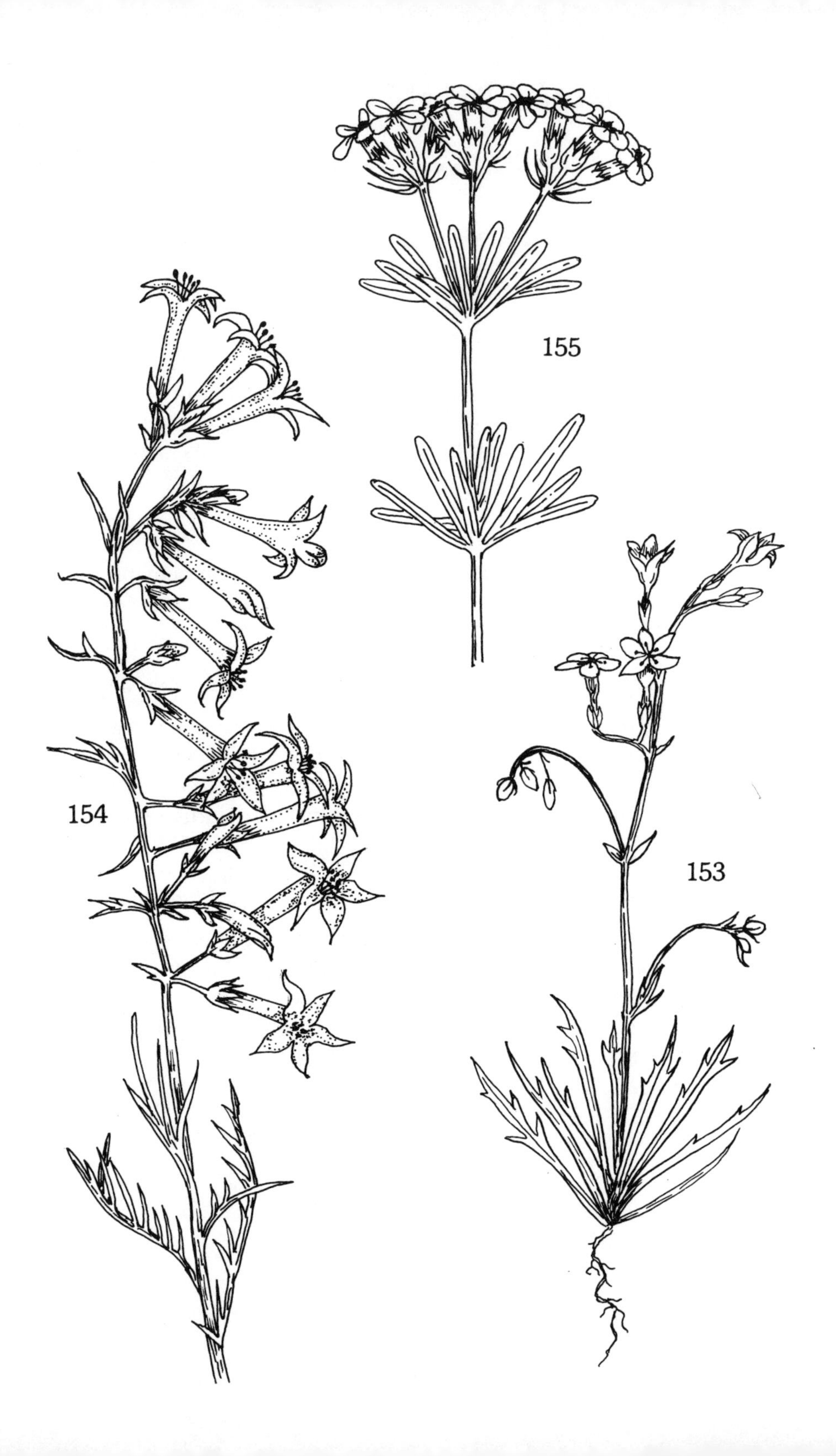
155
154
153

156. **Phlox** *Phlox nana*

Phlox means "flame" and refers to the brilliance of the flowers. The plant is a root perennial and branches underground so that the branches above ground look like individual plants. This kind of branching may produce loosely spreading plants or they may be crowded into mats, carpets, or cushions. The leaves are opposite.

The flowers form singly at the tips of the branches. The buds are convolute but spread out in a characteristic salverform with five lobes at the top of the slender tube. The stamens, of unequal length, are hidden in the flower tube.

157. **Desert Phlox** *Phlox tenuifolia*

Phlox tenuifolia is one of several species that have been brought under cultivation. It is used, like shrubbery, to plant in flower beds. The flower color, as with *Phlox nana*, varies from white to purple.

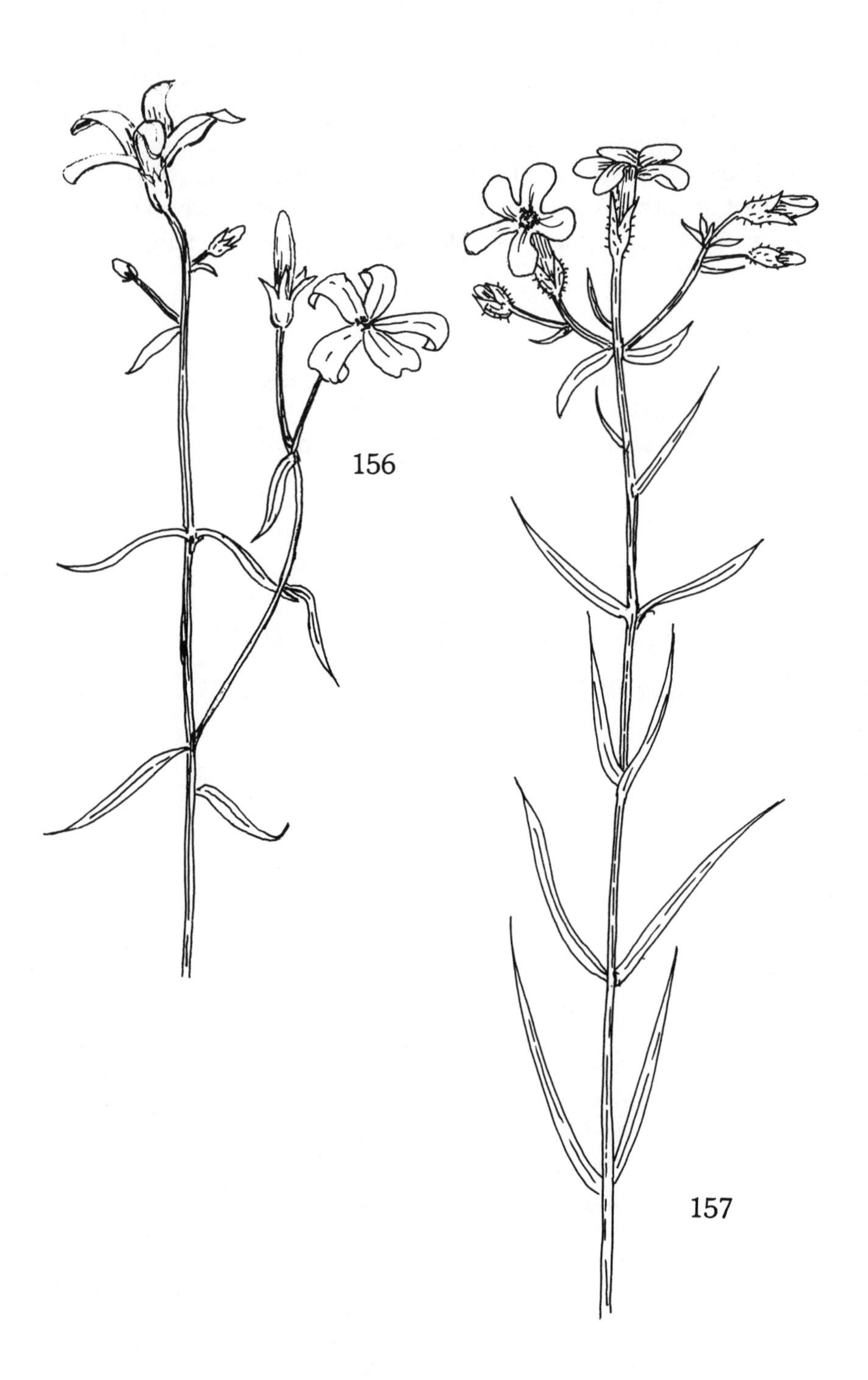
156
157

HYDROPHYLLACEAE

Waterleaf Family

The name waterleaf is a direct translation of Hydrophyllaceae and probably refers to the fact that the plant tissues are watery or juicy. Many members of the family are native to the southwestern United States. Leaves of the plants are formed singly at the nodes or are arranged in a basal rosette. Flowers are of several colors—blue, purple, white, or even yellow. The inflorescence is cymose.

158. **Baby Blue-Eyes** *Nemophila menziesii*

The genus name of Baby Blue-Eyes means "grove loving." The species name is for the Scottish botanist Archibald Menzies (1754–1842), who was also a surgeon. He visited California many times with the ship *Discovery*, captained by George Vancouver, the English navigator and explorer. The plant and its subspecies is well distributed in southern California, penetrating into the western edge of the Arizona desert. The flowers are blue, dotted or veined with purple. The leaves may be pinnately divided into nine to eleven oblong, toothed segments.

159. **Wild Heliotrope** *Phacelia distans*

Wild Heliotrope is also called Scorpion Weed because of its coiled inflorescence, resembling a the scorpion's tail. These plants are found in the shade of shrubs at low elevations of the desert. The blue flowers bloom from March to June.

160. **Lacy Phacelia** *Phacelia tanacetifolia*

The genus name, *Phacelia*, refers to the clustered flowers of this plant, and the species name means "tanzy-like leaves." The plant is found growing in the shade of Cat's-Claw, Ironwood, and Creosote Bushes. Wild Heliotrope and Lacy Phacelia are look-alikes as to the flower color, but the latter is a larger plant. As is often true of other members of the waterleaf family, Lacy Phacelia grows on the edge of the California desert and laps over into Arizona.

158
159
160

BORAGINACEAE

Borage Family

Members of the borage family differ widely in appearance, but almost all of them have coiled, cymose inflorescences. The bases of the flowers are funnels or tubes with horizontal, salverform, spreading lobes at the top. The borages are not important economically but are much used as ornamentals.

161. **Fiddleneck** *Amsinkia intermedia*

Fiddleneck is a rough plant covered with bristles. Its one-sided, coiled inflorescence looks like a fiddle head, hence the name. The flowers are orange colored. Young plants are good for forage, but the ripe nutlets, when eaten, are said to cause cirrhosis of the liver.

162. **Bearded Forget-me-not** *Cryptantha barbigera*

The "beard" of this Forget-me-not refers to the hairiness of the leaves and stems. The flowers are white and borne on long stems.

163. **Narrow-leaved Forget-me-not** *Cryptantha angustifolia*

The species name means "narrow-leaved," but this is not a very good name for this plant because the leaves are not really narrow. The flowers are white. Like the other *Cryptanthas*, the plant is covered with stiff hairs that lie flat instead of being bristly. The plant is common along disturbed roadsides, and harvester ants may be seen there collecting the seeds.

164. **Nevada Forget-me-not** *Cryptantha nevadensis*

The Nevada Forget-me-not grows in a wide range of altitudes—from two hundred to two thousand meters. Sometimes the plant looks almost like a vine, particularly when it supports its limber stems on shrubs.

165. **Broad-nutted Comb Burr** *Pectocarya platycarpa*

The Broad-nutted Comb Burr has broad, toothed margins on its nutlets, which is a distinguishing characteristic of the comb burrs. Figure 165 shows a detail of the four nutlets with their toothed margins. The flowers are white and the leaves are narrow.

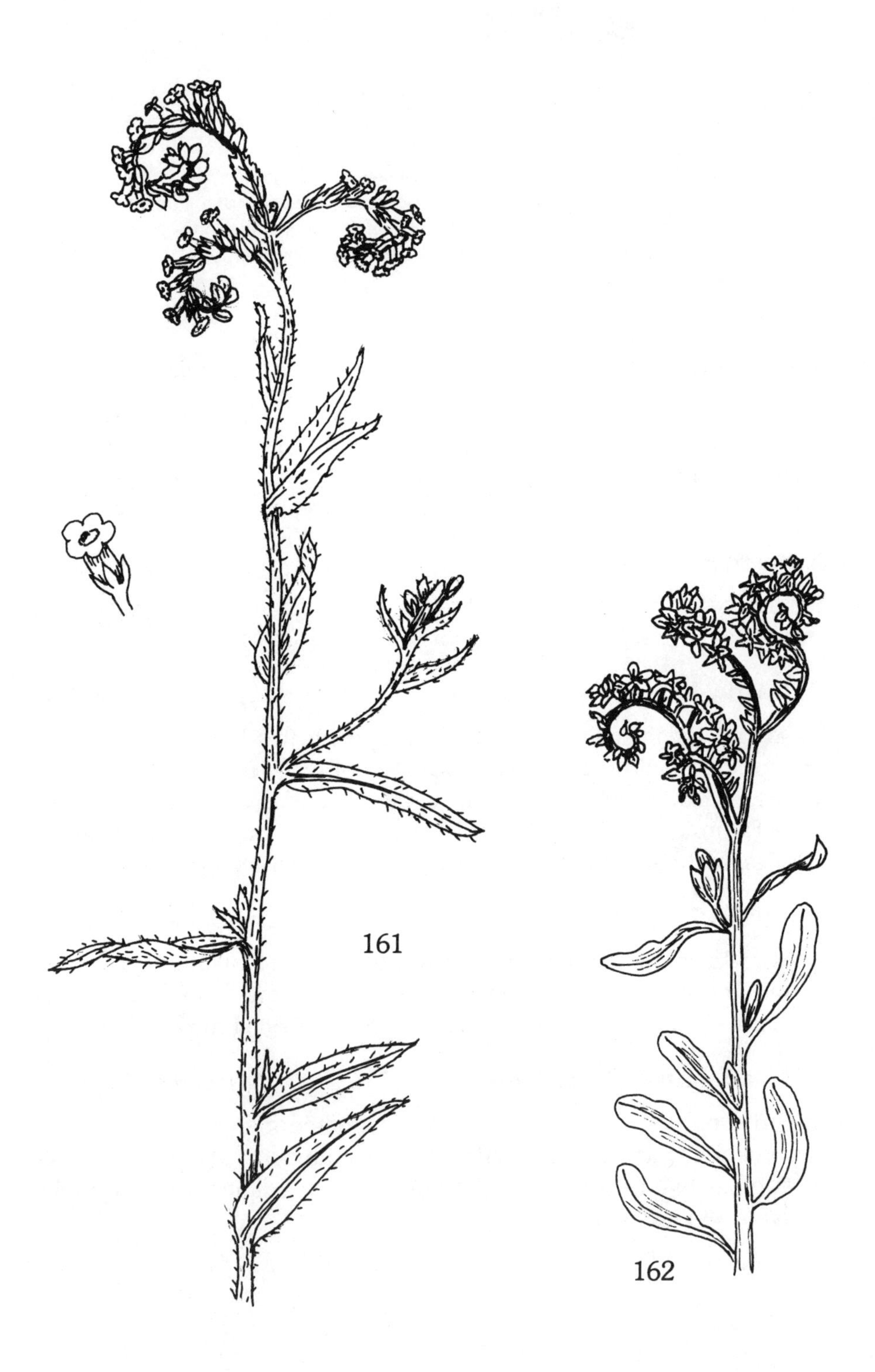
161
162

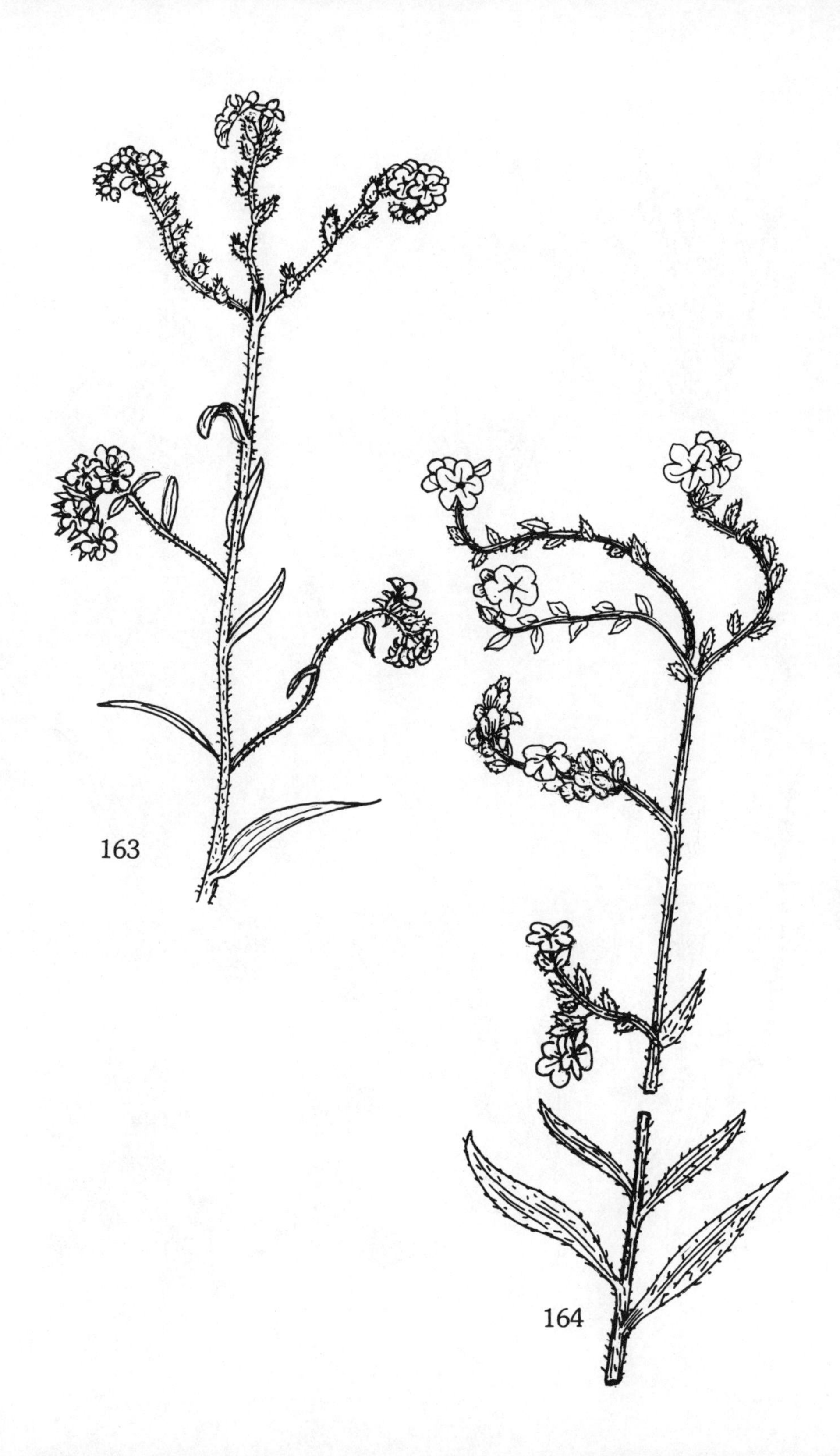
163
164

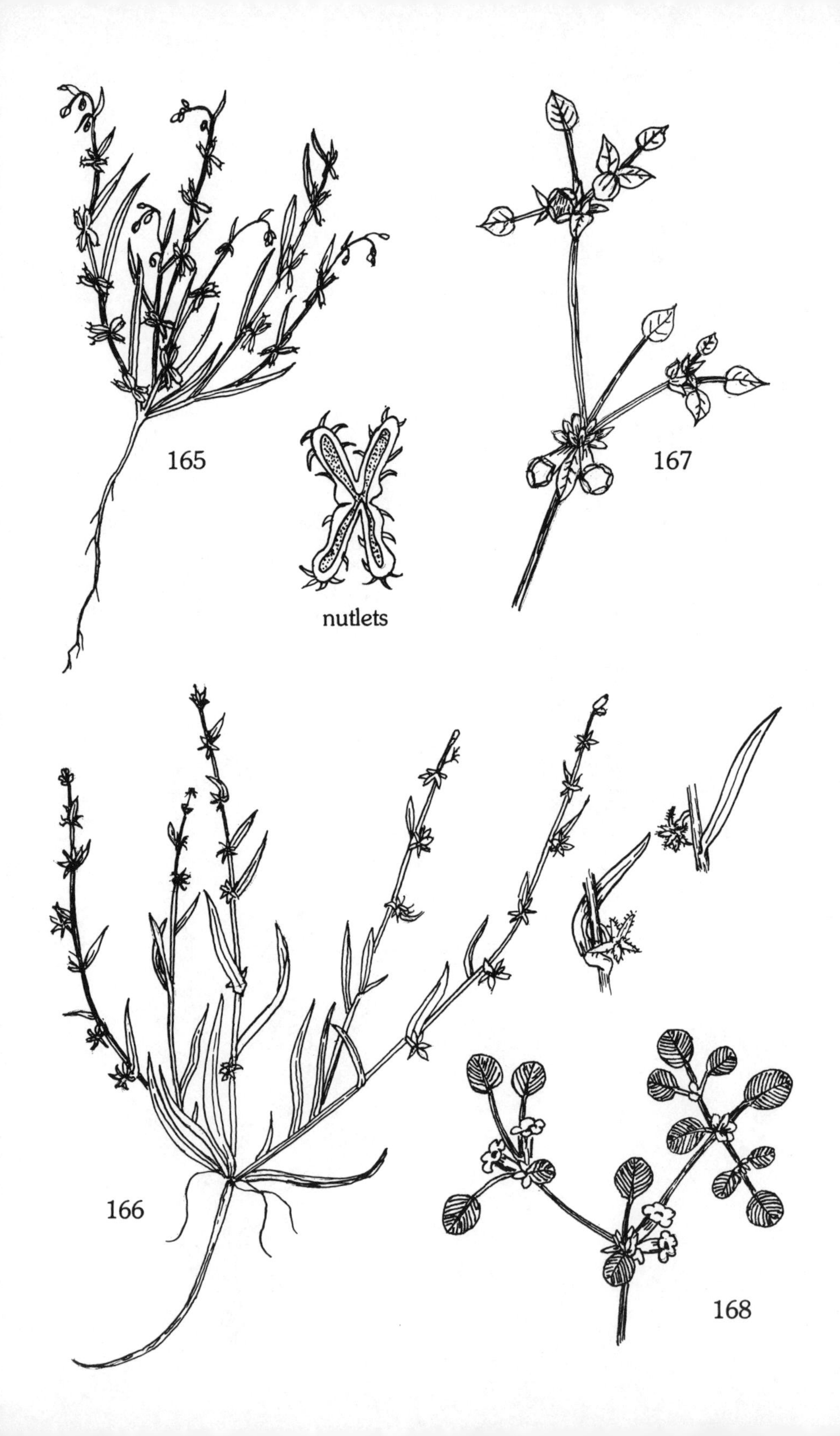
165
nutlets
167
166
168

166. **Arch-netted Comb Burr** *Pectocarya recurvata*

The Arch-netted Comb Burr has bent-backed nutlets. These comb burrs grow in the mountain regions of the desert. The stems lie flat on the ground. The leaves are narrow and the flowers white.

167. **Palmer Coldenia** *Tiquilia palmeri*

Palmer Coldenia is found in the Southwest on sand, clay, and silt soils. Like so many desert plants it needs a wet winter season to come to bloom. The flower is bluish white. The stems form a trailing mat that may grow enough to cover an area almost a meter in diameter.

168. **Plicate Coldenia** *Tiquilia plicata*

Plicate means "plaited," folded like a fan. This refers to the leaves, which only appear plaited because of the prominent, pinnately arranged veins. The plants grow in sandy flats at low altitudes in the deserts. The stems form gray-green mats, smaller than those of Palmer Coldenia. The flowers are light blue.

VERBENACEAE

Verbena Family

The verbena family comprises herbs and shrubs but no trees or vines. The plants of this family are mostly square-stemmed; leaves are opposite or whorled; flowers are perfect, having both stamens and pistils in the same flower. The flowers are usually two lipped and arranged in spikes or heads. The fruit is two to four nutlets or drupes. Some of the members found in flower gardens are Verbena, Lemon Verbena, Lantana, and Vitex.

169. **Verbena** *Verbena gooddingii*

Verbena is an old Roman name meaning "holy herb." *Verbena gooddingii* is a beautiful perennial found in the western part of Arizona and similar places in the Southwest. It grows at an altitude of around 1,600 meters and has a long flowering time, blooming from February to October. The plant consists of several branched stems. The inflorescence is a spike with the flowers at the tip in a flattened cluster. The flowers are purple, with five petals almost radially arranged, but the outer lobes are larger than the inner ones. The opposite leaves are three lobed with coarse toothing.

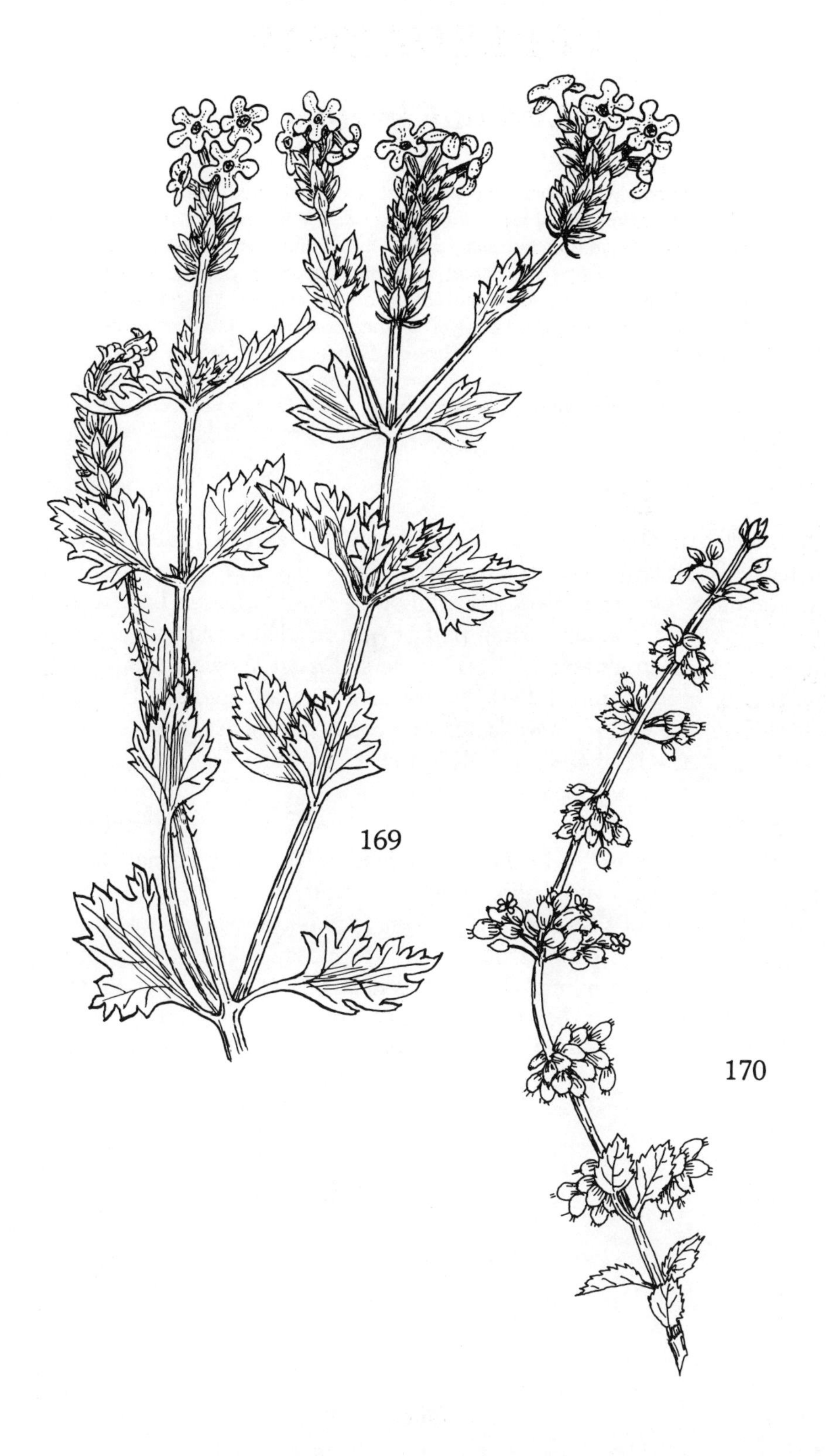
169
170

LABIATAE

Mint Family

Many aromatic oils, such as peppermint, spearmint, and menthol, are produced by the members of this family. The genus Mentha *includes producers of favorite odors and flavors. Among these are the cultivated rosemary, lavender, sage, thyme, marjoram, savory, and basil. There are wild ones that produce agreeable odors and tastes. The botanical name of the family, Labiatae, refers to the two-lobed upper and three-lobed lower lips of the flowers. This makes five petals, which are joined at the base, forming a funnel. As with the above mentioned verbenas and several other families, the stems are square, with opposite leaves.*

170. **Desert Lavender** *Hyptis emoryi*

The species name is for Major W. H. Emory (1812–1887), director of the Mexican Boundary Survey. The genus name *Hyptis* means "reflexed." This refers to the turned back lower lip of the corolla. Desert Lavender is a shrub found in the southwestern part of Arizona. Its habitat is washes and canyons up to an altitude of 1,600 meters. Desert showers bring out the sweet odor of the shrub. Livestock browse desert lavender and bees make honey from the nectar. Verdins and gnatcatchers nest in the branches and line their nests with the wooly calyx lobes of the plant.

171. **Betony** *Stachys palustris*

Another common name for Betony is Hedge Nettle, so named because some of the species live where hedges are cultivated. The species name, *palustris*, means of the marshes. Betony grows in moist mountain areas. Its square stem, two-lipped flower, and opposite leaves well represent characteristics of the mints. The plant is hairy. The flowers grow in threes in the axils of the leafy bracts. They are pale purple with darker spots on the lower lip, which is bent straight down.

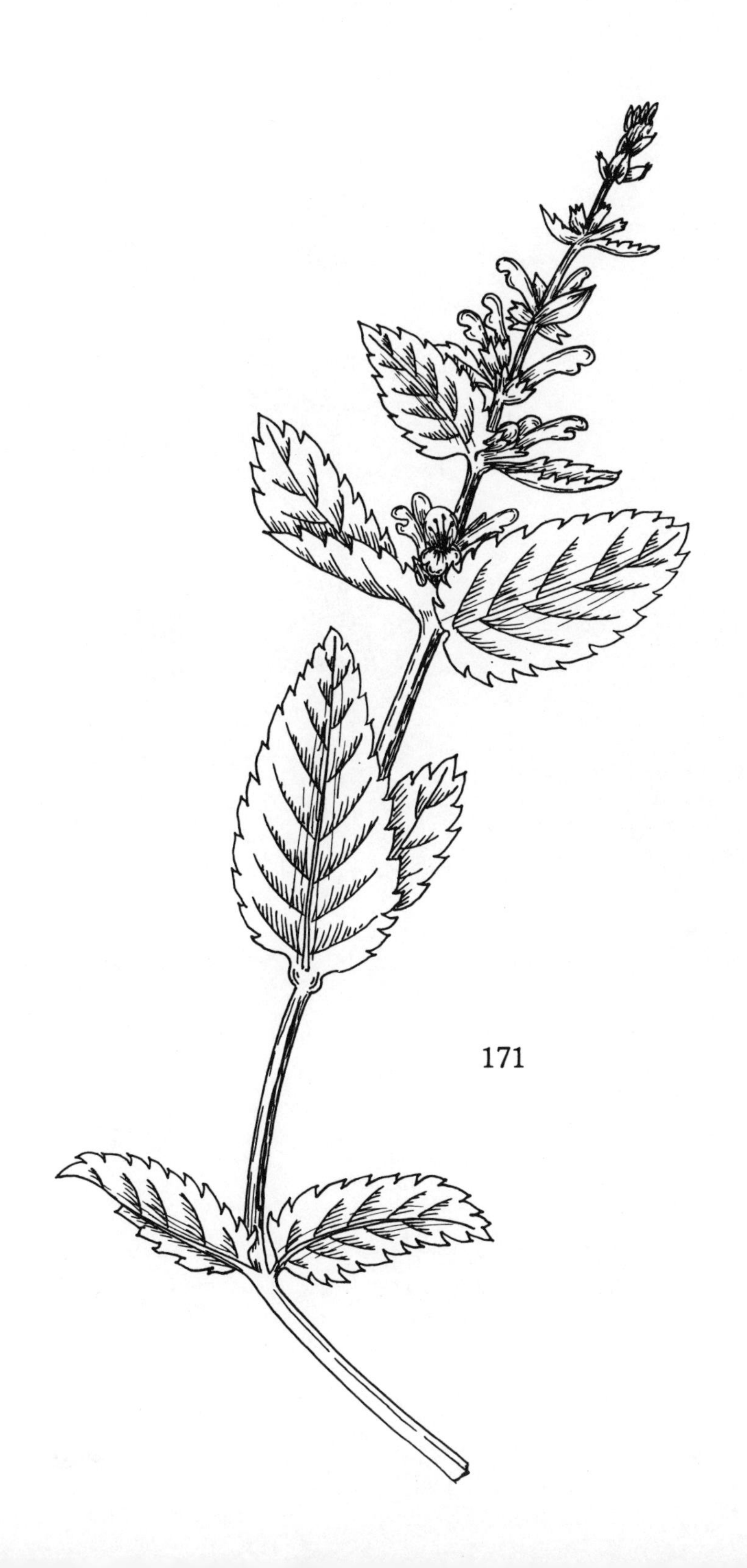

171

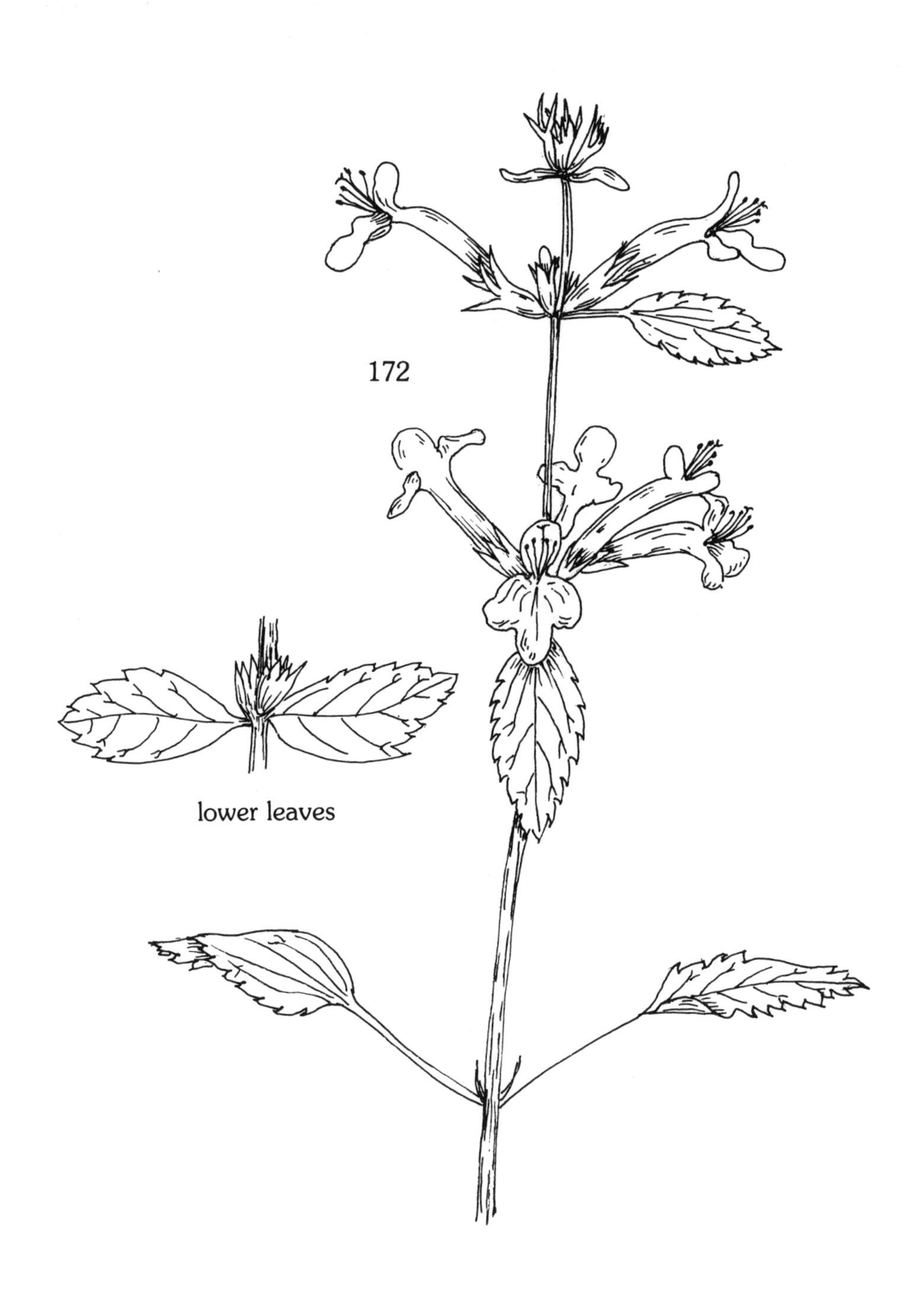
172
lower leaves

172. **Texas Betony** *Stachys coccinea*

Texas Betony has brilliant red flowers. The plant may grow to be almost sixty centimeters high. The lower leaves have shorter petioles than the upper ones. Both the stems and the undersides of the leaves have long hairs.

173. **Chia** *Salvia columbariae*

Chia is a medium-sized plant growing up to fifty centimeters in height. It grows on hillsides and smells like sage. This odor gives it another common name, Desert Sage. Flower stalks bearing a few leaves grow out of a basal rosette of leaves having one or two lobes, pinnately arranged. The blue flowers occur in closely packed whorls. The corolla has an indented upper lip, two side lobes, and a two-lobed lower lip. Chia seeds used to be an important part of the food of Indians. They were eaten raw or parched. Ground into flour, the seeds were mixed with water, sugar, and lemon to make a beverage.

Seeds were placed under the eyelids to help remove dirt particles and swallowed to treat inflamed digestive organs. Neither of these uses seems very soothing, but a poultice made from the seeds for treating gunshot wounds, may have been quite helpful. *Chia*, a word of Mayan origin, means "strengthening." This probably refers to the medicinal properties of the plant.

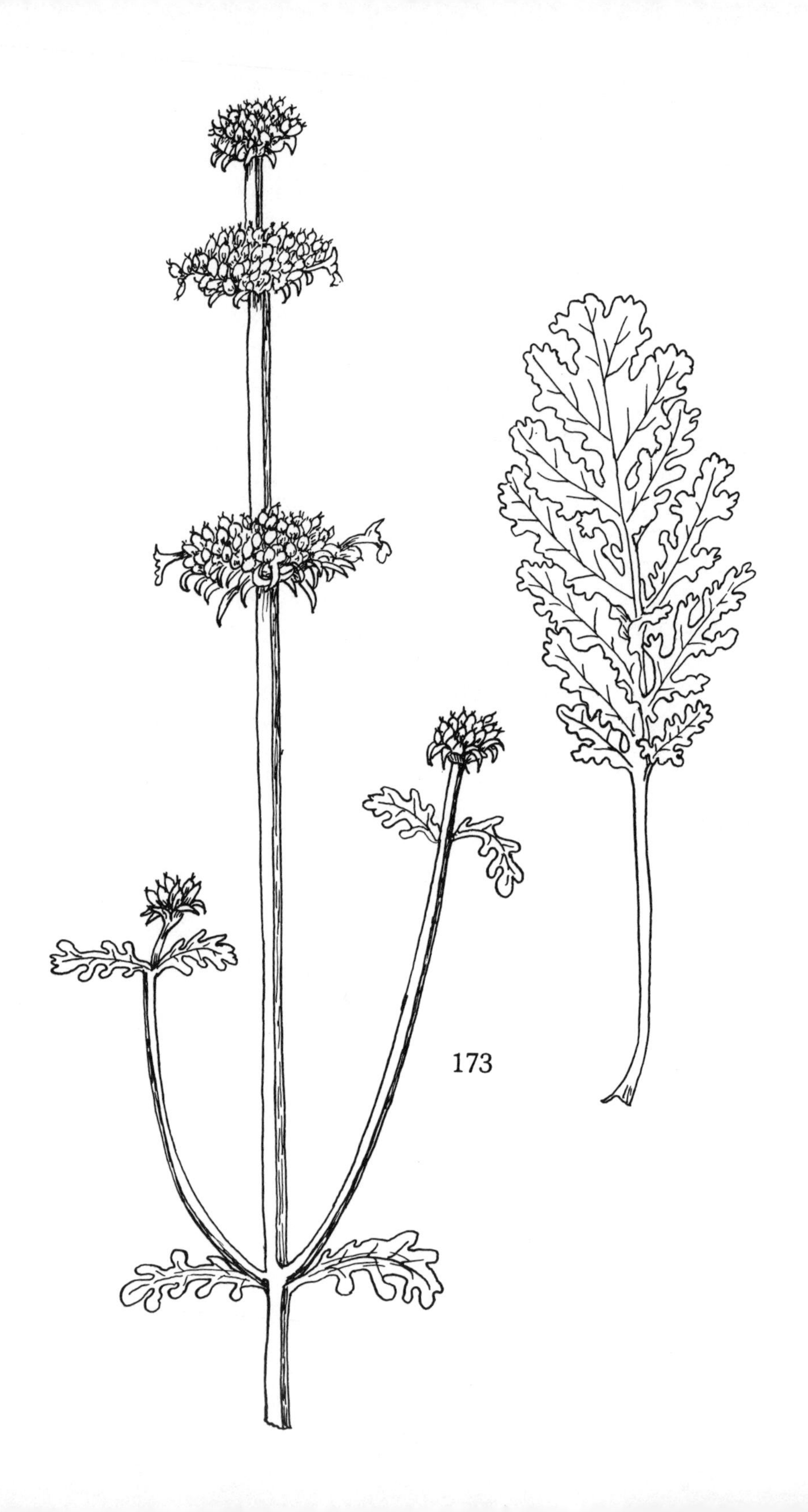

173

SOLANACEAE

Potato Family

The two thousand species of Solanaceae comprise herbs, vines, and small trees, widely distributed in temperate and tropical zones. Among them are many food plants, medicinals, and ornamentals. The genus Solanum *furnishes the Irish potato and eggplant. The genus* Lycopersicum *gives us the species* esculentum, *the tomato. Drug plants include Belladonna, Jimson Weed, Tobacco, and the members of the pepper genus* Capsicum. *The Jimson Weed gives us the drug stramonium. Poisonous alkaloids used as sedatives come from Henbane. Two species of Tobacco furnish nicotine. There are many varieties of* Capsicum, *the red peppers. Among them are the pimentos, paprika, chilis, bell peppers, and tabasco—the beautiful and bright berries of this family.*

174. **Desert Thorn Apple** *Datura discolor*

According to Lehr's *Catalogue*, there are four species of *Datura* found in Arizona and other southwestern states. The *Daturas* are the thorn apples and jimson weeds. They are large, poisonous plants.

Datura discolor has the characteristic funnel-shaped flower of the genus. The corolla is white, tinted with lavender. The numerous flat seeds are formed into a prickly capsule.

The Cahuilla Indians were given an extract of the plant at the time of their initiation into manhood, at which they danced until they became dizzy.

175. **Desert Tobacco** *Nicotiana trigonophylla*

Desert Tobacco is perennial and flowers the year around. The genus name, *Nicotiana*, comes from a sixteenth-century French ambassador to Portugal, Jean Nicot, who brought tobacco back to France. The plants are found in desert washes and canyons. They were used for smoking by the Yuma and Havasupai Indians, who grew them in the ashes of Mesquite that was burned for that purpose.

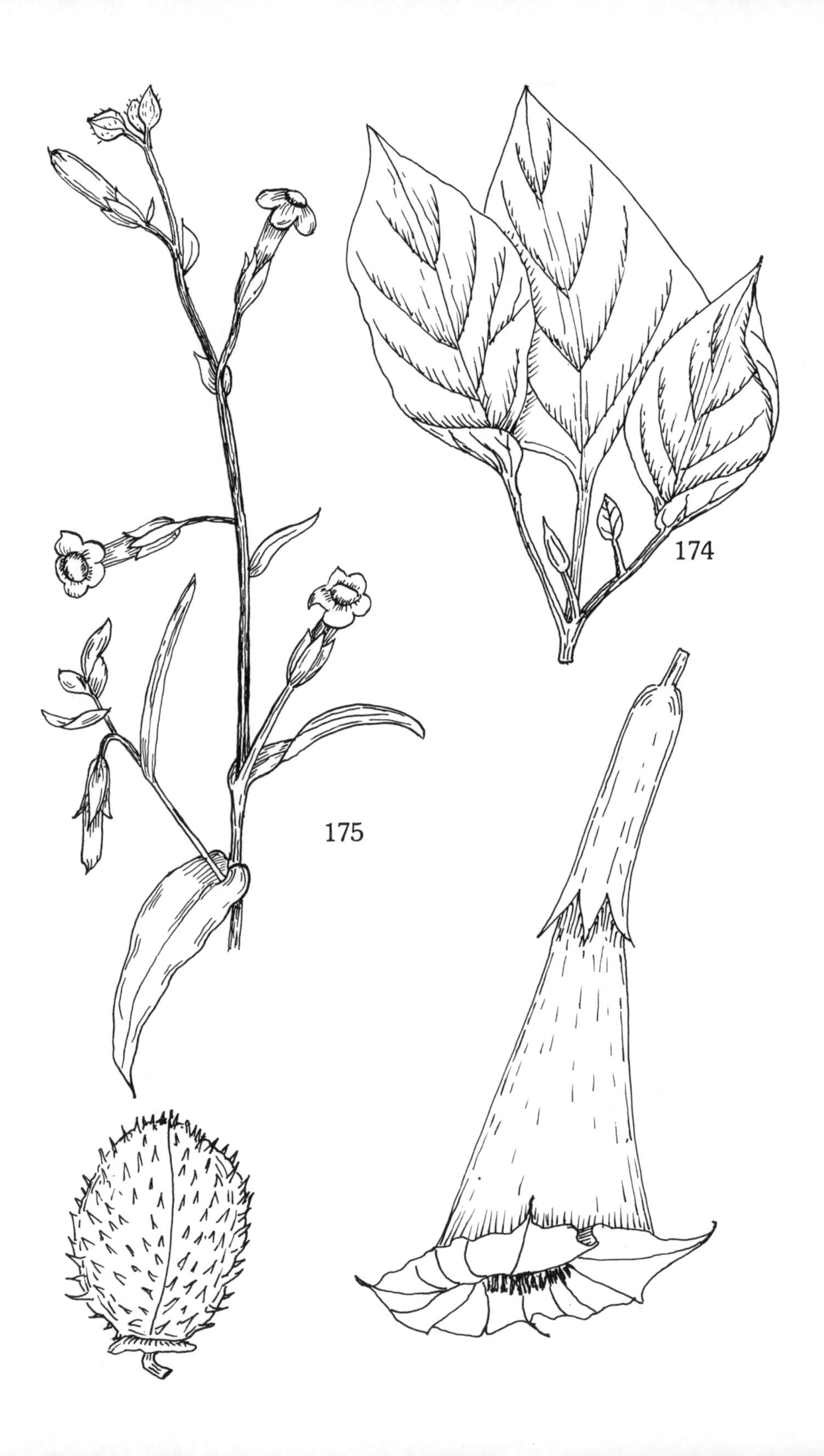
174
175

176

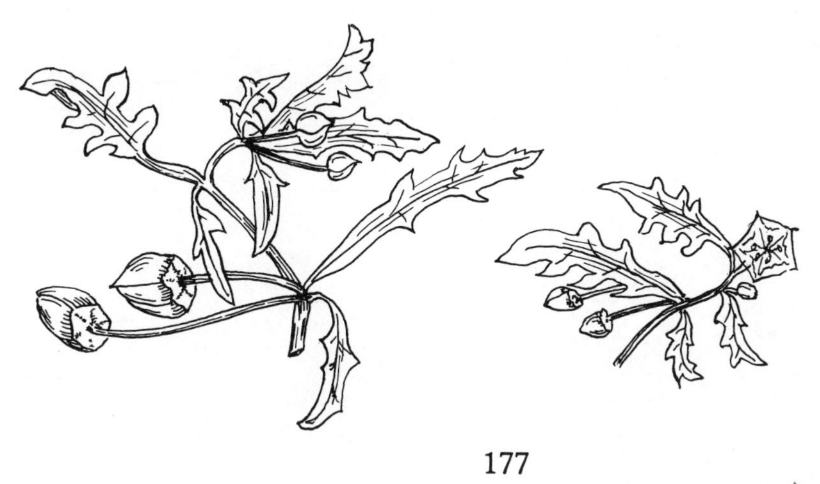

177

176. **Ground Cherry** *Physalis crassifolia*

The inflated, mature calyx of the Ground Cherry defines the genus name *Physalis*, Greek for "bladder." These green globes give another common name to the plant, Chinese Lantern, since they hang like little lanterns from the stems. The berries inside the "lanterns" are edible, either raw or cooked. They look like miniature tomatoes and can be made into delicious preserves. The flowers are creamy yellow.

177. **Purple Ground Cherry** *Physalis lobata*

The Purple Ground Cherry, sometimes called husk-tomato, grows on roadsides, plains, and mesas. It is a low-spreading plant with branches ten to thirty centimeters long.

It grows on dry soil in northern Arizona, where it is associated with Sagebrush. It has a long flowering period—from early spring to August.

178. **Douglas Nightshade** *Solanum douglasii*

This white-flowered nightshade grows on rocky slopes and in canyons. The plants are around fifty centimeters in both height and width. They have entire, dark green leaves. The flowers have a purple ring around the yellow cone made by the anthers. The berries are black.

179. **Wild Potato** *Solanum jamesii*

Another species, *Solanum fendleri*, has the same common name as *Solanum jamesii*—Wild Potato. Both species are much like our cultivated potato, although the tubers of the Wild Potatoes are smaller.

An interesting way of preparing Wild Potatoes for use as food was devised by the Hopi Indians, who cooked them by wrapping them in salt-impregnated clay and putting them in hot coals. The Hopis are also said to have made yeast from the Wild Potato.

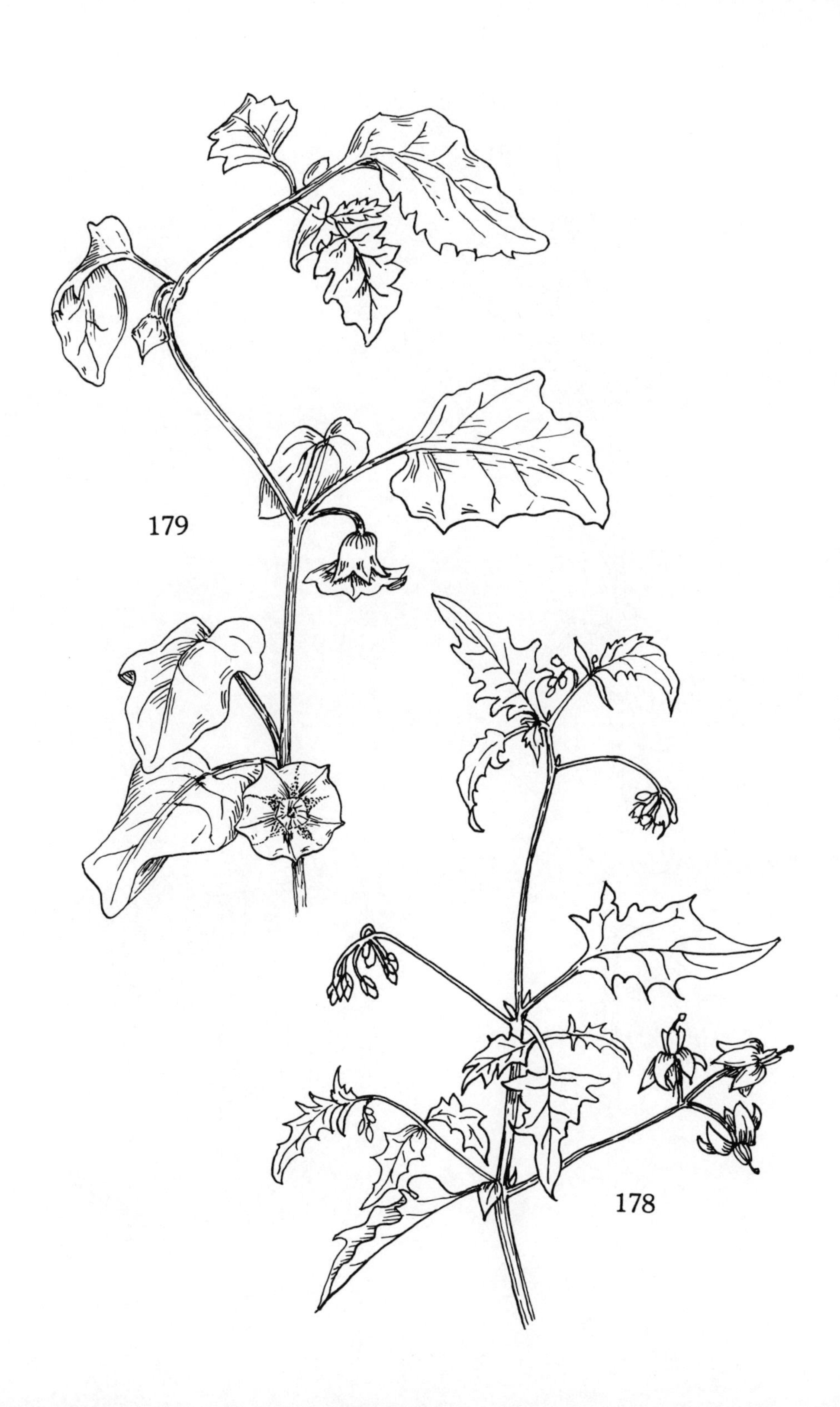
179
178

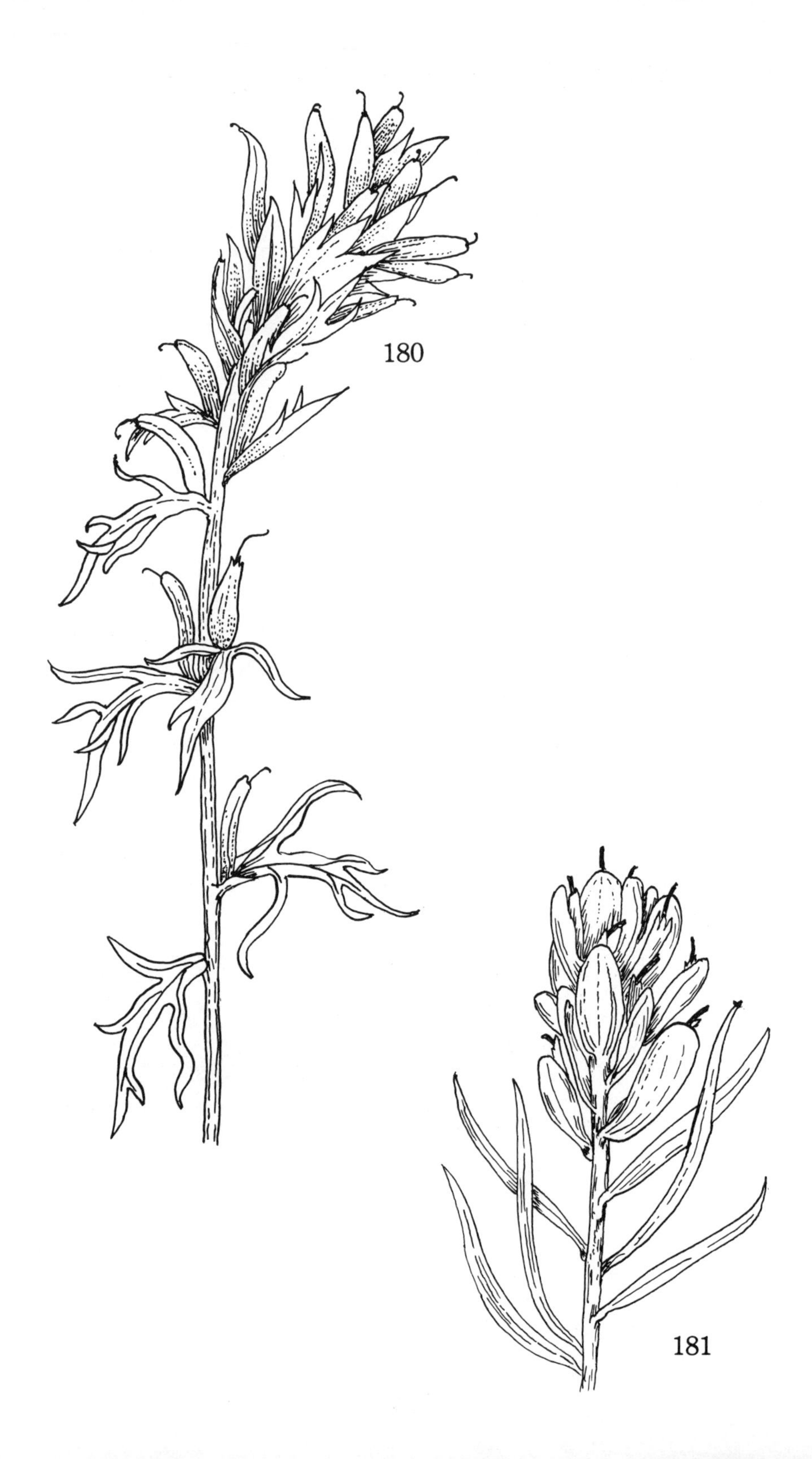
180
181

SCROPHULARIACEAE

Figwort Family

Other common names for the figworts are snapdragon and foxglove. The scientific name Scrophulariaceae is based on the belief that one species, Scrophularia nodosa, *was a remedy for scrofula. The drug digitalis comes from the foxglove.*

The foxgloves, snapdragons, beardtongues, monkeyflowers, and slipperworts are all popular ornamentals of gardens and greenhouses.

As with the mint family, the figworts are two lipped. The flowers are bilaterally symmetrical. Two lobes of the corolla form the upper lip and three the lower. There are two to four stamens with sometimes a sterile fifth. When there are four, they are two pairs of different lengths. The fruit is a pod that splits into two parts.

180. **Indian Paintbrush** *Castilleja chromosa*

Everywhere it grows, Indian Paintbrush is a favorite plant because of its scarlet flowers in a dense terminal cluster. The plants are around thirty centimeters tall. The plant is covered with short stiff hairs. The leaves are irregularly pinnatifid with narrow segments.

181. **Long-leaved Paintbrush** *Castilleja linearifolia*

As the species name *linearifolia* suggests, the Long-leaved Paintbrush has long narrow leaves instead of pinnatifid ones, as with the Indian Paintbrush.

The plant is not covered with hairs like the species *Castilleja chromosa.* Long-leaved Paintbrush blooms even longer than Indian Paintbrush—from April to October.

182. **Blue Snapdragon Vine** *Maurandya antirhinifolia*

The genus name *Maurandya* is for Catherina Pancratia Maurandy, botany teacher at Carthagena. This plant, a vine climbing by means of its flower and leaf stalks, grows in southern Arizona. The beautiful and unusual shape of the leaves is hastate—spear or arrowhead shaped. The flowers are showy, with two well-defined sets of petals.

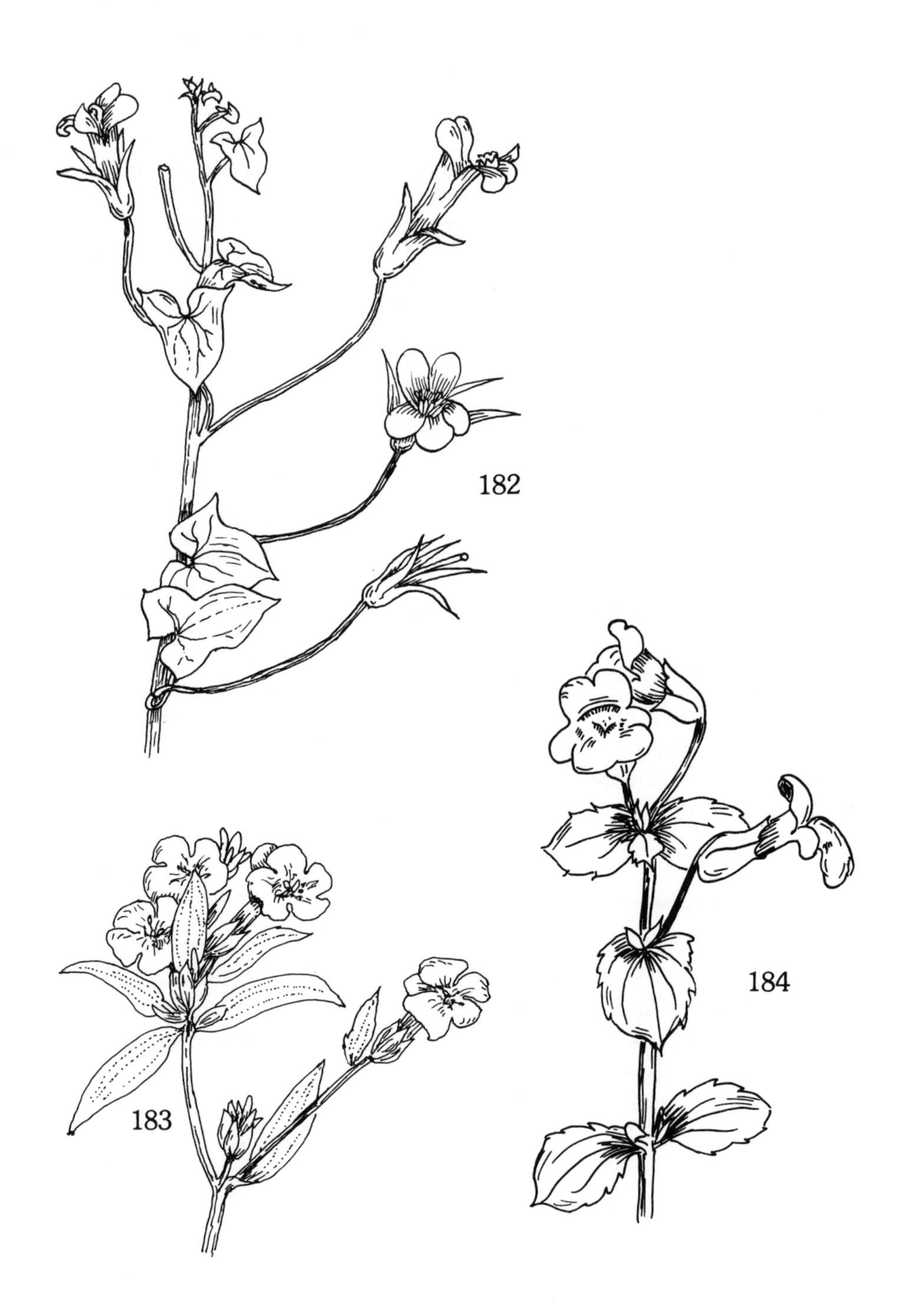
182
183
184

183. **Bigelow Monkeyflower** *Mimulus bigelovii*

Bigelow Monkeyflower has very large flowers for such a small plant. It grows in northwestern Arizona in canyons and washes and in similar places of the Southwest. In these dry habitats other species of this genus cannot survive.

All the *Mimulus* species of the desert are easy to recognize because of their similarity to the more familiar ones that live in moister habitats.

Bigelow Monkeyflower is reddish purple. The leaves are opposite, lanceolate to broadly ovate to obovate.

184. **Common Monkeyflower** *Mimulus guttatus*

Like Bigelow Monkeyflower, the Common Monkeyflower lives in washes and canyons. The plant is more spreading than Bigelow Monkeyflower. The leaves are variable but mostly obovate and sinuate-dentate. The flowers are bright yellow, spotted with red. The stems and leaves can be used in salads and as greens.

185. **Ghost Flower** *Mohavea confertiflora*

The genus name *Mohavea* is from the Mohave River, where this plant was first collected. It is common on sandy or gravelly soil in the deserts. The leaves are alternate and ovate-lanceolate. The corolla is pale yellow and the lips are decorated with lines of purple spots. Three of the five stamens are infertile.

186. **Mohave Owl Clover** *Orthocarpus purpurescens*

Mohave Owl Clover is a small annual plant that looks much like Paintbrush on account of its spike of colorful flowers. The upper lip of the flower is purplish red and the lower lip is white, tipped with yellow. The bracts and stems are purplish too, which adds more rich color to the spike. The blooming time is from late April through May. The leaves are pinnatifid and deeply divided into linear segments. All species of Owl Clover are grazed by cattle and sheep. The leafy flower stem looks like a small brush, which gives it its Spanish name, Escobita, meaning "little broom."

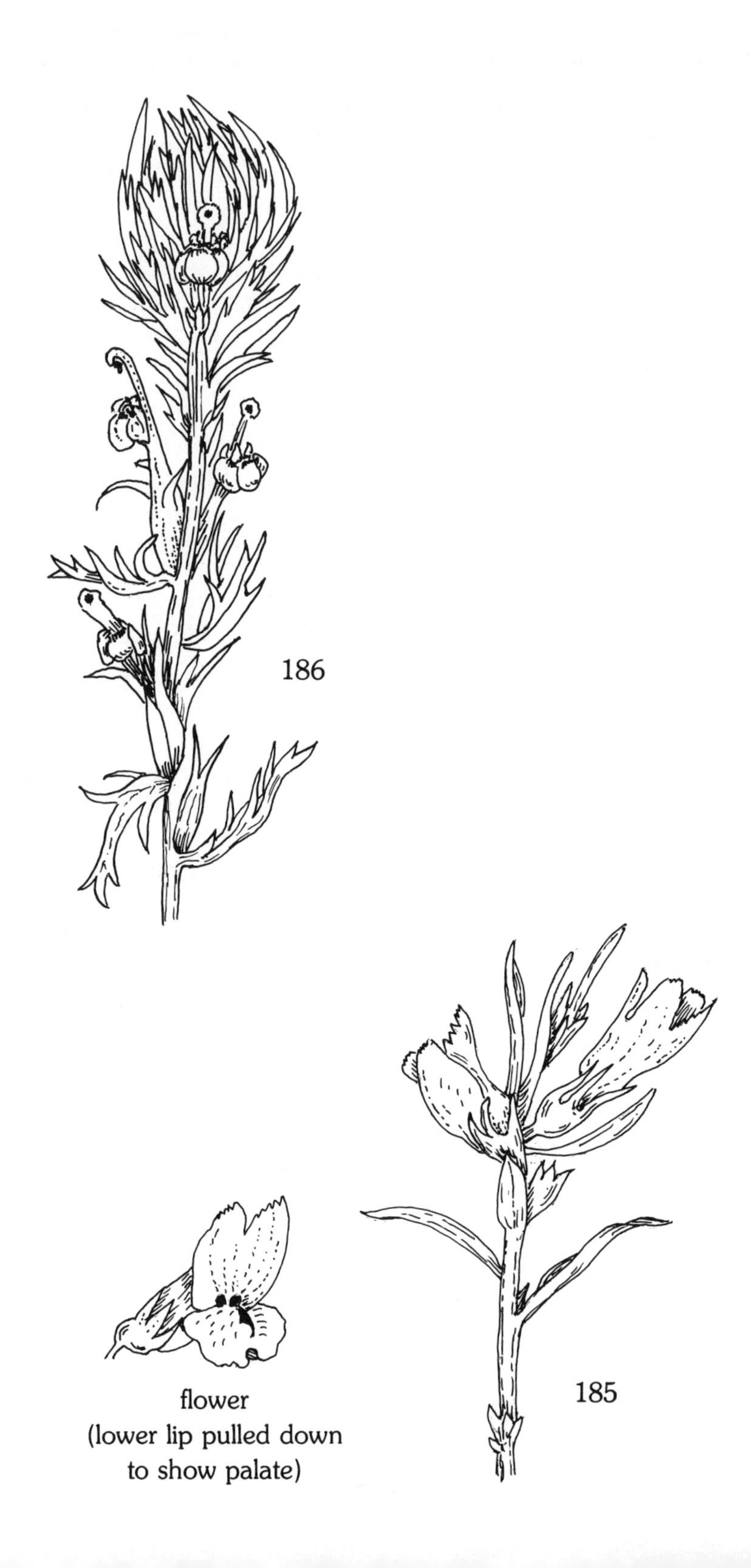
186
185
flower
(lower lip pulled down
to show palate)

187. **Mohave Beardtongue** *Penstemon pseudospectabilis*

The genus name *Penstemon* means "five stamens." Most members of the figwort family have four stamens, and the penstemons might as well have, for their fifth stamen has no anther and consequently no pollen. The common name, Beardtongue, refers to the brush of hairs on the tip or side of the sterile stamen.

Mohave Beardtongue is a tall plant sometimes reaching a height of fifty centimeters. The erect stems bear terminal inflorescences of rose-purple flowers that bloom from April to June. The lower leaves on the stem are lanceolate to ovate and the upper ones are connate-perfoliate (see Figure 187).

Spanish New Mexicans boiled the stems with the flowers and drank the brew for kidney trouble and to cure colds. Juice from boiling the flowers was used for poulticing running sores, renewing skin, and treating burns.

188. **Death Valley Penstemon** *Penstemon fruticiformis*

The species name *fruticiformis* means "formed like a shrub," and the Death Valley Penstemon is a small shrub growing twenty-four to thirty centimeters high. Descriptions of the color markings on the white flowers differ in different taxonomic works. They vary from purple to lavender-blue.

189. **Bush Penstemon** *Penstemon microphyllus*

The Bush Penstemon is another shrubby penstemon, taller than the Death Valley Penstemon, sometimes reaching a height of fifty centimeters. It is one of the food plants of the checker-spot butterfly, the most common butterfly in Southern California.

The habitat of the Bush Penstemon is the Juniper areas of desert mountains. The corolla is sulphur yellow. The leaves are small and elliptic, and the fruit is the usual many-seeded capsule characteristic of penstemons.

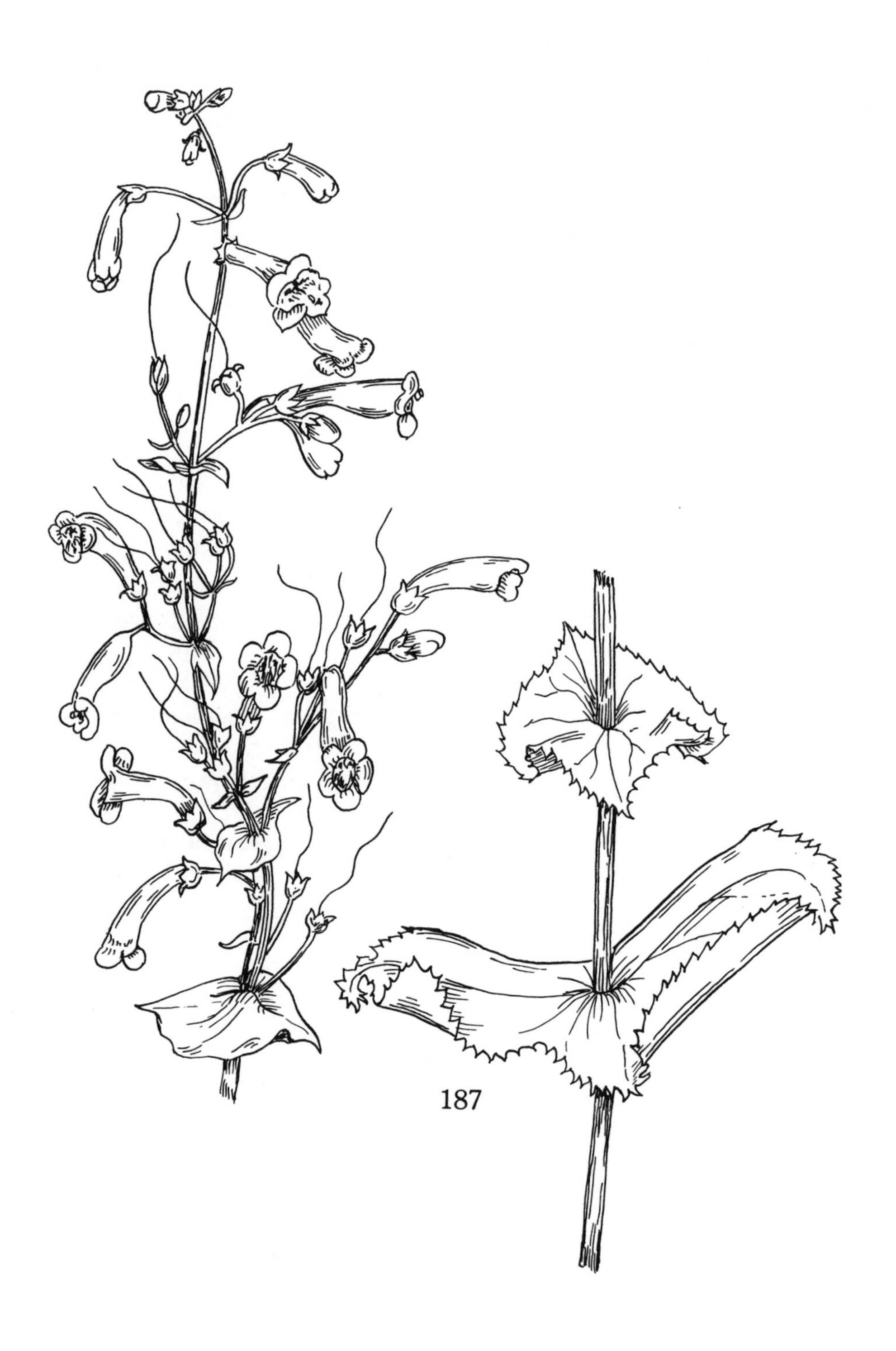

187

190. **Beardtongue** *Penstemon subulatus*

Penstemon subulatus is one of the species of the genus that has a "beard" on the fifth stamen, hence the common name, Beardtongue, is applied to all other penstemons that have this beard on the fifth stamen. The species *Penstemon subulatus* has beautiful scarlet flowers that bloom through April and May in the central and southern areas of Arizona as well as similar habitats of the southwestern United states. The upper and lower lips are almost alike and the tube is inflated. In the references it is called "fat."

191. **Speedwell** *Veronica wormskjoldii*

Veronica is an erect plant from eight to sixteen centimeters tall. The leaves are entire, opposite, sessile, and ovate to oblong. The flowers are dark blue. The plant grows in damp spots of the high deserts in Arizona.

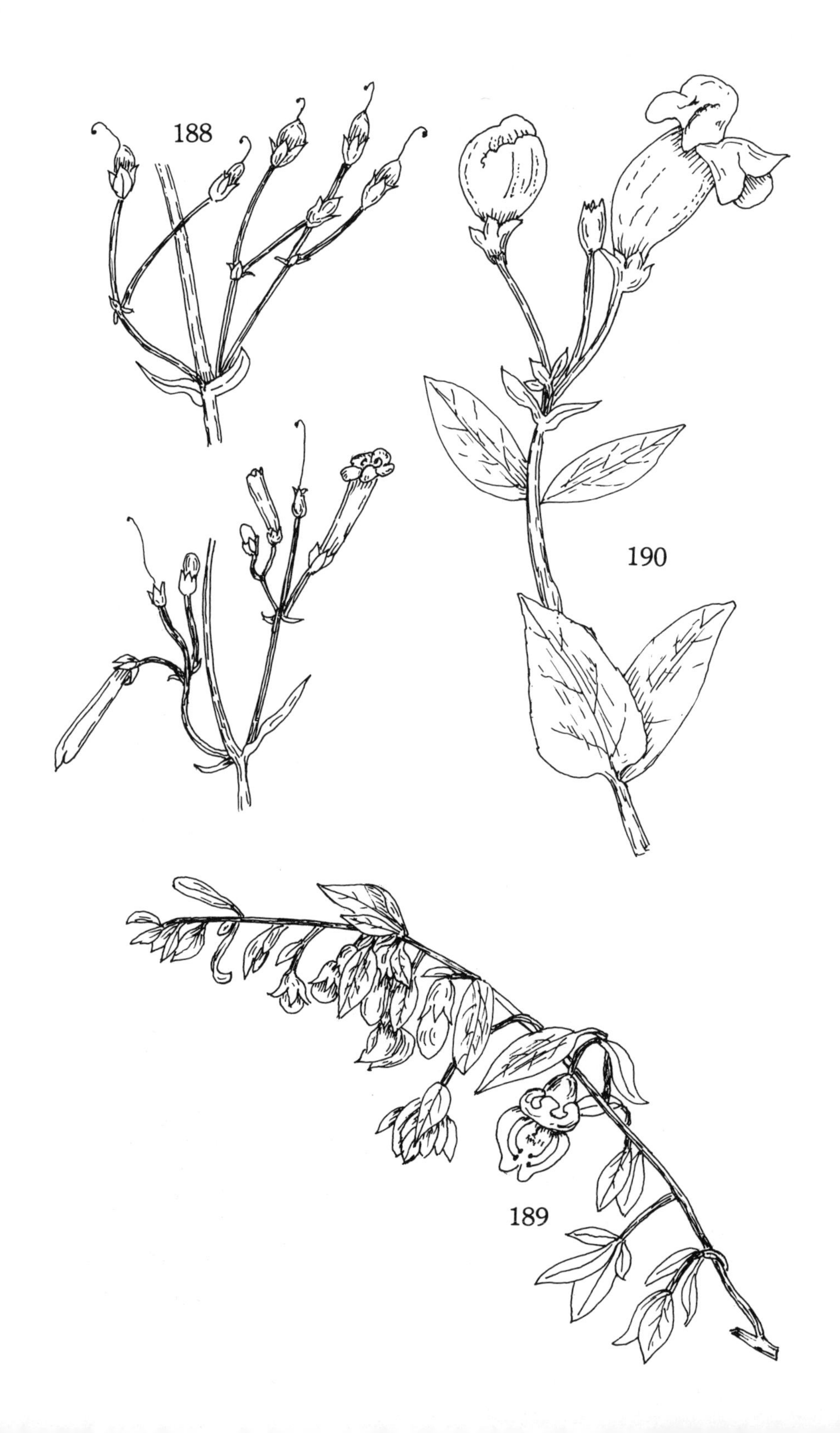
188
190
189

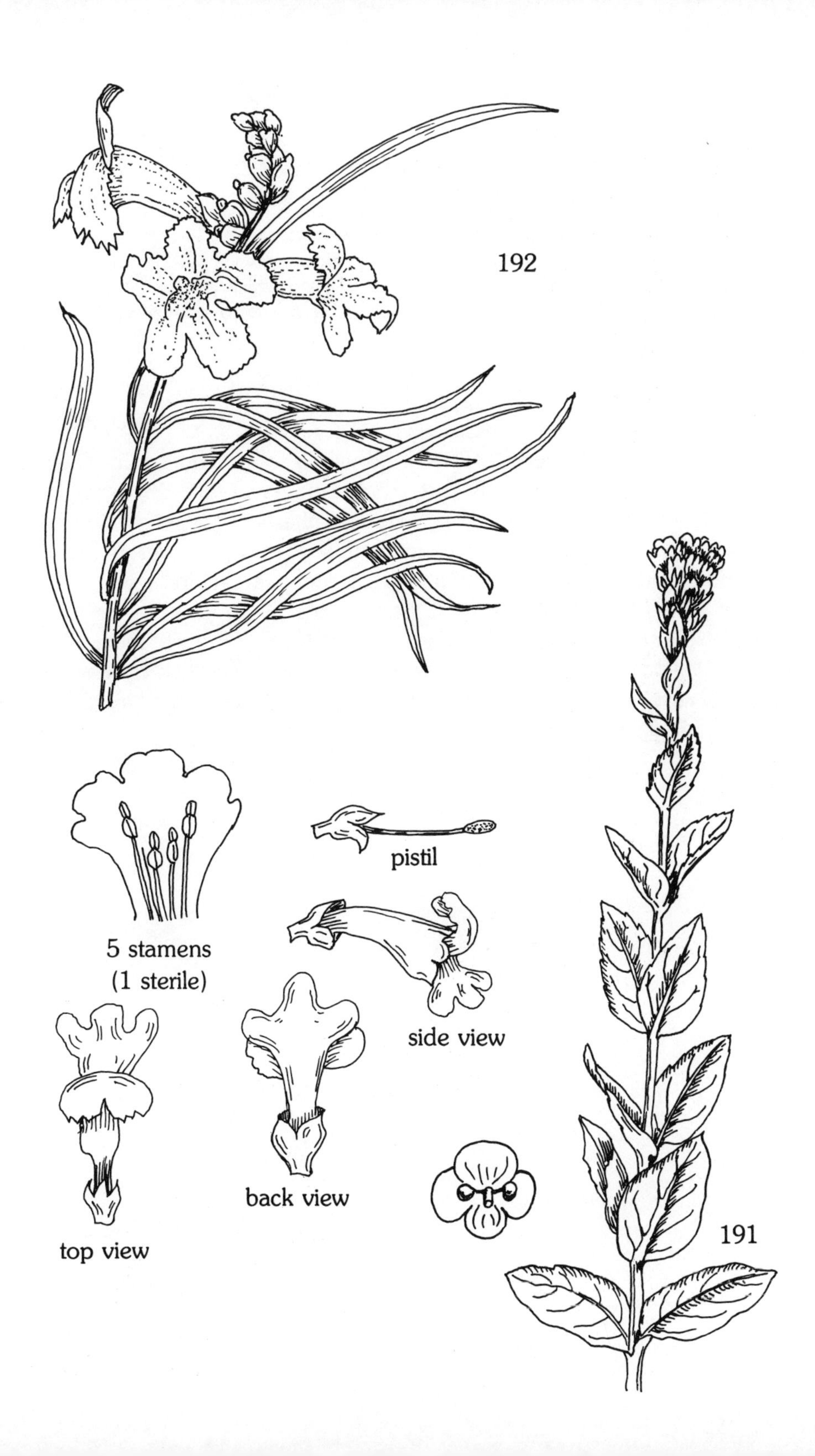
192
5 stamens
(1 sterile)
pistil
side view
top view
back view
191

BIGNONIACEAE

Bignonia Family

Members of the bignonia family are shrubs or small trees. Leaves are nearly all opposite, simple or compound. Flowers are in racemes or panicles. Corollas are two lipped. As in the figwort family there are five stamens, one sterile. The fruit is a two-valved, elongated, many-seeded capsule.

192. **Desert Willow** *Chilopsis linearis*

Desert Willow is also called Catalpa. It grows up to nine meters in height. The upper leaves are alternate but the lower leaves are opposite and linear or linear-lanceolate. Both opposite and alternate leaves are smooth margined. The fragrant flowers are pink with streaks of lavender and spots of lavender and purple. They look a great deal like Catalpa flowers and produce fruits similar to the pods of the Catalpa.

The hard strong wood of *Chilopsis* is used to make fence posts. The Desert Willow is the food of the white-winged moth. The two-centimeter-long pupa cases of the moth can be found on the plants in late spring. Tea can be made from the dried flowers.

OROBANCHACEAE

Broomrape Family

It is interesting that the broomrape family is also called the cancer-root family because some of the members are parasitic on the roots of other plants. Except for this parasitism, the family has much in common with the Figworts.

The broomrapes have labiate flowers like the figworts but are unlike them in having four stamens instead of five. They are parasites, so they have no chlorophyll. The plants are yellowish, red, or almost colorless. The leaves are often reduced to alternate scales without chlorophyll. The stems are unbranched.

193. **Cooper Broomrape** *Orobanche cooperi*

One has difficulty choosing among the common names for *Orobanche cooperi* because all names that have been given it suit the plant so well. Besides Cooper Broomrape, it is called Strangleroot, Burrow-Bush, Strangler, and Cancer-Root.

As a root parasite it appears to prefer White Bur-Sage as a host plant, but it is reported to parasitize other plants as well.

The plant is sticky and covered with fine hairs. The flowers are purple and have golden spots at the edge of the tube.

194. **Tufted Broomrape** *Orobanche fasciculata*

The Tufted Broomrape is a more slender plant than Cooper Broomrape. It bears only a few flowers at the top of the stalk in comparison to the many-flowered spike of Cooper Broomrape. The flowers are all yellow or purplish. Tufted Broomrape is parasitic on Sagebrush and Buckwheat.

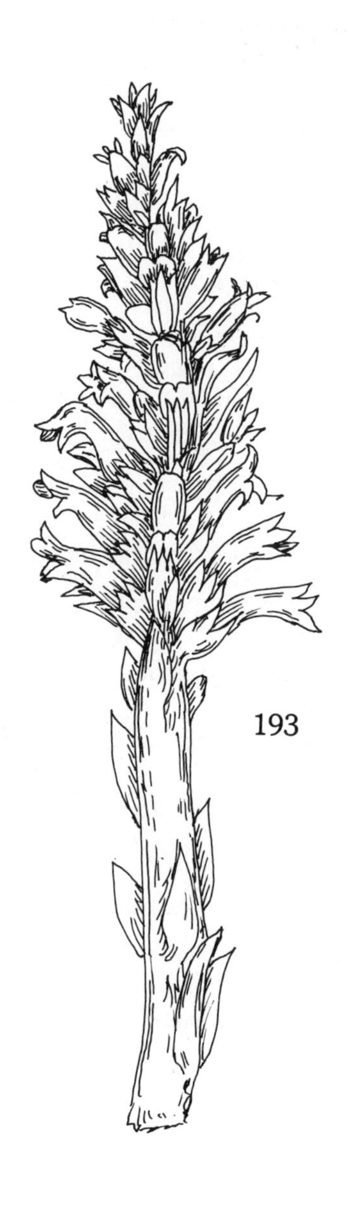
193

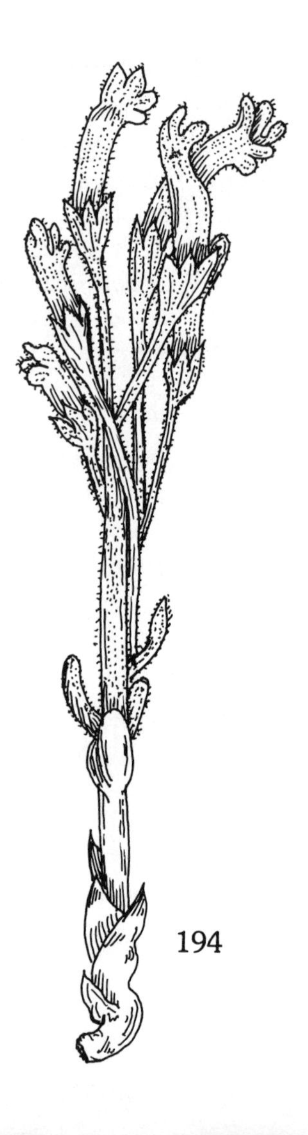
194

ACANTHACEAE

Acanthus Family

Both herbaceous and shrubby members of this family are perennial. The flowers are two lipped, but the lobes of some are so much alike that they seem almost radially symmetrical. The leaves are opposite, simple, and entire.

195. **Chuparosa, Desert Honeysuckle** *Anisacanthus thurberi*

Chuparosa is easily recognized by the honeysuckle-like flowers that account for it also being called Desert Honeysuckle. Chuparosa blooms nearly throughout the whole year. This makes it a good browse for cattle and sheep when other food is scarce. It is not a vine like true honeysuckles, but a shrub with thin, white, flaking bark. The long-tubed flower is normally red but is sometimes yellow or orange.

196. **Chuparosa, Honeysuckle** *Beloperone californica*

Beloperone californica shares a common name with *Anisacanthus.* They are, of course, similar. The honeysuckle-like flowers furnish nectar to both insects and hummingbirds. Sparrows and linnets eat the flower bases, which contain nectar. The Papago Indians eat the blossoms.

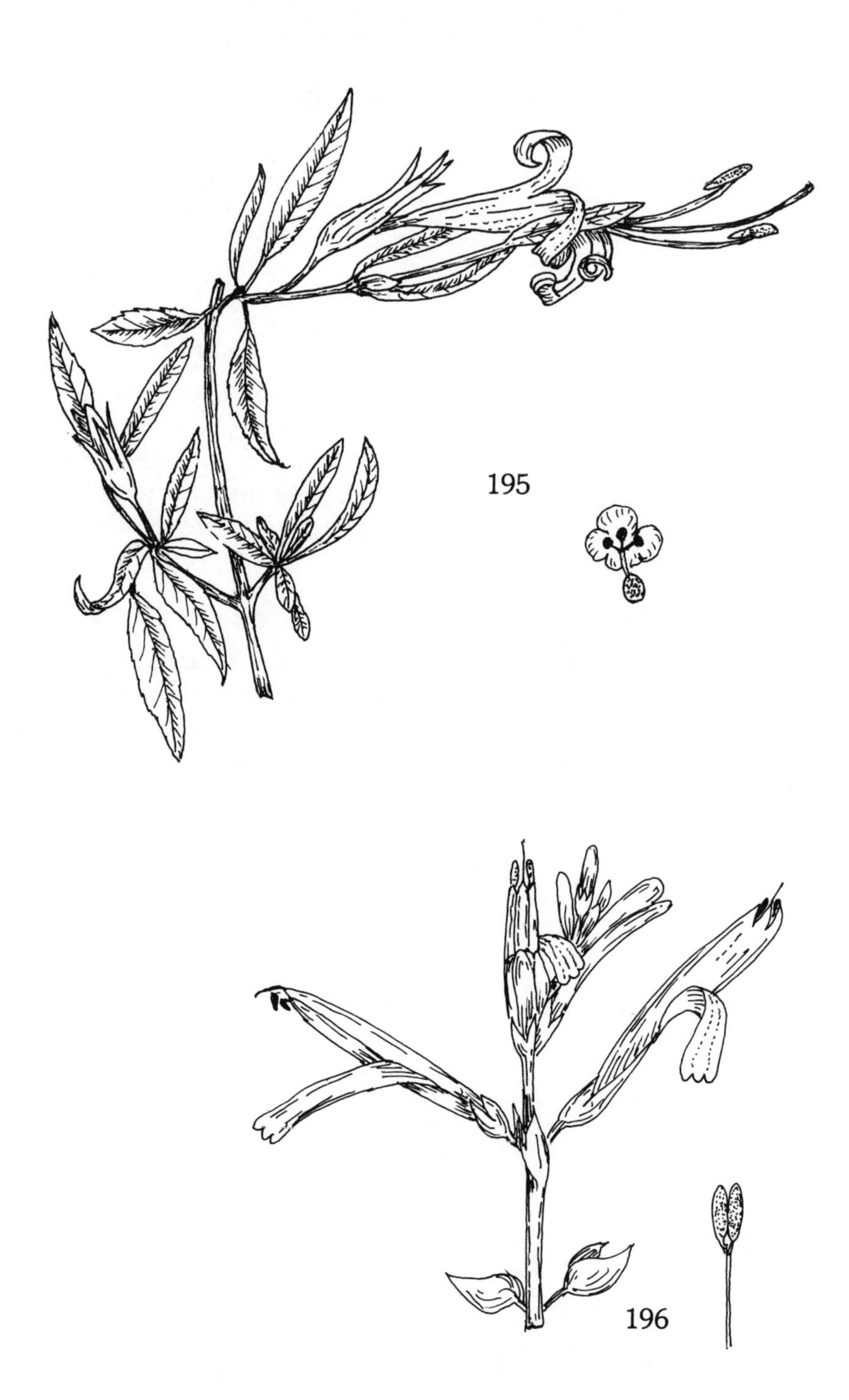
195
196

PLANTAGINACEAE

Plantain Family

The leaves of this family are usually all basal and prominently ribbed. The flowers are small and form crowded spikes. Some species are nuisances on lawns, but the desert species are excellent forage for sheep and cattle.

The cleaned and dried seeds of one of the plantains, known in commerce as Spanish or French psyllium seed, are used for the treatment of chronic constipation.

197. **Pursh Plantain** *Plantago purshii*

Pursh Plantain is a short wooly annual. The seeds are known as Indian wheat. The lanceolate leaves are basal and have prominent ribs, as do those of the whole family.

198. **Spiny Plantain** *Plantago spinulosa* var. *oblonga*

The spines are most prominent on mature plants. They are at the tips of the lower bracts. The *oblonga* refers to the broadly oblong calyx divisions. This is a rare plant and therefore it is fortunate that there is no commercial use for it.

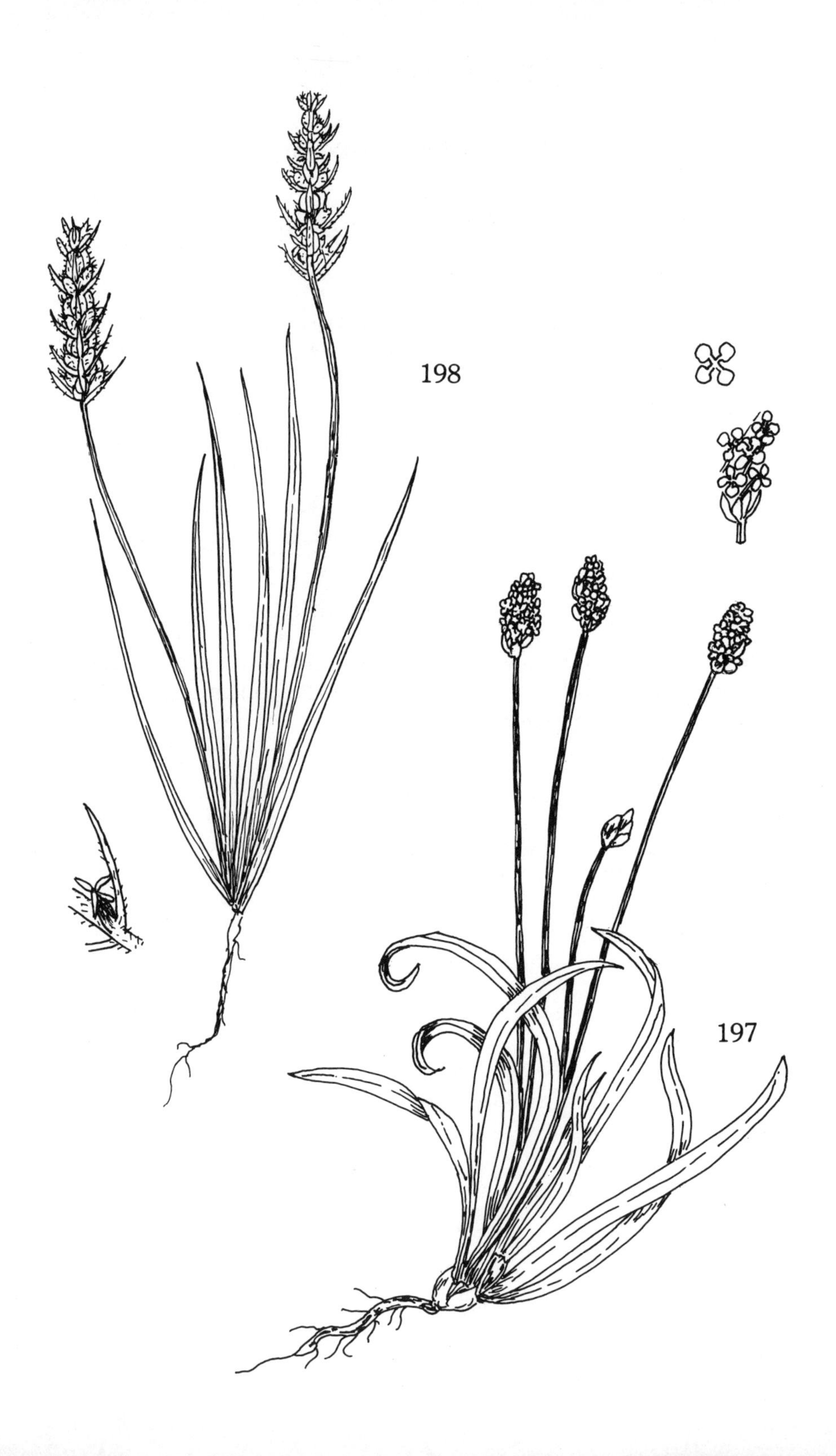
198
197

RUBIACEAE

Madder Family

*The madder family is a large tropical family. To it belong some important plants. Perhaps the best known are the coffee tree (*Coffea arabica*) and the quinine tree (*Cinchona *spp.).*

*The dye plant, Madder (*Rubia tinctoria*), has been supplanted by aniline dyes. Southwestern species of madders are of no economic value.*

There is a legend that the manger of the baby Jesus was filled with these plants, so they are sometimes called bedstraw. Bedstraw was somtimes used in England as ticking in place of wheat straw.

Among the products of tropical bedstraws are coffee, quinine, and ipecac.

199. **Goosegrass** *Galium aparine*

Galium aparine is a worldwide annual plant. The stems have turned-back prickly hairs. The leaves are linear and lanceolate or oblanceolate. As well as stems, the leaves and fruits are equipped with hooked hairs that cause them to cleave (or adhere) to clothing and fur. This gives these plants the common name Cleavers. The long, weak stems trail among other plants for support.

The seeds have been roasted to use as a substitute for coffee. Geese eat the plants—hence the name goosegrass. The plants are sometimes even chopped up to feed to geese. They are easy weeds to pull up in the spring because their roots are small and few. When they ripen in the fall, the seeds become a nuisance to hikers.

200. **Northern Bedstraw** *Galium boreale*

Northern Bedstraw has linear-lanceolate leaves in whorls of four at each node. The stems are square in cross-section. At the stem tops there are lovely, fragrant masses of tiny, saucer-shaped, white flowers. As with other Bedstraws, the whole plant is covered with stiff, back-curving hairs.

Northern Bedstraw is used as food by ducks, geese, and white-tailed deer.

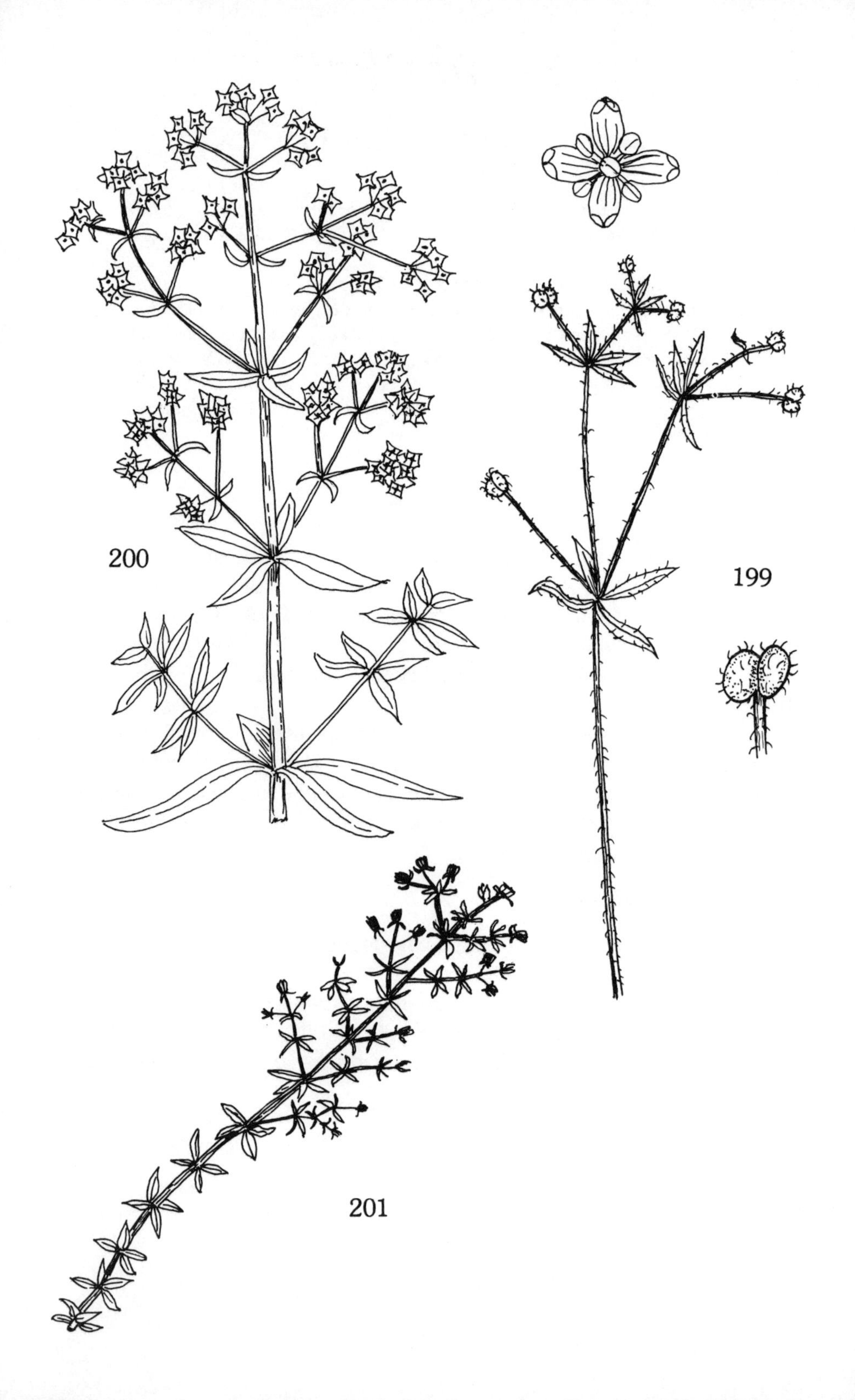
200
199
201

201. **Desert Bedstraw** *Galium stellatum* var. *eremicum*

The species name *stellatum* means "star-like" and is said to refer to the star-shaped hairs on leaves and stems. Actually the hairs are not star-like, but simple; the name could refer to the star-like arrangement of leaves. The variety name, *eremicum*, is appropriate, however, for this desert-living plant because it comes from the Greek word for "lonely."

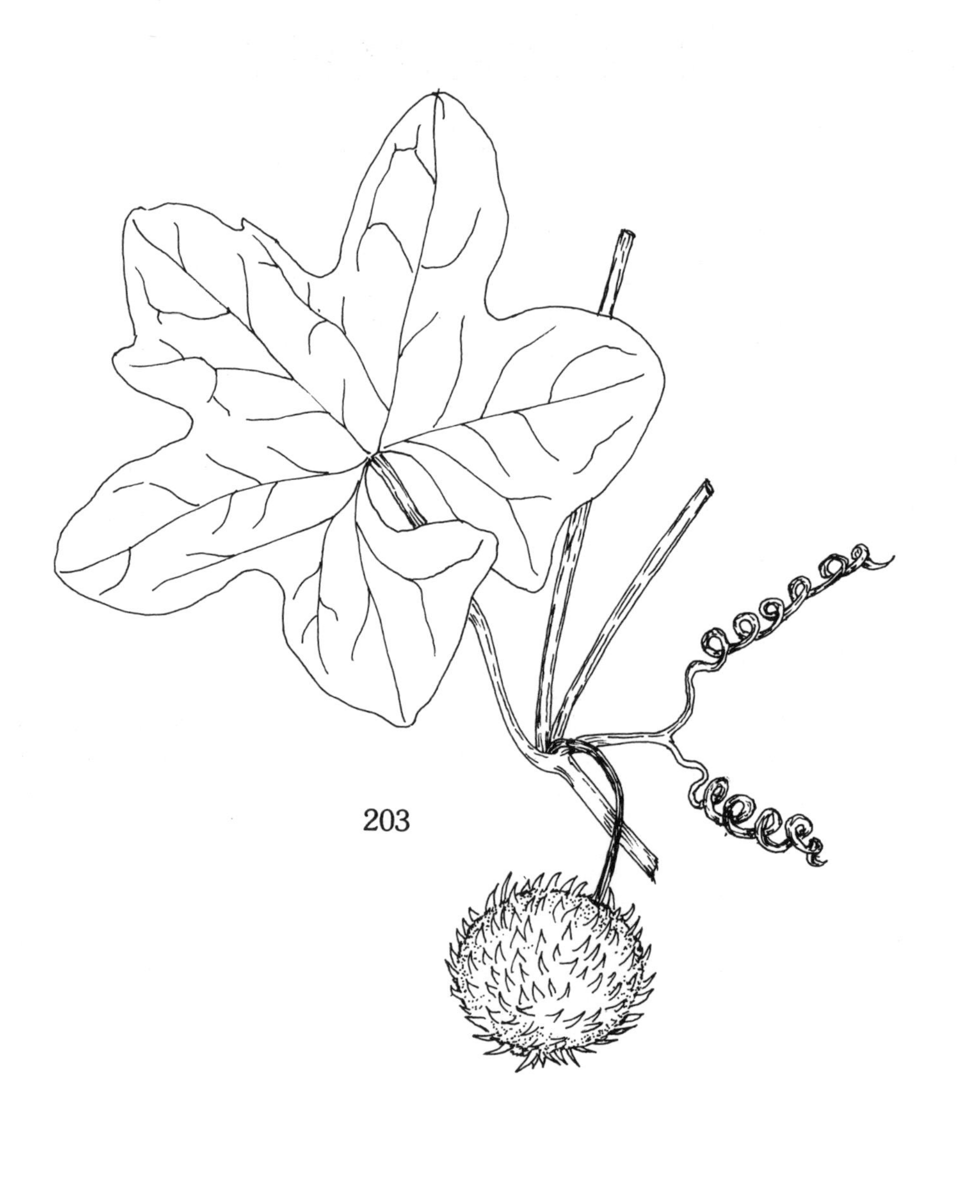

203

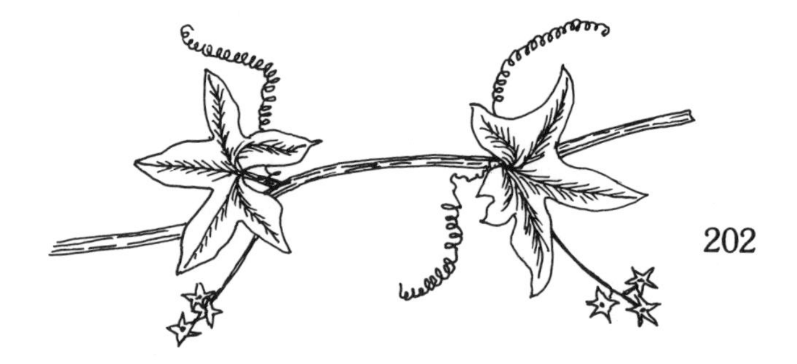

202

CUCURBITACEAE

Gourd Family

The gourd family is made up of vines with coiling tendrils. The leaves are palmately lobed, cleft or divided. Except in one species the staminate and pistillate flowers are on the same plant. Melons, pumpkins, cucumbers, and gourds belong to this family. There are no species of economic importance occurring naturally in the southwestern deserts and mountains, but some of the vines are cultivated as ornamentals.

202. **Brandegea** *Brandegea bigelovii*

Brandegea is a cucurbit of southwestern Arizona. It is a perennial vine found climbing over shrubs, sometimes so thickly as almost to smother them. The palmately lobed leaves are oddly marked on the upper side with little blisters. The small staminate flowers are in clusters and the pistillate ones are single or paired. The fruit is a thorny pod. The genus is named for Mary Katherine Brandegee and her husband T. S. Brandegee, who worked in plant taxonomy on the west coast during the later half of the nineteenth century and the first quarter of the twentieth. They spent their last years at the herbarium of the University of California. The species is named for the eminent botanist John M. Bigelow.

203. **Wild Cucumber** *Marah gilensis*

Wild Cucumber is also called Big Root on account of its large, tuberous root. The rounded leaf lobes number from three to five to seven. The three or four stamens make round heads in the axils of the leaves. The pistillate flower grows in the same axil as the staminates. The fruit is round and spiny.

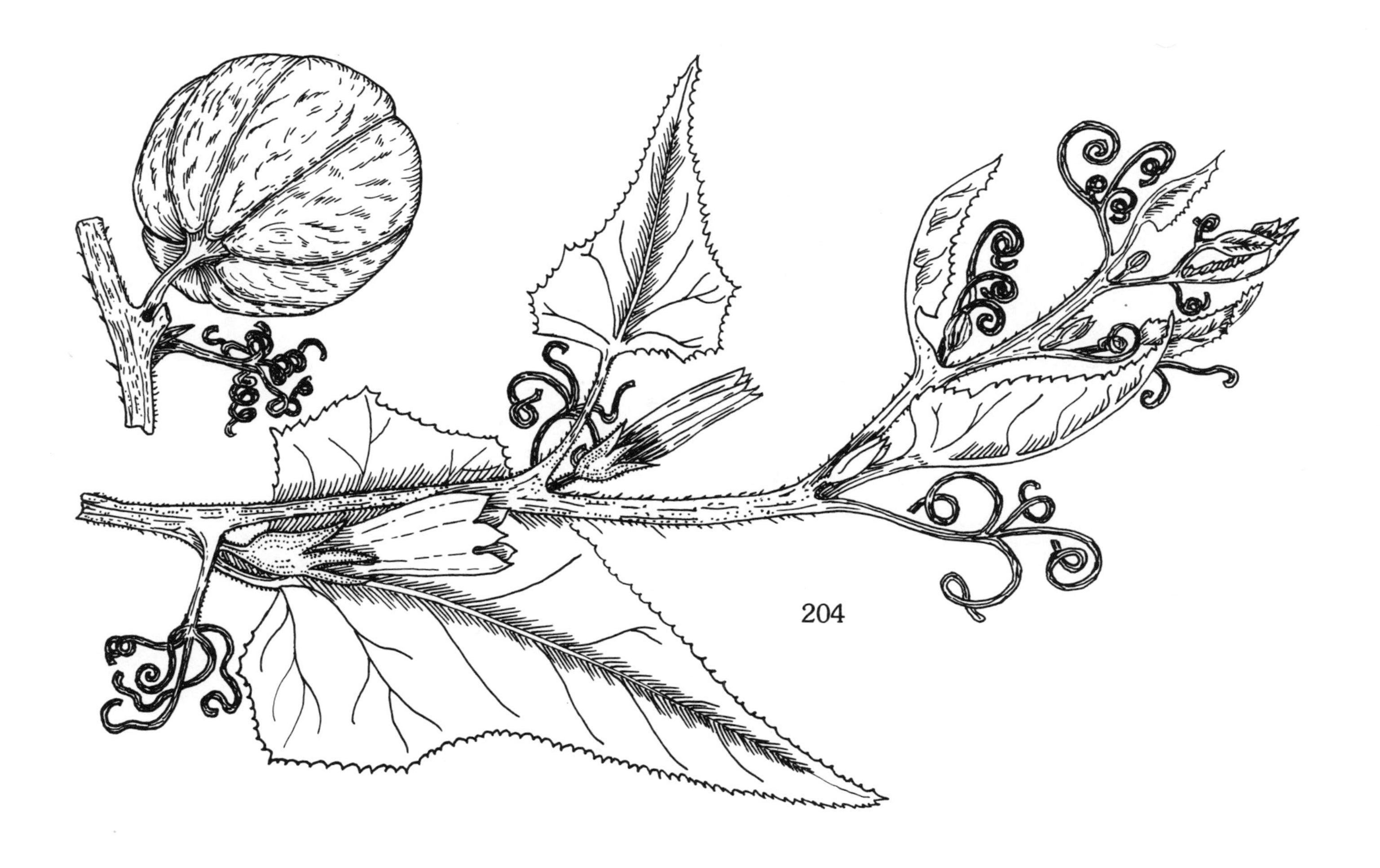

204

204. **Buffalo Gourd** *Cucurbita foetidissima*

Buffalo Gourd, like other gourds, has bell-shaped, yellow, pistillate flowers. The staminate flowers have three stamens with their tops twisted around each other. Both male and female flowers are borne singly in leaf axils. The fruits are mottled dark and light green, but turn yellowish at the first frost. The species name *foetidissima* means "bad smelling."

205. **Coyote Melon** *Cucurbita palmata*

The Coyote Melon has palmate leaves, the five divisions of which, unlike those of the Buffalo Gourd, are sharply pointed and somewhat serrate. The veins of the leaves are downy. The fruit is dark green, with lighter green stripes, and is about six centimeters in diameter.

205

CAMPANULACEAE

Bellflower Family

This family is also known as the bluebell family, but there are plants in other families that are commonly called bluebells. Thus Bellflower seems a better name for this one, especially because the scientific name begins with the root word "campanula," which means "little bell." The bellflowers are pretty well scattered all over the world and are universally admired. Cultivated bellflowers include the Scotch Bluebell, English Harebell, and Canterbury Bell.

206. **Bellflower** *Campanula parryi*

Members of the genus *Campanula* have linear-lanceolate upper leaves. The lower leaves are oblanceolate, spatulate, ovate, or cordate. The flowers are blue and showy, thus providing cultivated ornamentals. Species *parryi* has one-flowered erect stems.

207. **Harebell, Bluebell** *Campanula rotundifolia*

Harebell is another plant for which the species name—*rotundifolia*, meaning "round leaf"—is not actually descriptive because the leaves are mostly linear or linear-lanceolate. The slender stems are much branched. The flowers are in clusters on branches instead of growing atop a single stem, as in *C. parryi*.

208. **Alpine Harebell** *Campanula uniflora*

Alpine Harebell is a small relative of the Bellflower and Harebell. Like Harebell, it has a one-flowered stem. It has linear stem leaves, but the basal leaves are rounded.

209. **Venus Looking Glass** *Triodanis perfoliata*

Many taxonomic books list Venus Looking Glass under the genus name *Specularia*. This may be a better name than *Triodanis* because it means "mirror"; the flat, shiny seeds are the little "mirrors."

The plant is erect and may be sparingly branched. The leaves are cordate and clasping. The flowers form in clusters of one to three in the axils of the leaves. Usually only one flower per axil matures at a time. Venus Looking Glass is not a mid-desert plant. It grows at the edge of high mountain deserts.

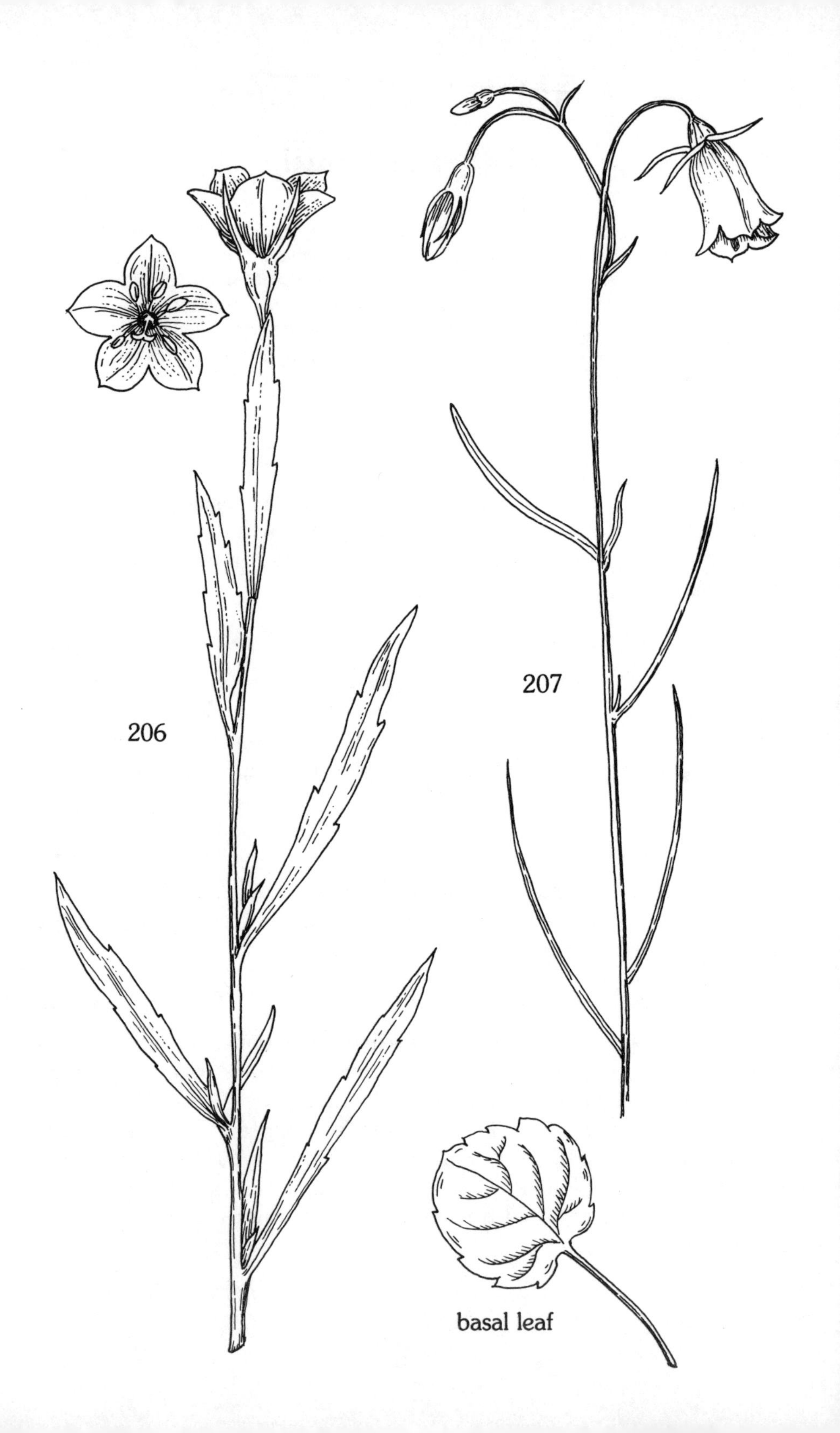
206
207
basal leaf

208

209

COMPOSITAE

Composite Family

The composite family is perhaps the largest seed plant family. These plants are considered very difficult to classify, but this problem can be solved by learning the fundamental characteristics and using a good ten-power hand lens to examine the plants.

The inflorescence is called a head and is made up of numerous flowers (as you can see if you split open the head of a dandelion or sunflower). Each flower of the dandelion head has a strap-shaped corolla of five fused petals that form a short tube at the base. Inside each base is a ring of five stamens. The ovary is at the bottom of the tube and is one seeded. At the top of the ovary, surrounding the style, is a tuft of white hairs, the pappus, which is a modified calyx. The stigma, at the top of the style, is in two parts.

Examination of the head of a sunflower reveals two kinds of flowers. One kind, the ray flowers, located around the outside of the head, are like the ones described for dandelions. The other kind, the central flowers, do not have strap-shaped corollas. The five petals are joined in a radially symmetrical tube ending in five teeth.

210. **Yarrow** *Achillea millifolium*

The alternate leaves of Yarrow are divided into many fine segments, but the general shape of the leaf is lanceolate. The leaves have a strange but pleasant odor. The heads are in flat-topped clusters of white and sometimes pink flowers.

Before the manufacture of synthetic medicines, Yarrow leaves, fresh or steeped, were much used to staunch blood. The genus name, *Achillea*, comes from Achilles, the great hero of the Trojan War. He was supposed to have used Yarrow on his famous heel wound.

Yarrow has been substituted for hops in the brewing of beer and is supposedly a potent love charm. It is used in lawn-making but has to be cut frequently to keep it from forming flower stalks.

210
211
212

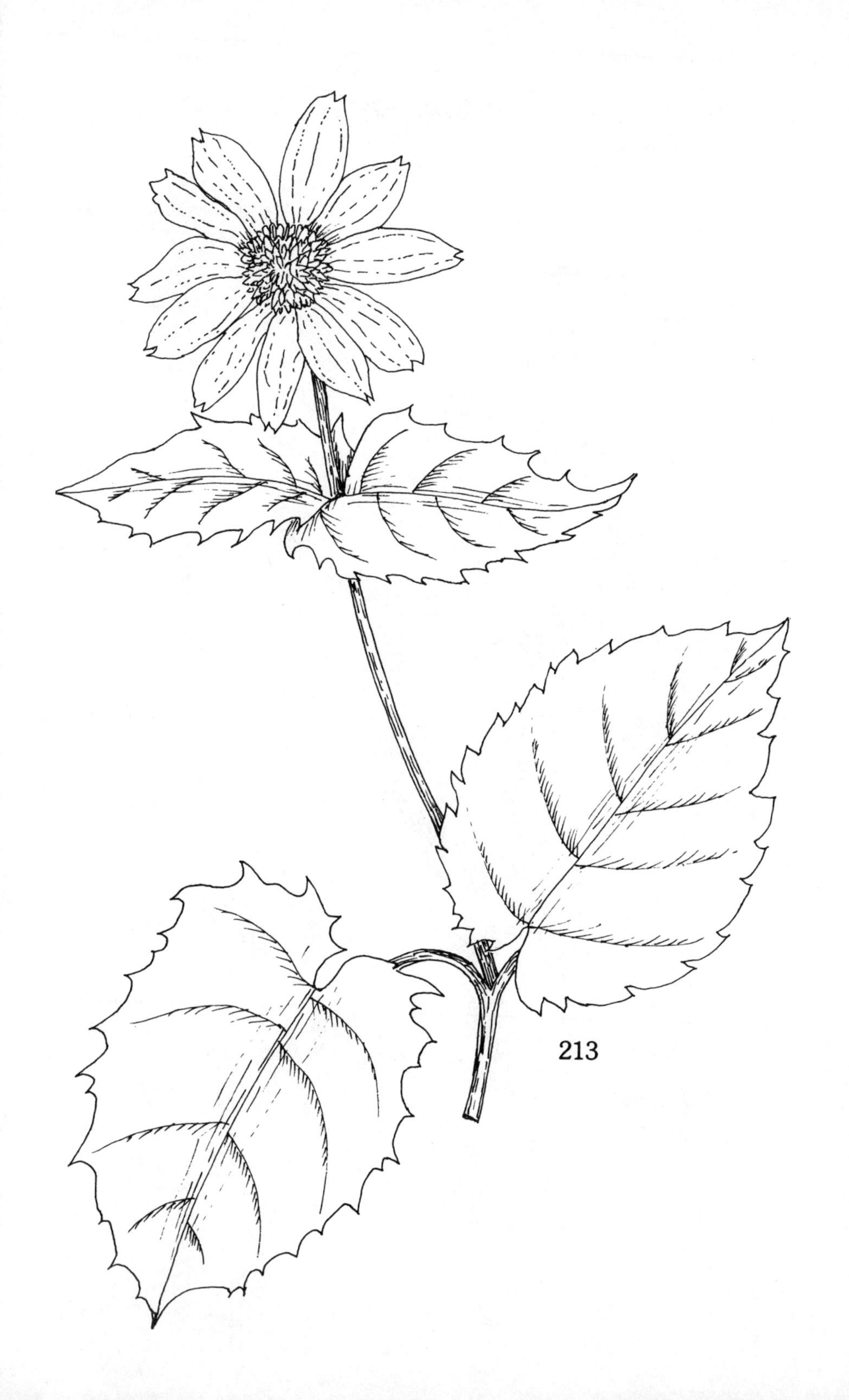
213

211. **Mountain Dandelion** *Agoseris glauca*

The Mountain Dandelion has basal rosettes of lanceolate leaves. The blades may be lobed. The flower stalk is leafless and has only one head. The flowers are ray flowers, and the corolla is yellow or orange.

212. **Big Sagebrush** *Artemisia tridentata*

Big Sagebrush is a many-branched shrub that varies in height from just twelve centimeters to one and one-third meters. It is an inhabitant of high mountain deserts. The wood burns with great heat and a fragrant odor.

The seeds can be ground into meal. Tea made from the leaves has many uses—to wash hair and eyes, to apply as an antiseptic, and to drink as a cold remedy. The plant also makes good pasture for goats and sheep. Nesting in the shrubs may be found the gray vireo, the black-throated sparrow, the sage sparrow, the gnatcatcher, and the hummingbird.

213. **Arnica** *Arnica cordifolia*

Arnica cordifolia is a perennial plant that can be identified by its opposite, cordate leaves and large, beautiful, long-stemmed flower heads. It has both ray and disk flowers, and the corollas are yellow orange. The flower heads are the most attractive of all species. The arnica tincture used for soothing bruises and sprains comes from a European species.

214. **Mecca Aster** *Aster cognatus*

The Mecca Aster is a beautiful plant that usually grows in the crevices at the bases of bluffs. The common name, Mecca, is for the town close to its habitat in the Colorado desert.

The leaves are alternate and covered by fine glandular hairs. The flowers of the head are lavender with yellow centers. They appear after the winter rains or summer cloudbursts. An interesting detail about the plant, recorded in Jaeger's *Desert Wildflowers*, is that the night-flying moth *Thyerion ligeae* rests in the center of the flower head during the daytime.

215. **Porter Aster** *Aster porteri*

Porter Aster has smooth stems and leaves. The plant stem is sixteen to forty centimeters tall. The flower head disks turn from orange to dark red with age.

214
215

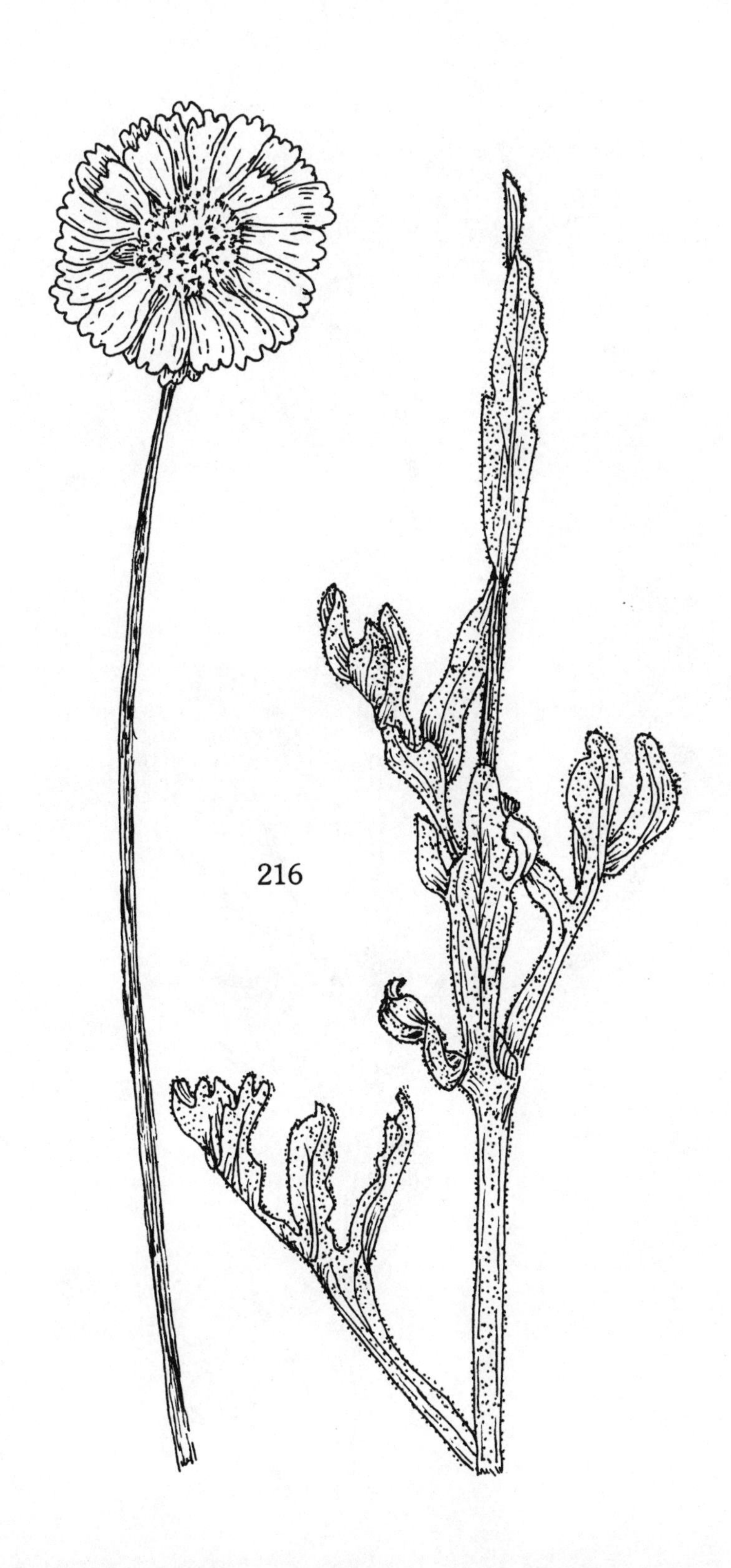
216

217

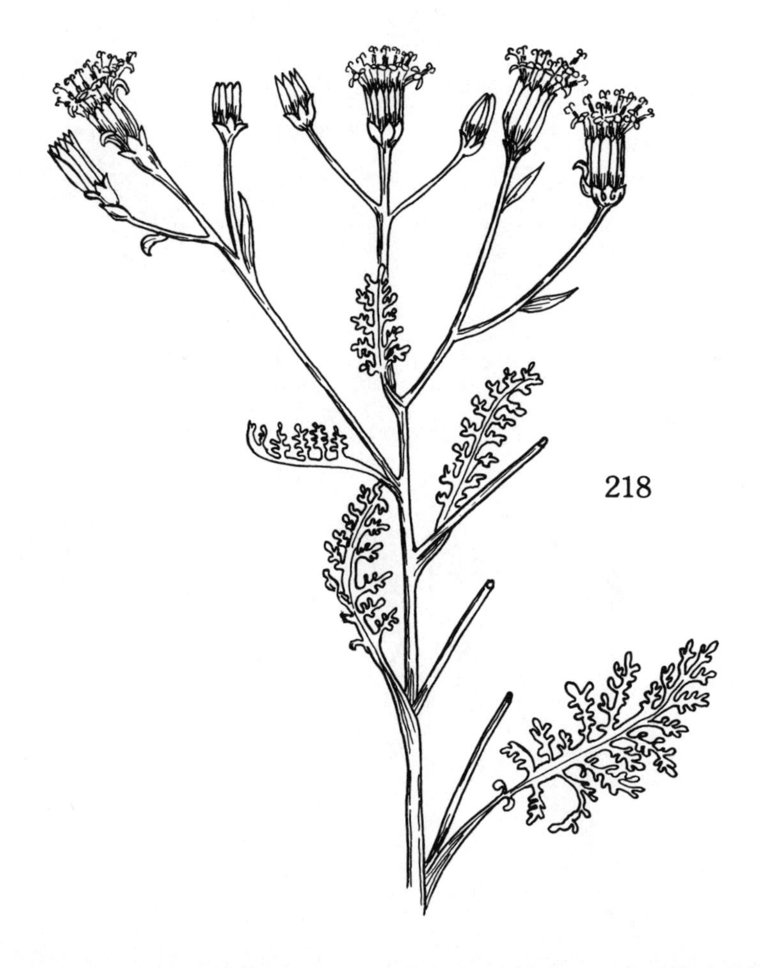
218

216. **Wild Marigold** *Baileya multiradiata*

The leaves of the Wild Marigold are mostly basal. The stems are woody; the flower head is called "paper daisy" because the petals turn pale and papery as they age. The plant has a long period of bloom. It is cultivated in gardens and for greenhouse sales.

217. **Yellow Tackstem** *Calycoseris parryi*

The name Tackstem comes from the tack-like glands that stud the stems. The yellow flowers of *Calycoseris parryi* distinguish it from *Calycoseris wrightii*, which has white flowers. Both have tacks on their stems.

218. **Douglas Pincushion** *Chaenactis douglasii*

Other common names for Douglas Pincushion are Dusty Maiden and Brides Bouquet. "Pincushion" refers to two white points in each of the many little flowers that make up the heads. The leaves are twice or even three times pinnate and become up to ten centimeters long.

219. **Sticky-leaved Rabbit Brush** *Chrysothamnus viscidiflorus*

Sticky-leaved Rabbit Brush blooms in the late summer and autumn. Sheep browse it, especially liking the flowering shoots. It is a small shrub, with twisted leaves and rounded or flat-topped clusters of small, yellow flower heads.

220. **Rabbit Brush, Chamiso** *Chrysothamnus nauseosus*

The Rabbit Brushes of the southwestern growth areas are slightly different from the northwestern ones. Chamiso inhabits the Sagebrush area of the deserts. It blooms in early fall with heads of rayless, golden yellow flowers. Many insects pollinate them.

The leaves and four-winged fruits are eaten by rodents and hoofed browsers, especially sheep. The foliage is covered with silvery scales. The plant is an indicator of tillable soil in Arizona.

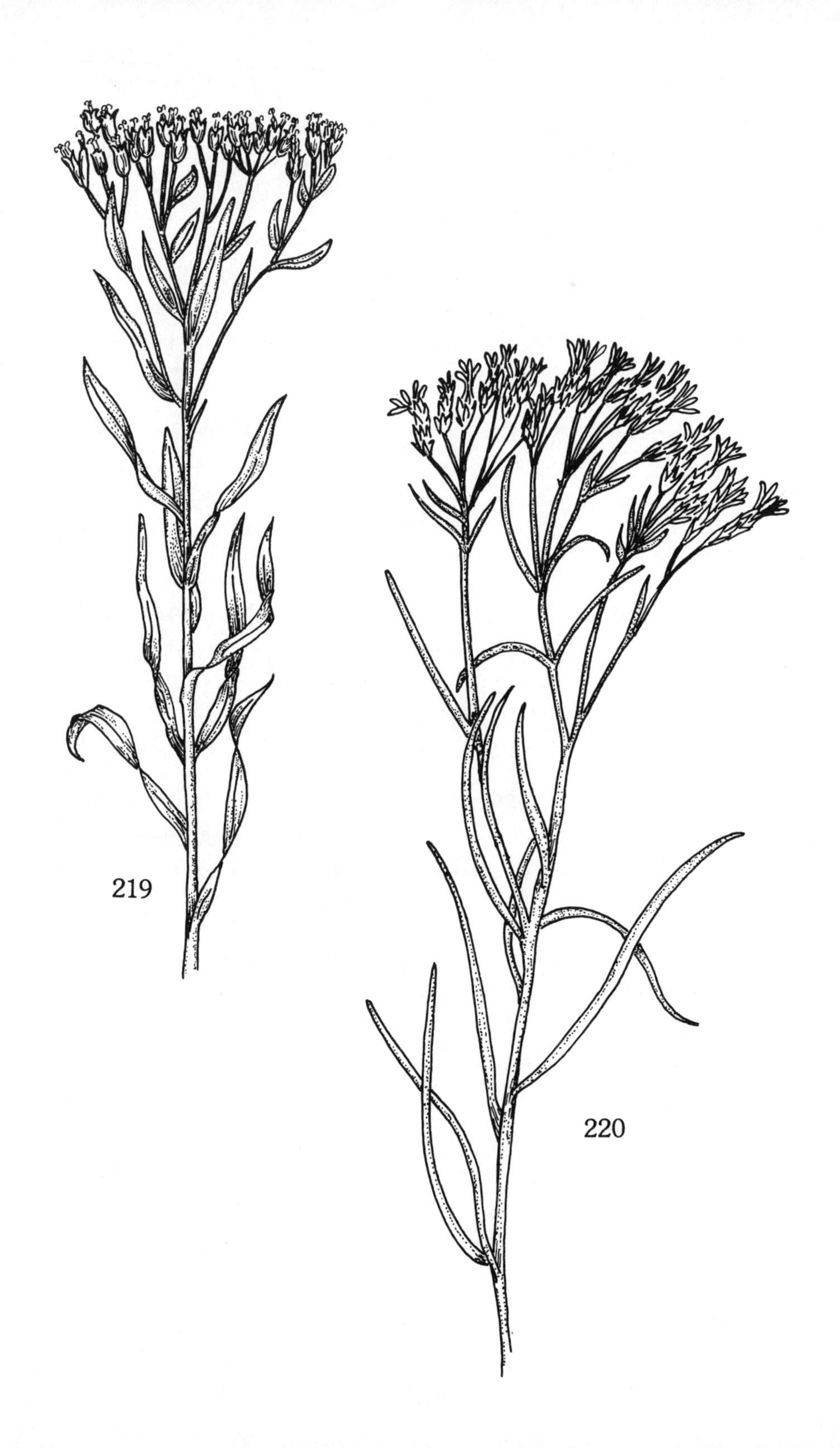

219
220

221. **Brittle Bush** *Encelia farinosa*

In the years when moisture is sufficient to bring most beautiful bloom to the desert, the Brittle Bush turns the whole area yellow with its magnificent flowering, which usually begins in mid-March.

The plant reaches a height of one meter. Its stout, branching stems bear clusters of bright yellow ray flowers and reddish brown disk flowers. An interesting fact about Brittle Bush is that the gum that oozes from its stems was used by early-day Catholic priests as incense. The Indians chewed the gum and heated it to spread on painful areas of their bodies.

222. **Wooly Eriophyllum** *Eriophyllum lanosum*

Both the *Erio* part of the genus name and the species name *lanosum* mean the same thing—"wooly." The common name is, therefore, also repetitive. *Phyllum* means leaf.

223. **Spiny Goldenbush** *Haplopappus spinulosus*

The spines of the Spiny Goldenbush are on the tips of the leaf serrations. Several tall stems come from a perennial woody base to form the plant. The heads are radiate; the flowers yellow.

224. **Cheesebush** *Hymenoclea salsola*

Cheesebush is so named because the crushed leaves and stems smell cheesy. The plant is a meter high or less, and it is beautiful throughout its whole living season, when in flower and in fruit. The clusters of pearly flowers and the reddish silver involucres of the flowers (which persist in the fruit) make lovely color patterns.

225. **Bitterweed** *Hymenoxys acaulis*

Bitterweed is a perennial with several crowns, which are sometimes partly extruded above ground. Species of *Hymenoxys* can be difficult to distinguish from one another, but the genus is not hard to identify. The leaves are narrowly lanceolate. The ray flowers are yellow.

226. **Blackfoot Daisy** *Melampodium leucanthum*

Blackfoot Daisy is a plant of the rocky slopes and mesas, where it makes a beautiful showing with its heads of white rays clustered at stem tips. The leaves are opposite and narrowly lanceolate.

221

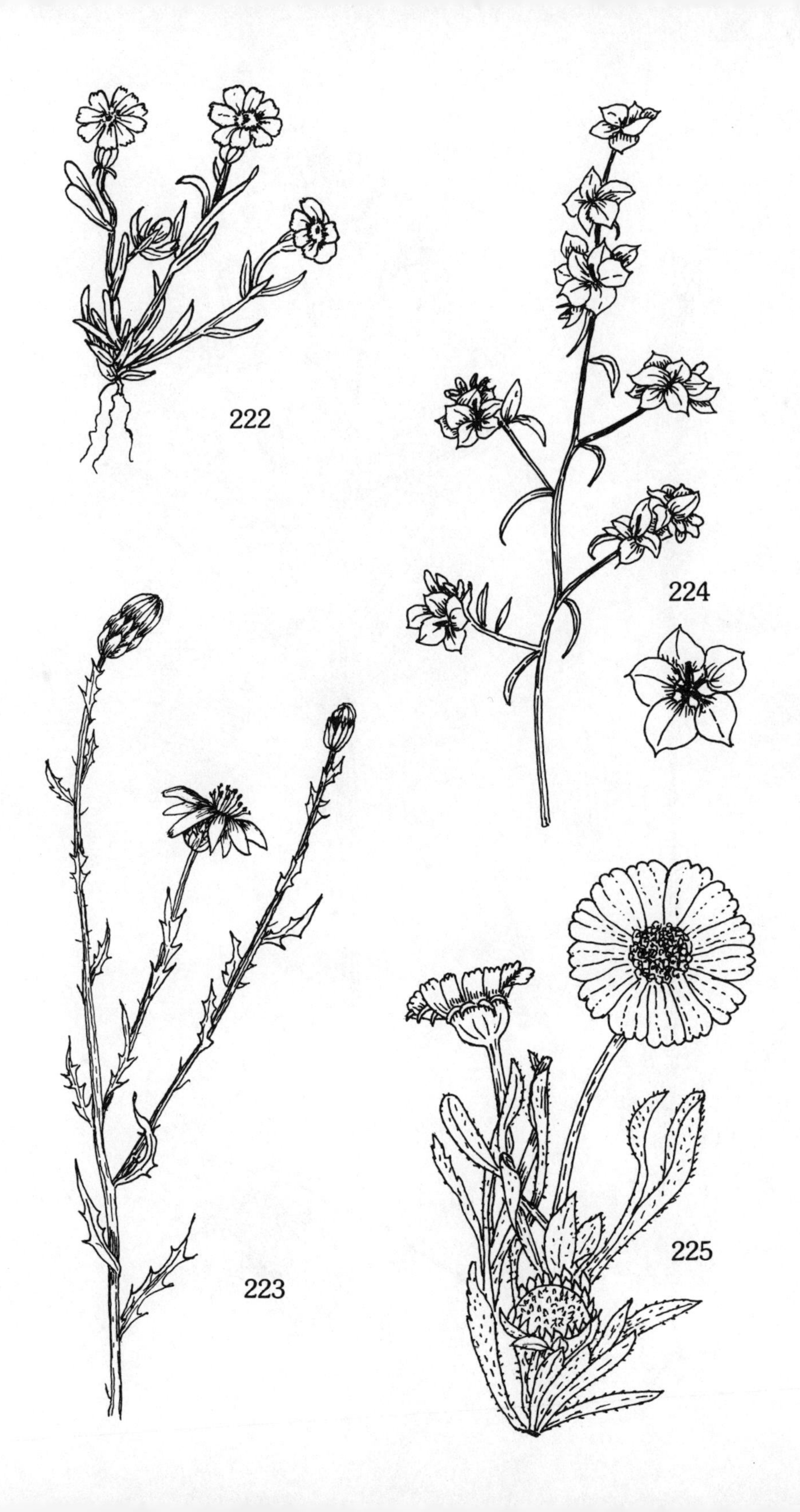

222
224
223
225

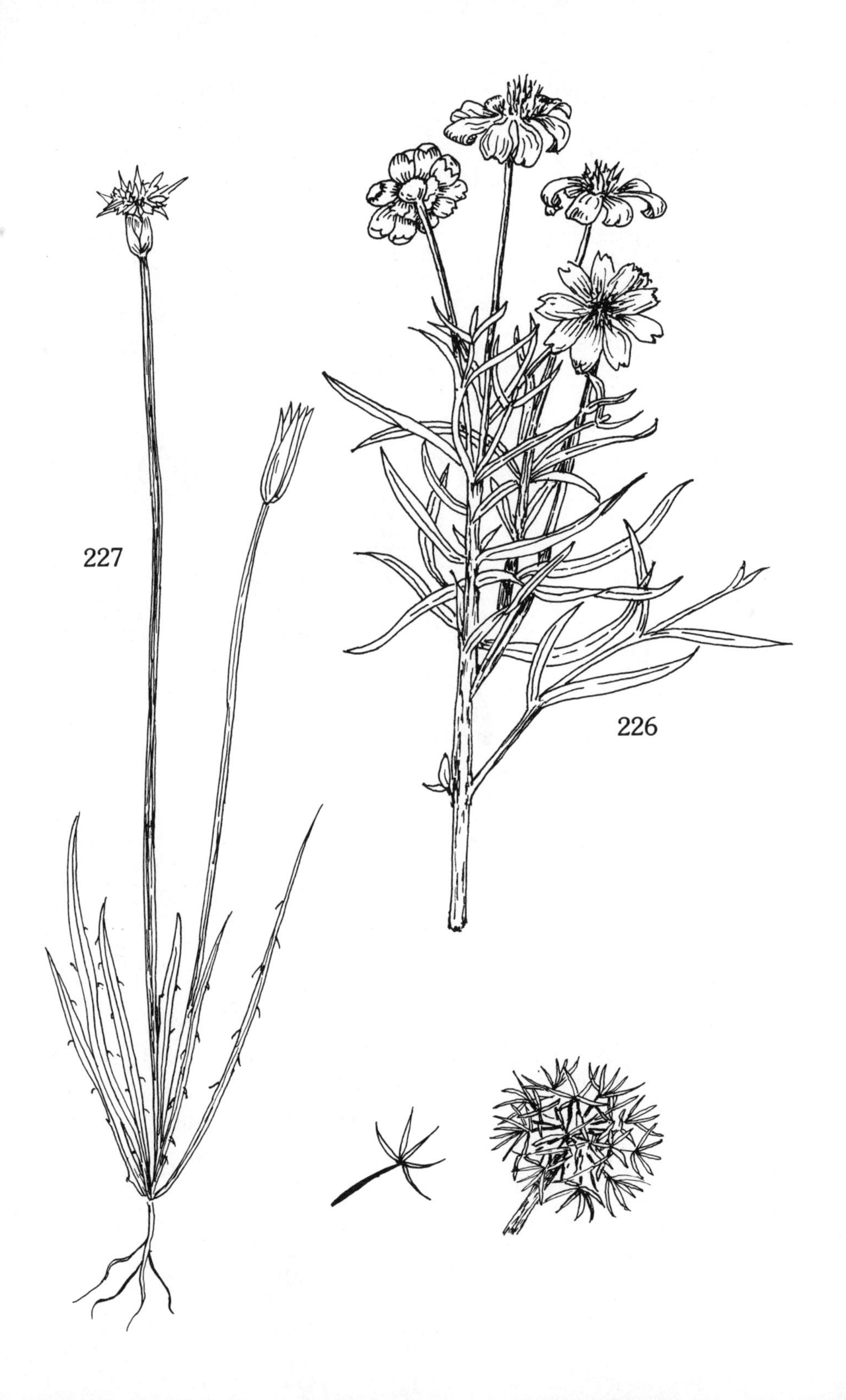
227
226

227. **Silver Puffs** *Microseris linearifolia*

Microseris linearifolia grows where Sagebrush does. The plant is thirty centimeters tall, with linear basal leaves. A head can have from five to one hundred flowers. The seed ball is most spectacular as each seed is tipped with a silvery paper star, hence the common name Silver Puffs.

228. **Mohave Desert Star** *Monoptilon bellioides*

Desert Stars are small annual plants with white to pinkish flowers. They live in sandy, rocky places. The plants may form good-sized mats in the sand. The linear leaves are borne singly.

229. **Spanish Needle** *Palafoxia arida*

Spanish Needle is said to have spread rapidly from California along the highways to the Arizona deserts. Like Desert Star, it is a small plant with white flowers. The pink color of the head is due to the color of the styles, not the petals.

A distinguishing characteristic of all *Palafoxias* is that the flowers are cut deeply into long, narrow petals. There are no ray flowers. *Palafoxia linearis* var. *gigantea* (not figured), which grows in the sand dunes near Yuma, Arizona, is really a giant. It grows from one to two meters in height.

230. **Tailed Pericome** *Pericome caudata*

Tailed Pericome is a tall, branched, odorous annual. The tails are the long ends of the bright green, hastate, opposite leaves. The flower heads are light yellow.

231. **Emory Rock-Daisy** *Perityle emoryi*

Perityle emoryi may be called a Rock-Daisy because it is so easily seen against rock walls where it shelters. It is a strongly scented annual. The leaves are indistinctly lobed and coarsely serrate. Both ray and disk flowers are present in the head, but the ray flowers are small and inconspicuous.

232. **Goldfields** *Lasthenia californica*

From early March to May *Lasthenia californica* spreads itself over wide areas of the desert to form great yellow fields, so the common name, Goldfields, is very appropriate. It is not a large plant—only four to sixteen centimeters in height.

228

229

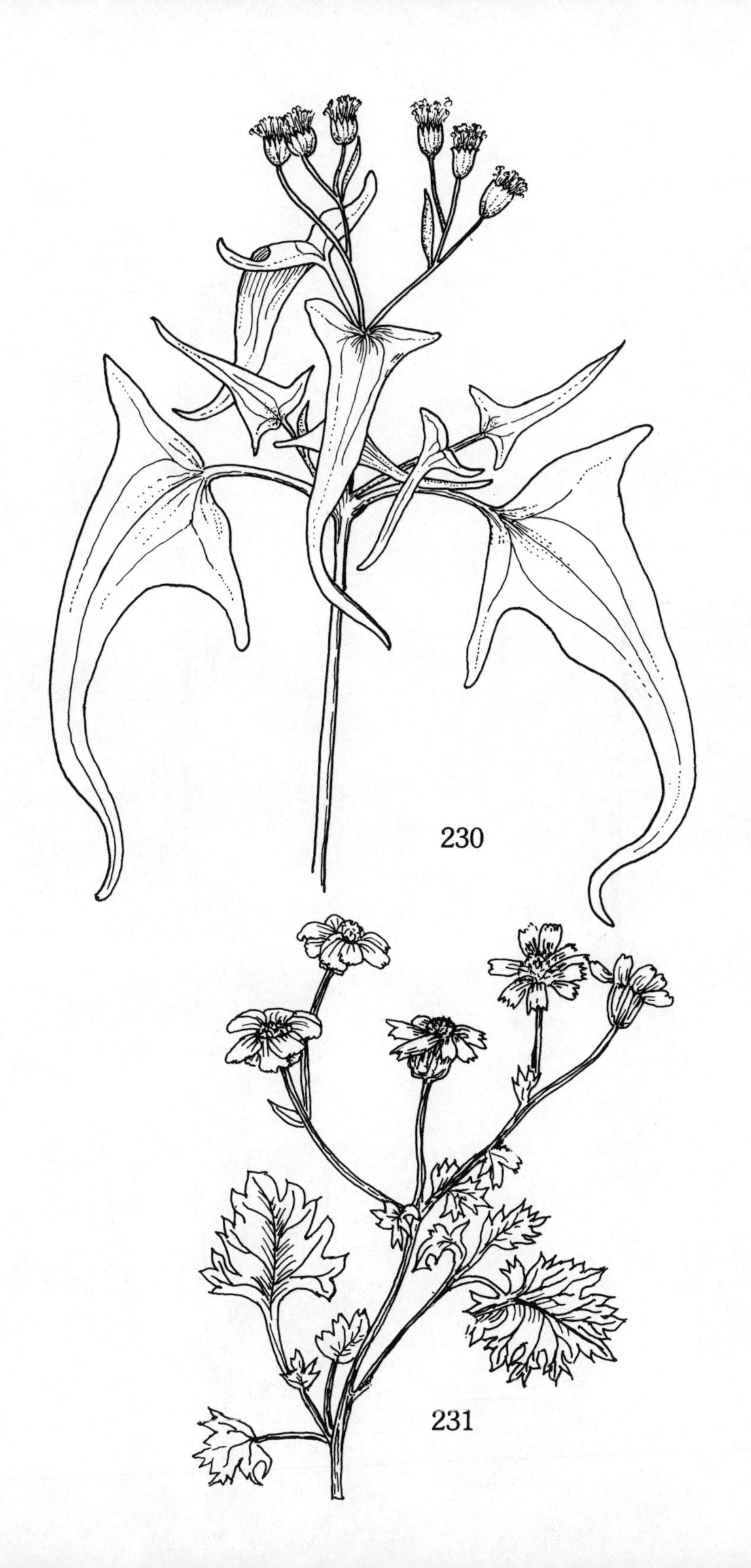
230
231

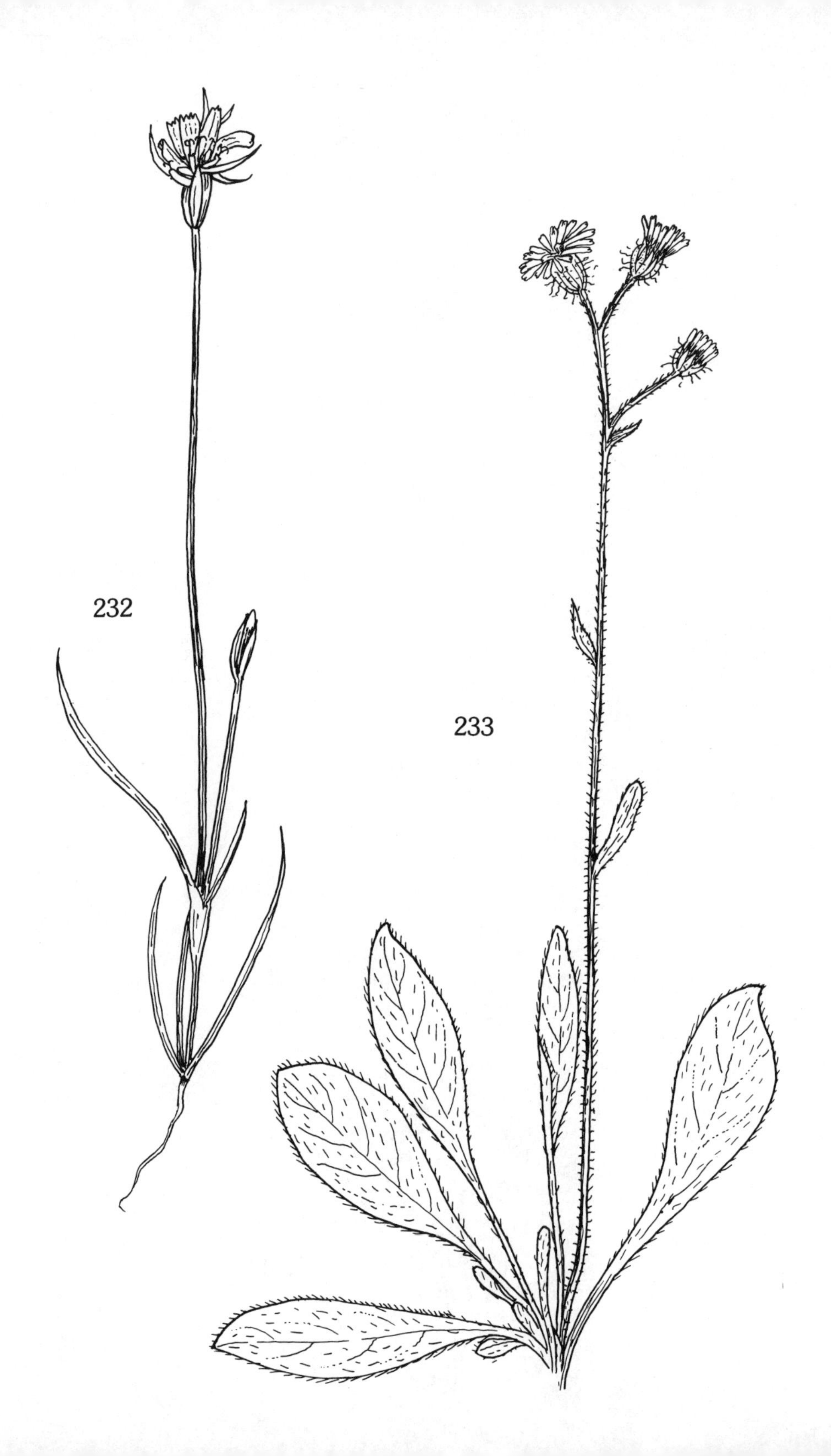
232
233

233. **Hawkweed** *Hieracium fendleri* var. *discolor*

This is the most common and widely distributed type of Hawkweed in the Southwest. The flower stem is leafless except for a few small ones along it. Stems and leaves are sprinkled with bristly hairs. The heads look a little like dandelions.

234. **Skinner Saxicola** *Perityle saxicola*

One peculiar thing about genus *Perityle* is that most of its members are distributed in the habitat of bare rock, where there is very little soil, and form large clumps there, hanging to the undersides of overhanging ledges. The plants are small, with yellow flower heads and yellow-green leaves.

235. **Desert Fir** *Peucephyllum schottii*

Also called Pigmy Cedar, this plant does look a bit like a member of the evergreen family, the fir. It is a perennial green shrub, with leaves resembling fir needles. The flower heads are disk shaped and there are no ray flowers.

236. **Arrow-Weed** *Pluchea sericea*

Arrow-Weed is so called because its straight stems were used to make the shafts of arrows. Indians used it to make other things, such as baskets, cages, and bins. A good-smelling tea was made from stem tips and was used for an eyewash. The plants make dense stands in places where there is a good water supply. The flower heads are purple.

237. **Odora** *Porophyllum gracile*

Porophyllum, the genus name, means "pore-leaf." This refers to the semitransparent spots on the leaves, which are oily glands that resemble pores. The natives of Baja California have called this plant Hierba del Veriodo—"herb of the deer." They made tea from the leaves to cure intestinal troubles. The common name Odora probably refers to the rank odor of the plant.

The many-branched plant is from fifteen to sixty centimeters tall. The leaves are alternate or opposite. The off-white corollas have purple veins. The herbage is relished by cud-chewing animals, such as cattle and deer.

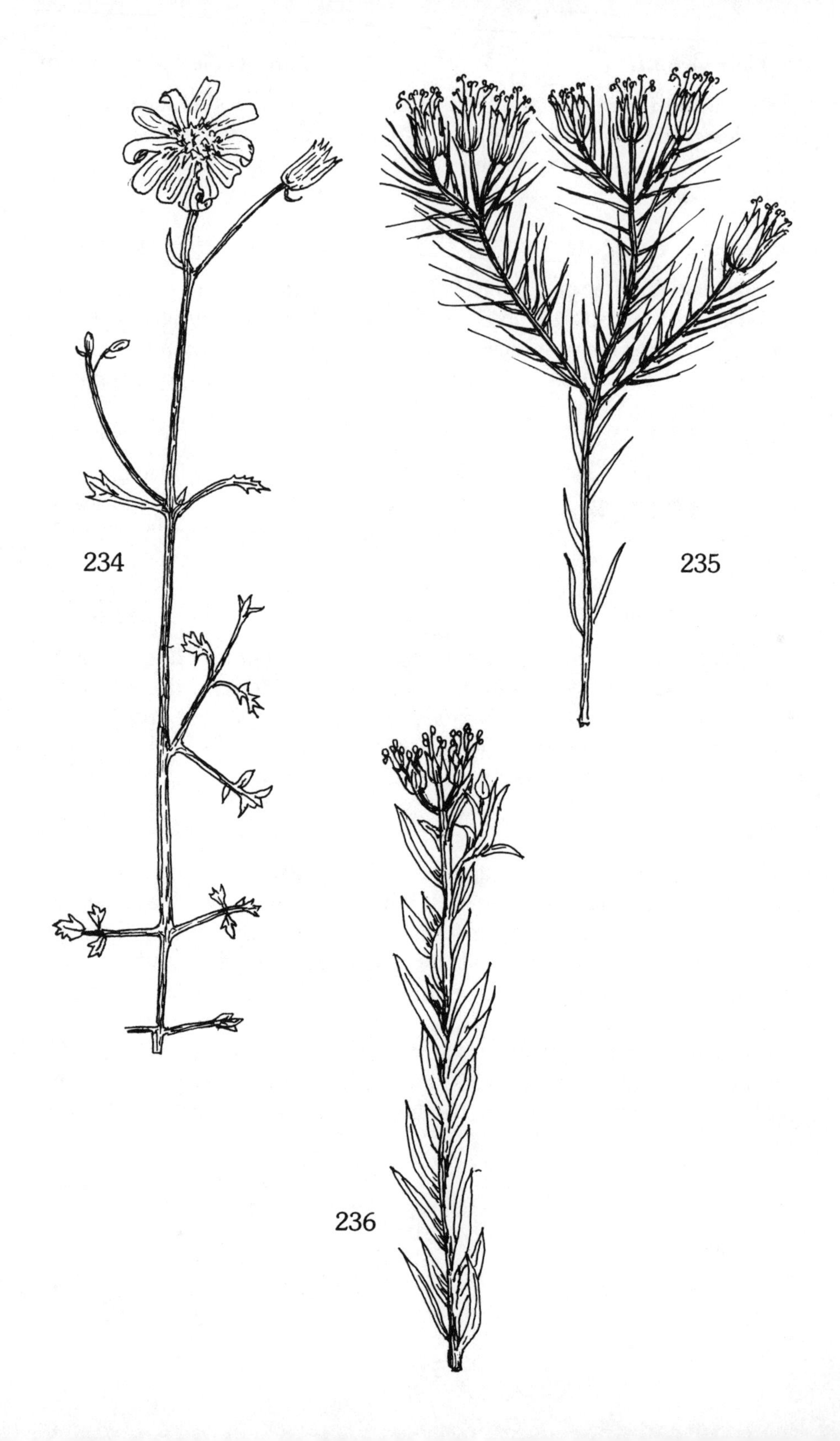
234
235
236

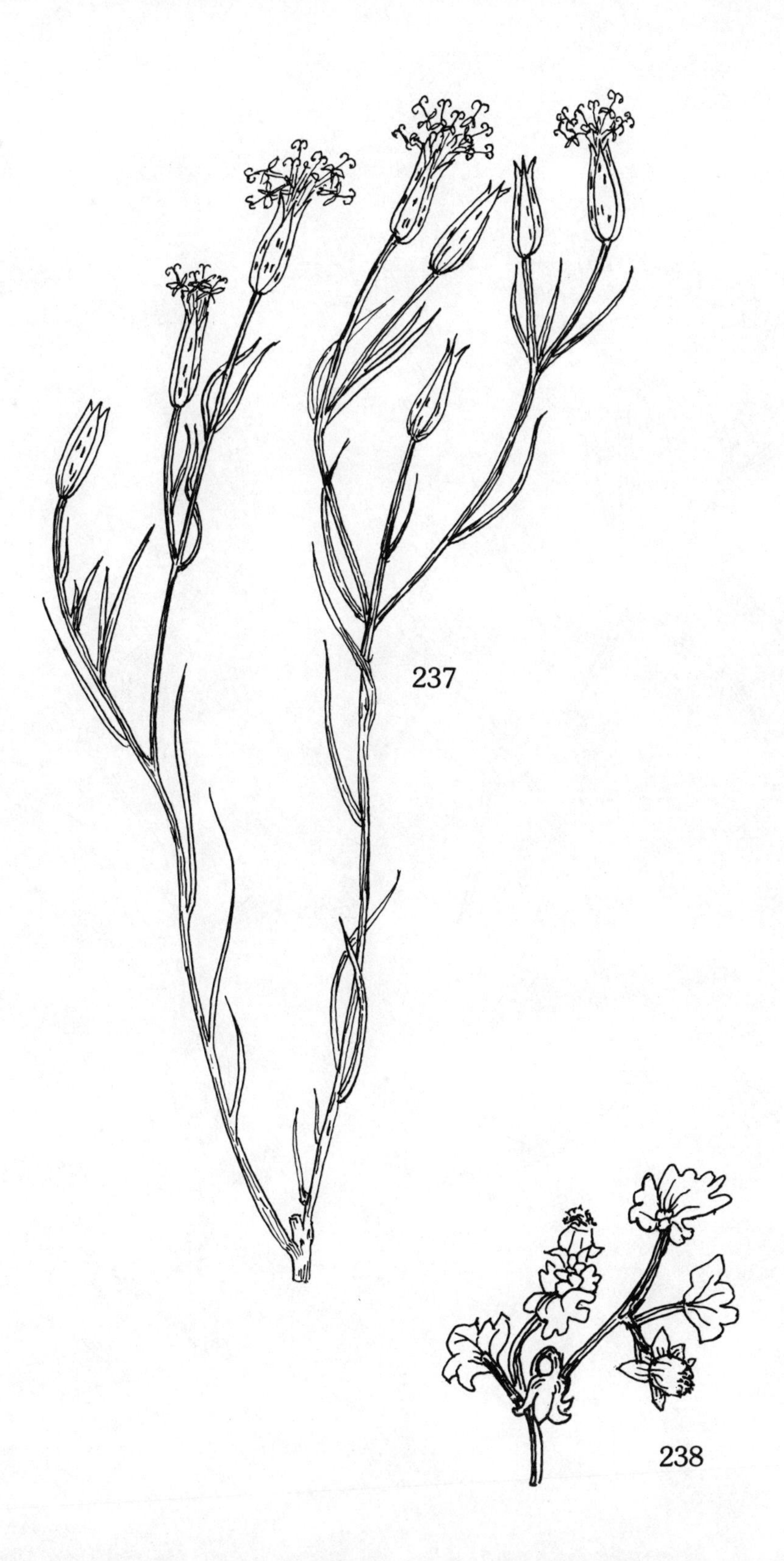
237
238

239

238. **Velvet Rosette** *Psathyrotes ramosissima*

This silvery, gray-green, velvet plant spreads itself close to the ground in a twenty-four-centimeter cushion or rosette. Due to its appearance it is called Turtle Back. It is easy to identify since no other desert plant resembles it. The yellow flowers, scattered all over the rosette, look like little buttons. Two other species besides *ramosissima* live in the desert.

239. **Paper Flower** *Psilostrophe cooperi*

This plant is called Paper Flower because its blooms turn papery with age. The flowers stay on the stems for weeks after they bloom and are still beautiful when in the old-age "paper" stage.

240. **Curly-headed Goldenweed** *Pyrrocoma crocea*

Pyrrocoma crocea is a tall plant with alternate, ovate, clasping leaves. There are one to three heads per stem. The heads are radiate. Figure 240 shows the tendency of the orange-colored rays to curl back as the flower heads age.

241. **Desert Chicory** *Rafinesquia neomexicana*

Other common names for Desert Chicory are Plume Seed and Goatsbeard. This plant is weak stemmed and tends to grow up through shrubs that support it. The leaves are pinnately toothed, though not compound. The fragrant flowers are rose-veined white. The heads have only ray flowers numbering up to thirty. Blooming time is from February through May.

The genus name *Rafinesquia* is for Constantine Rafinesque-Schmaltz, who was a brilliant botanist of the nineteenth century. His contemporaries disagreed with him, but much of his classification work is now accepted as correct.

242. **Fendler Senecio** *Senecio fendleri*

The flower heads of Fendler Senecio are in semi-flat-topped clusters. The basal leaves as well as the alternate stem leaves are shallowly pinnately lobed. Senecio is a very large genus; there are over thirty species in the southwestern states. The name *Senecio* comes from the Greek word *senex* meaning "old man." This name refers to the white beards on the seeds.

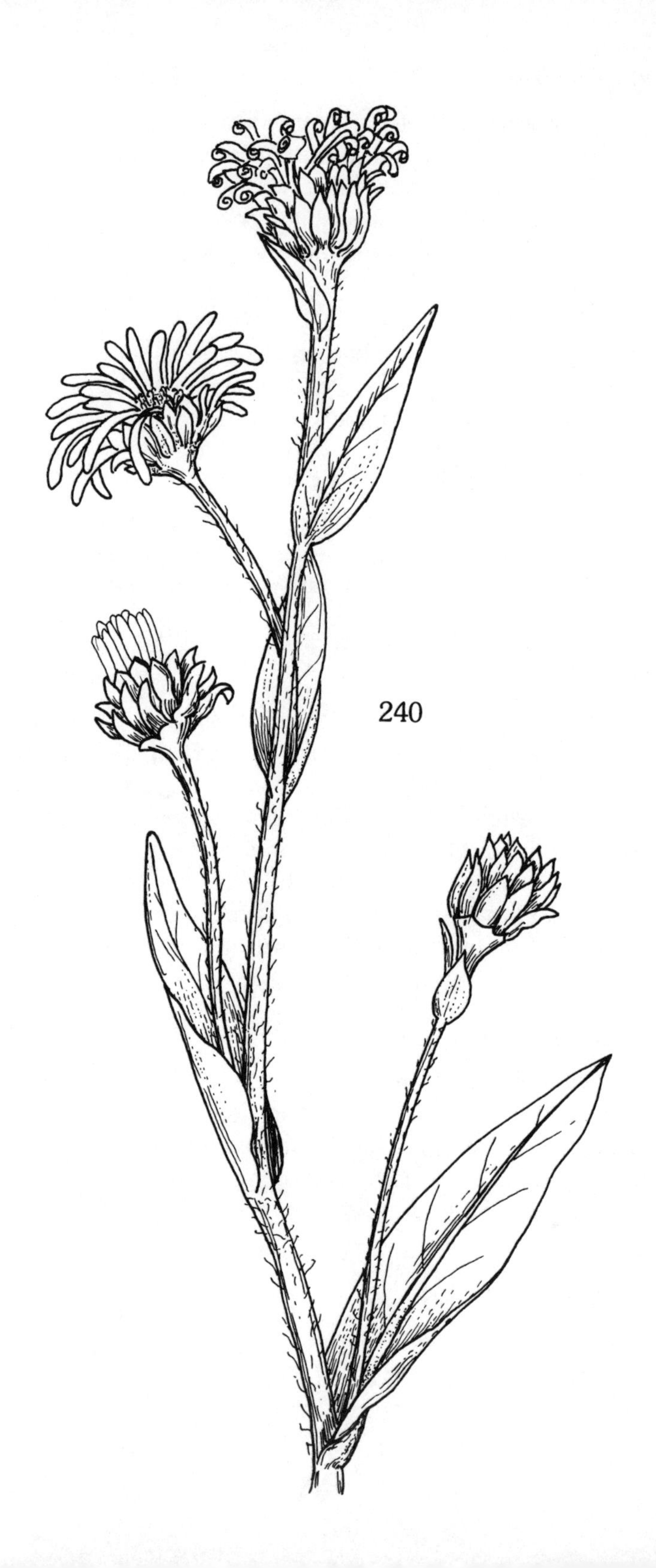
240

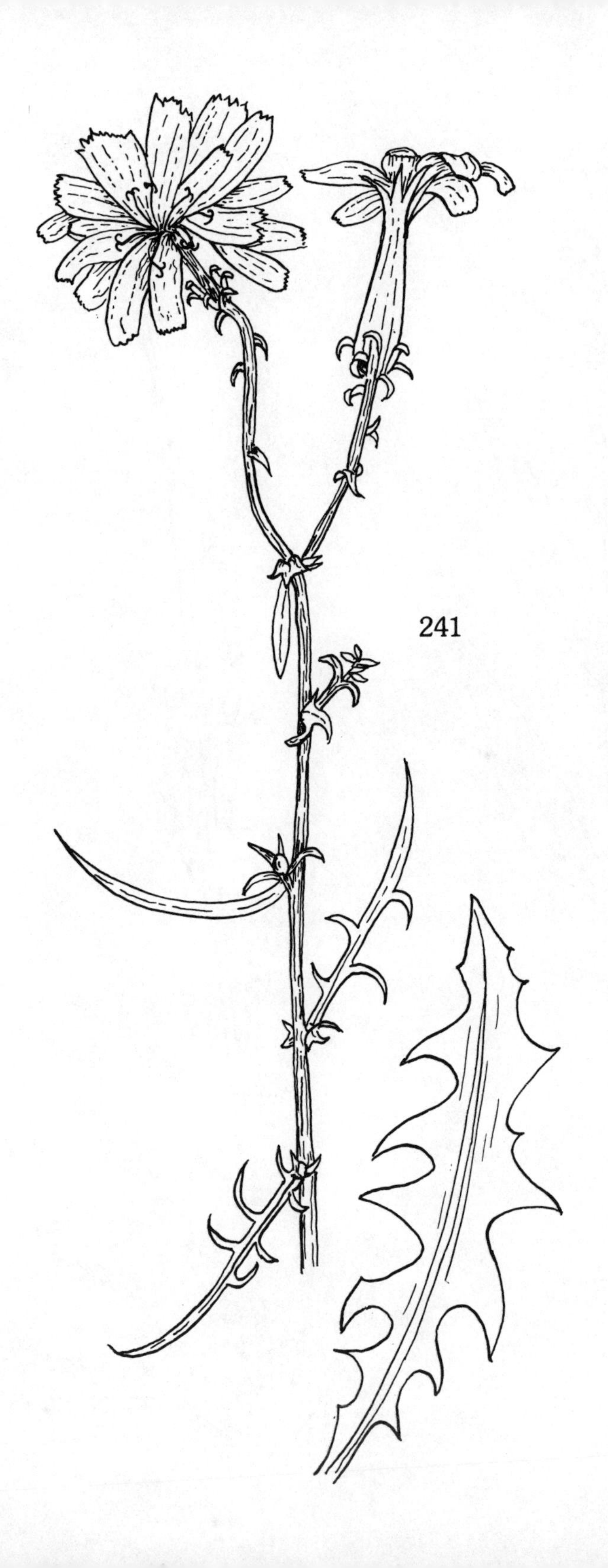
241

243
242

243. **Common Spring Senecio** *Senecio integerrimus*

Common Spring Senecio is also called Lambstongue Groundsel. The young plants have a "cobwebby" appearance. The alternate upper leaves are clasping and sharp pointed.

244. **Mohave Groundsel** *Senecio mohavensis*

Groundsel is an old English name for Senecio and it means "ground swallower," which means, in turn, "covering much ground." This meaning was true of the English species but not necessarily of the North American species.

The species *Senecio mohavensis* is not very common in the deserts of the southwest. The oblong leaves are coarsely toothed. The flowers are yellow. The habitat is sandy washes and canyons of southwestern Arizona.

245. **Arrowleaf Senecio** *Senecio triangularis*

This Senecio is named *triangularis* for its leaf shape, but not all Senecio plants have triangular leaves. They vary from that shape to ovate to lanceolate. All leaves have sharply toothed edges. The stalks may vary in size. Blooming time is from July to September.

246. **Groundsel** *Senecio neomexicanus*

Scenecio neomexicanus is widespread in Arizona as well as in New Mexico and Colorado. The stalked leaves are eight or more centimeters in length, including the petiole. The upper leaves are clasping and evenly toothed.

247. **Greenthread** *Thelesperma filifolium*

The stems of Greenthread are slender and smooth. The leaves are pinnately divided into thread-like segments. The bright yellow flowers are on tall stalks.

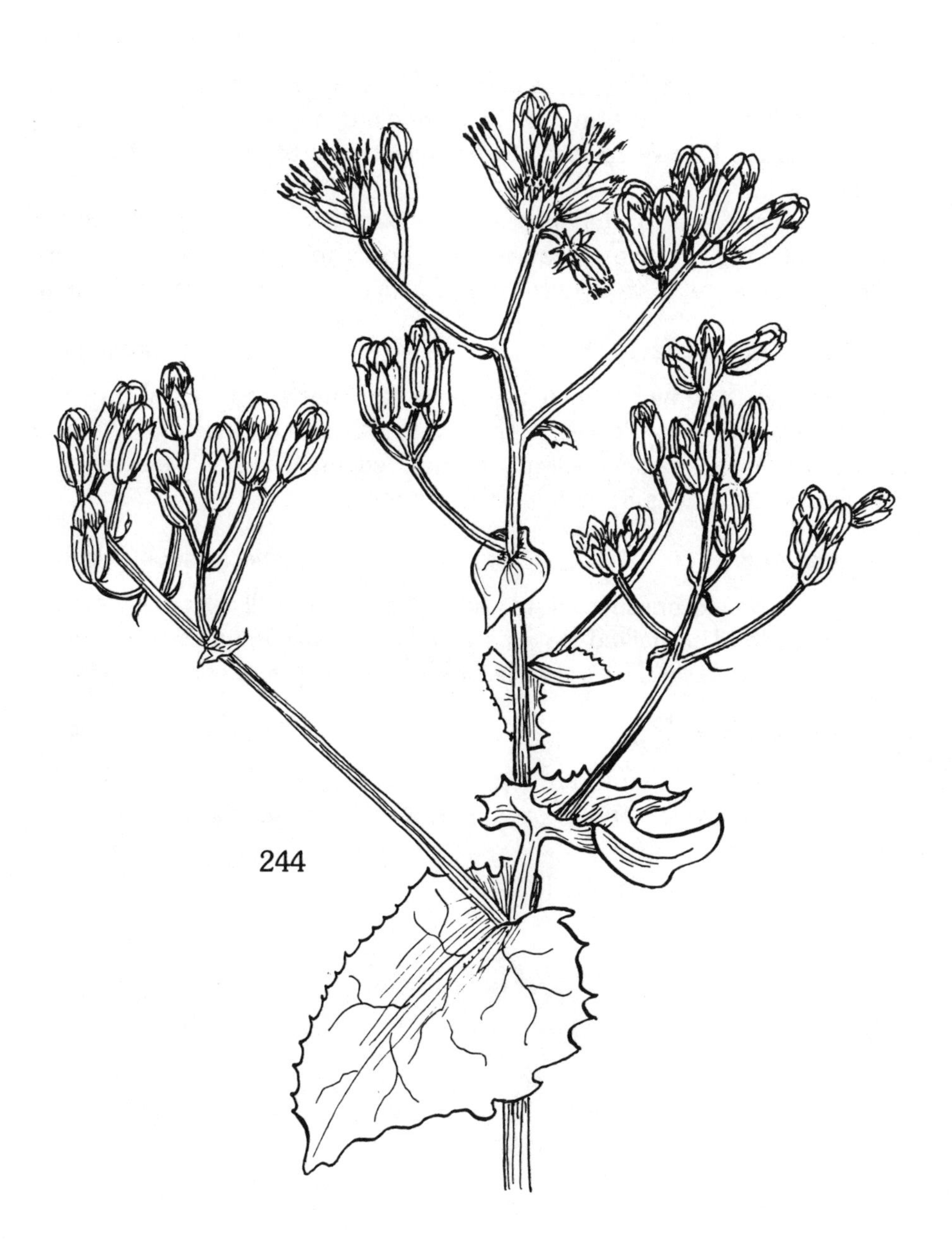
244

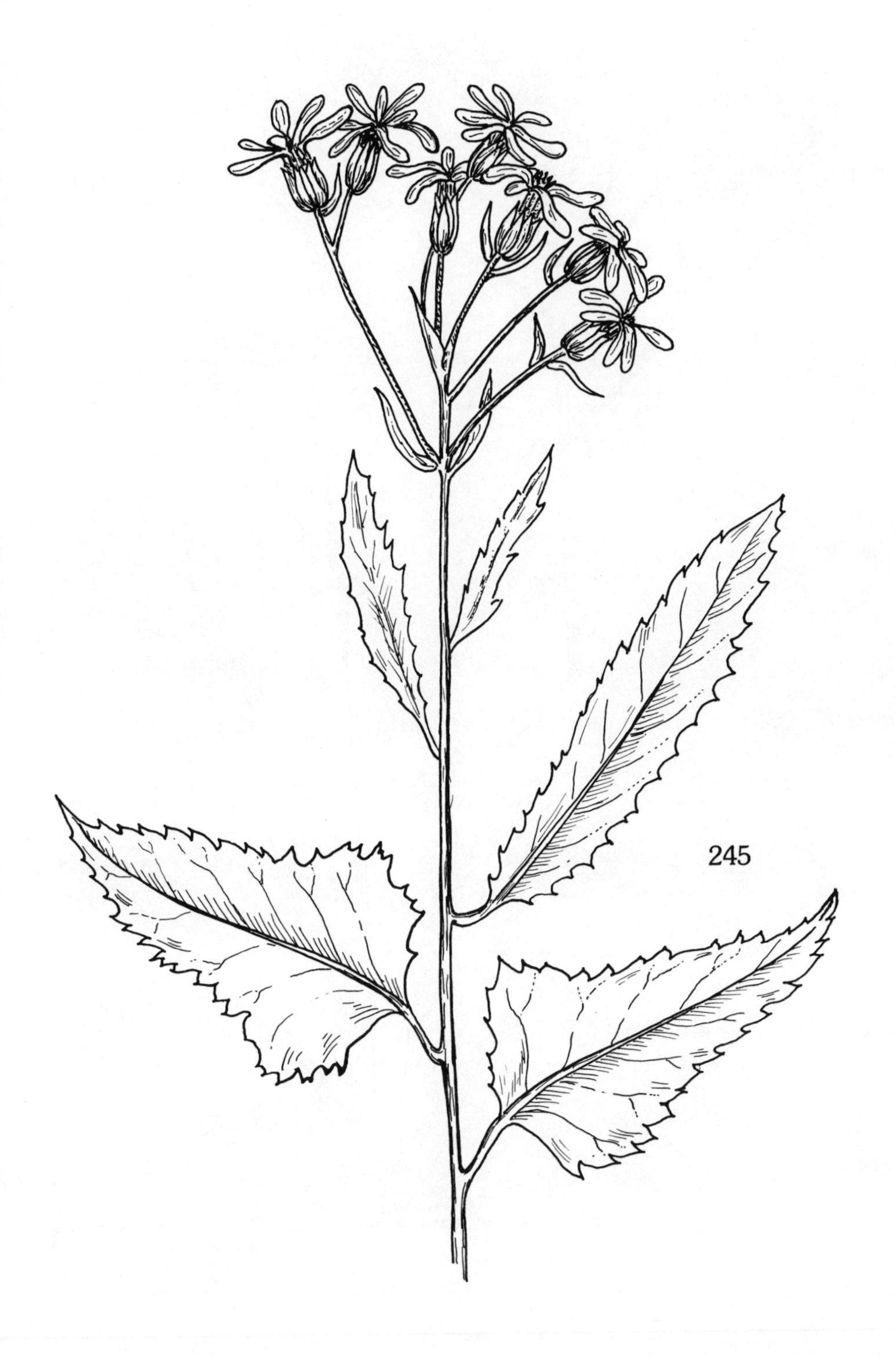
245

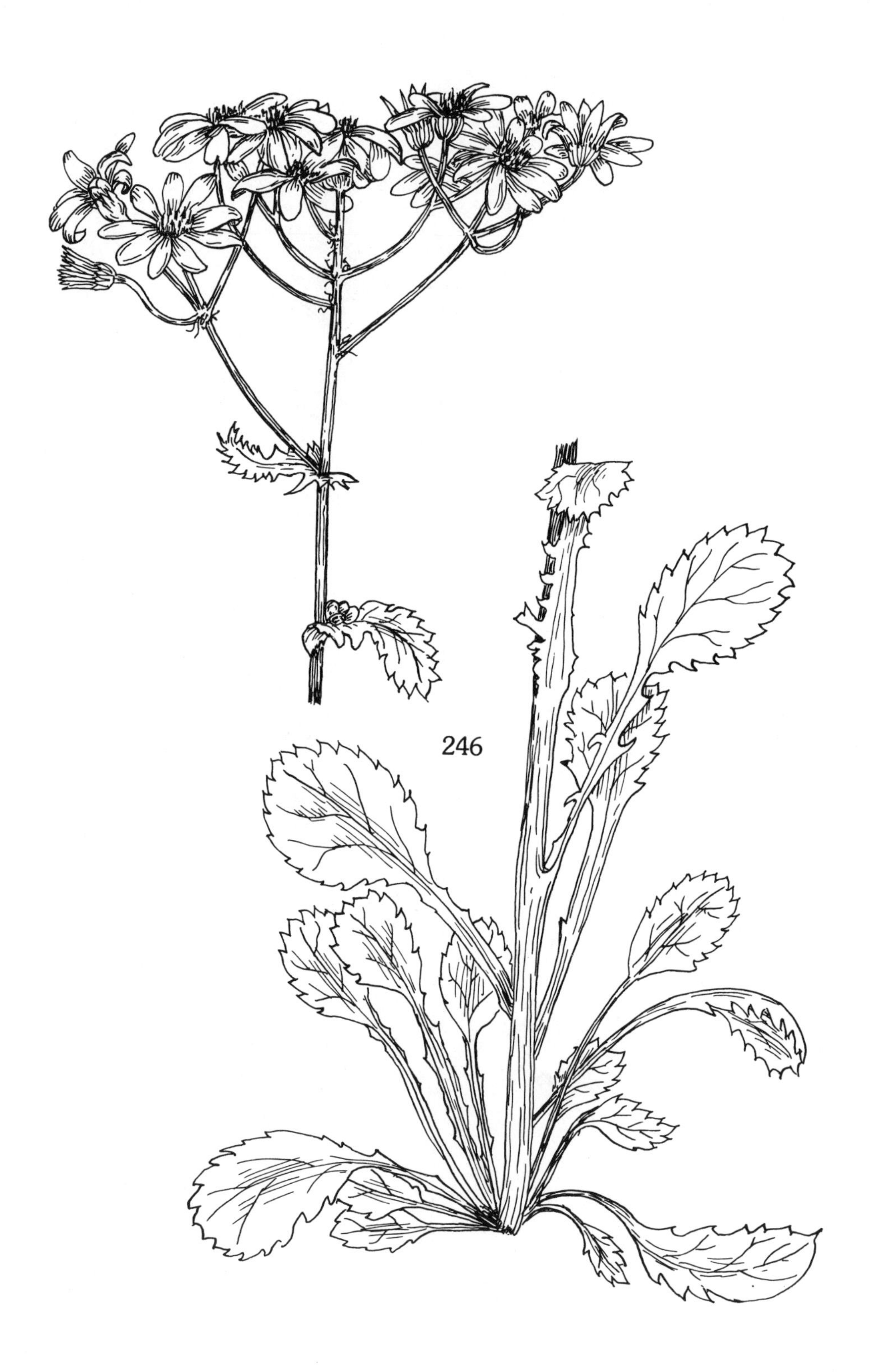
246

247

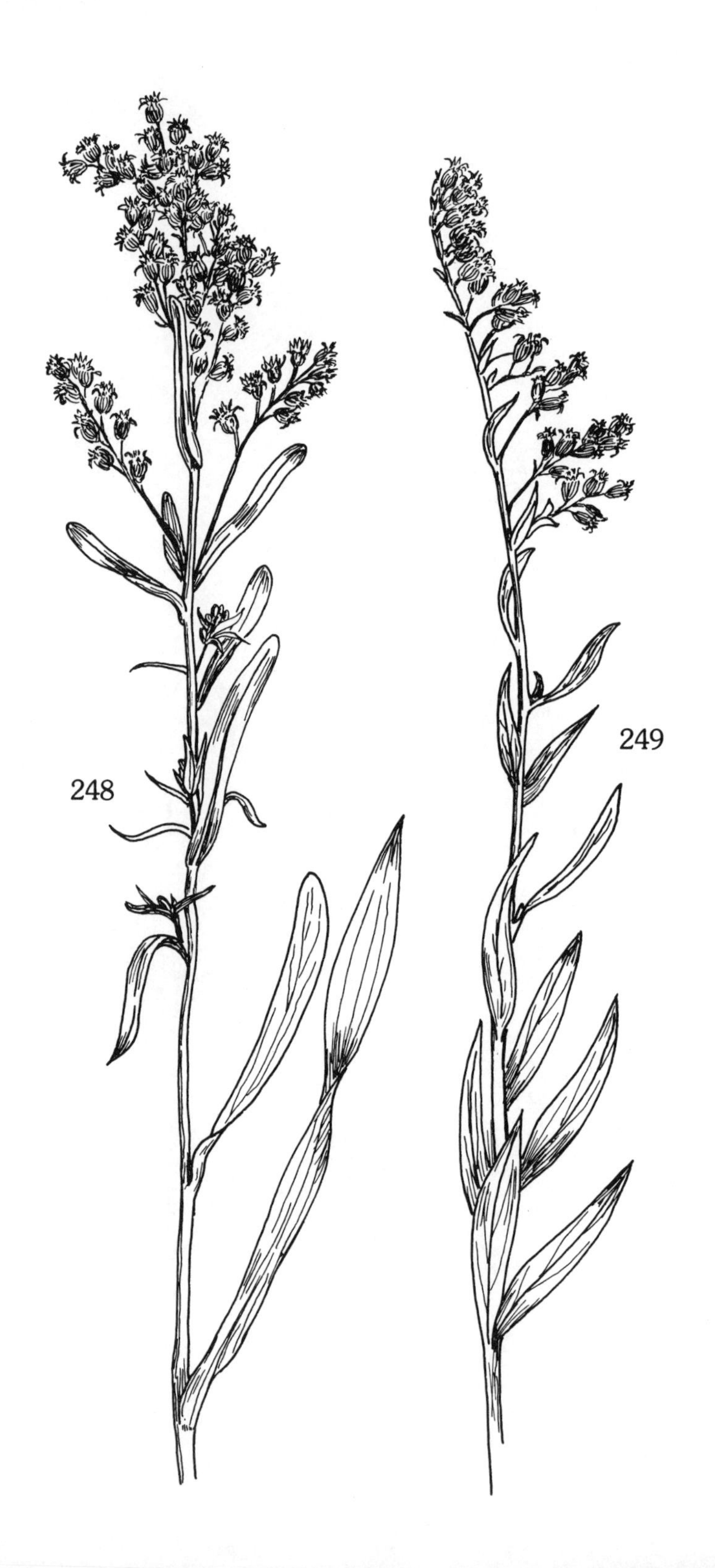
248
249

248. **Missouri Goldenrod** *Solidago missouriensis*

The goldenrods are quite distinctive as a group, but it is difficult to identify the species because the differences between them are so slight.

The two species figured in this book are distinguishable because *Solidago sparsiflora* has fewer flowers on the stalk than *Solidago missouriensis.* The Missouri Goldenrod tends to be much larger than the Few-flowered. It grows to a height of one meter. The basal leaves are around sixteen centimeters long. They are tapering and sparingly toothed. The stem leaves are narrow and toothless.

249. **Few-flowered Goldenrod** *Solidago sparsiflora*

The stems of the Few-flowered Goldenrod are not as smooth as those of the Missouri Goldenrod. The floral branches are arched and not crowded. In the Southwest both goldenrods bloom from June to October—a longer season for them than in Missouri.

250. **Wild Salsify, Oyster Plant** *Tragopogon major*

Like the tame Salsify, or Oyster Plant, the root of the wild one can be used as a vegetable. It has strayed from Europe to invade North America. It is beautiful its whole life. It is lovely to see the flowers in early morning with their yellow faces turned toward the sun. The fruit is a beautiful globe of silver bristles. It looks like a much enlarged dandelion seed head. These fluffy balls are much used for winter bouquets.

251. **Trixis** *Trixis californica*

Trixis is a shrub with alternate lanceolate leaves. The corolla is two lipped and the outer lip is three lobed. It lives in the shadier places of the desert—in rock crevices, under overhangs, and in the shade of other shrubs.

252. **Nevada Viguiera** *Viguiera multiflora* var. *nevadensis*

The leaves of Viguiera are not stalked. They occur in pairs and are lanceolate and entire. The few heads have ten to fifteen ray flowers. Blooming time is long—from May to October.

250

251
252

253

253. **Arizona Mule-Ear** *Wyethia arizonica*

Arizona is the meeting place of two species of the genus: *Wyethia arizonica* is a native of Arizona, and *Wyethia amplexicaulis* is a native of northwestern Colorado, Nevada, and Montana. The two are very much alike except that species *arizonica* is a hairy plant. Where the distributions of the two overlap, they hybridize, producing plants intermediate in appearance.

Both parent species and the hybrids have large leathery, elliptic basal leaves about twenty-four centimeters long. They look varnished and are sticky. Smaller leaves on the upper parts of the stem are clasping. There are several yellow heads at the stem top. The terminal one is the largest.

Appendix

Plant Characteristics Illustrated

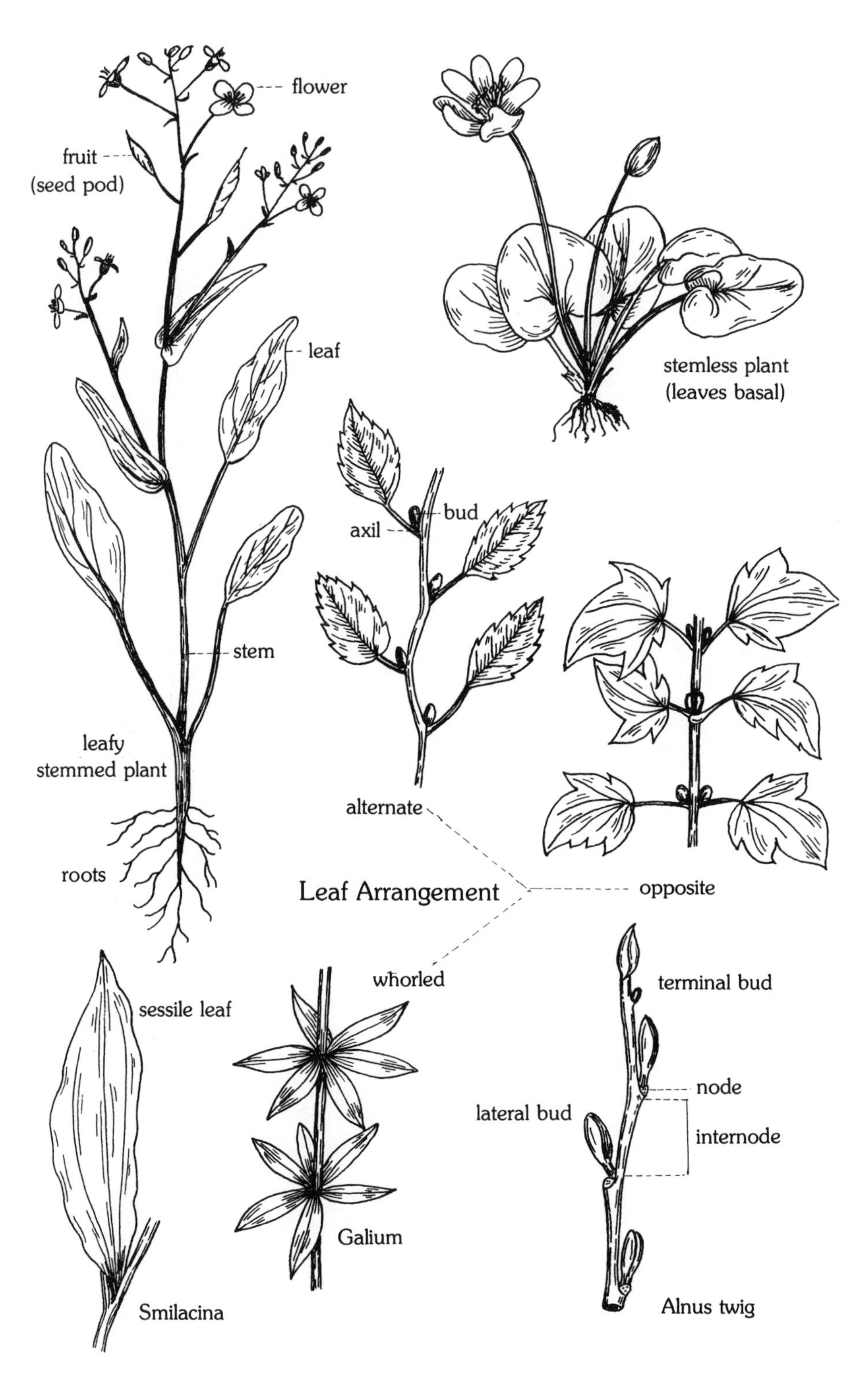

Plate A. The Plant

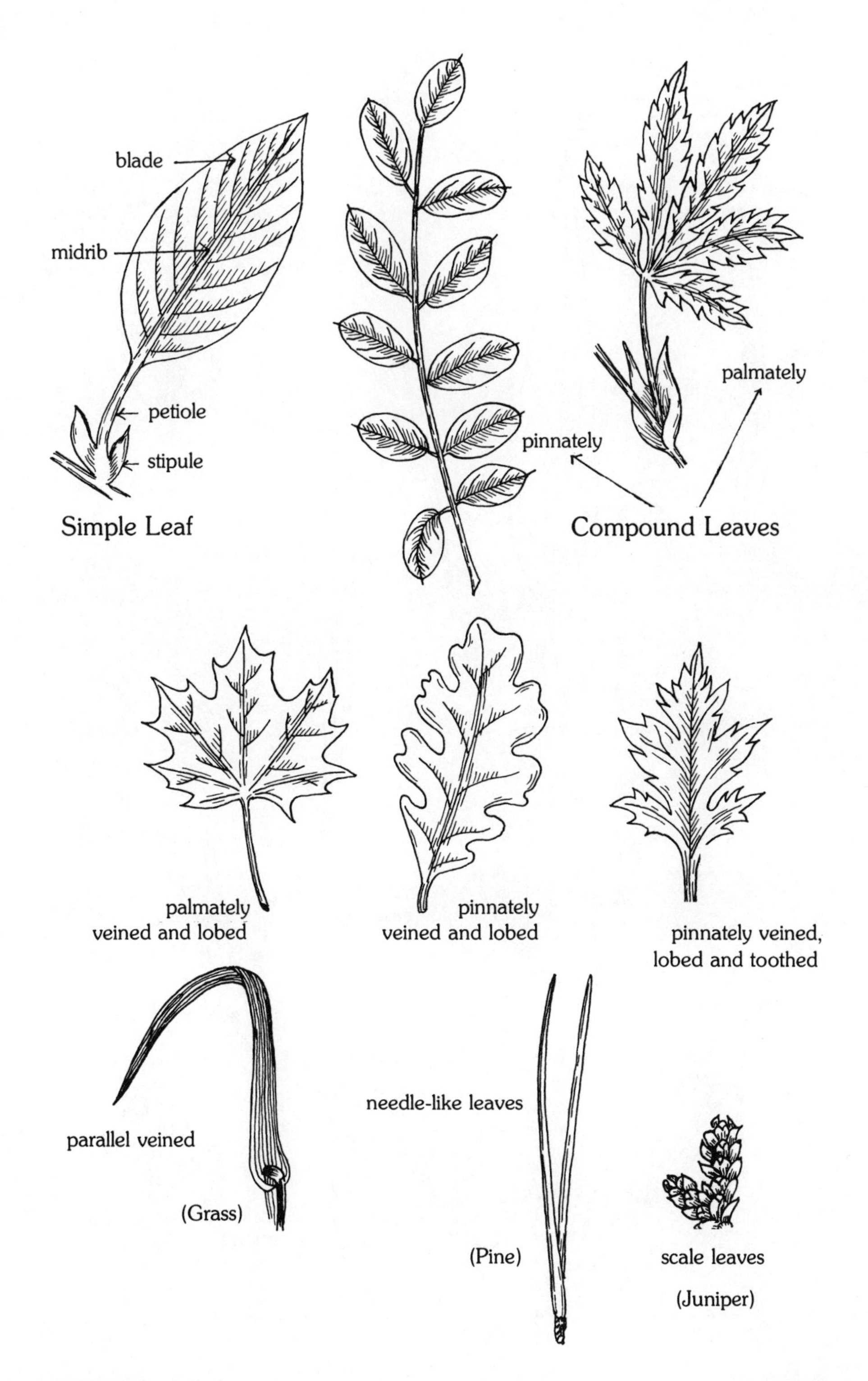

Plate B. Leaves

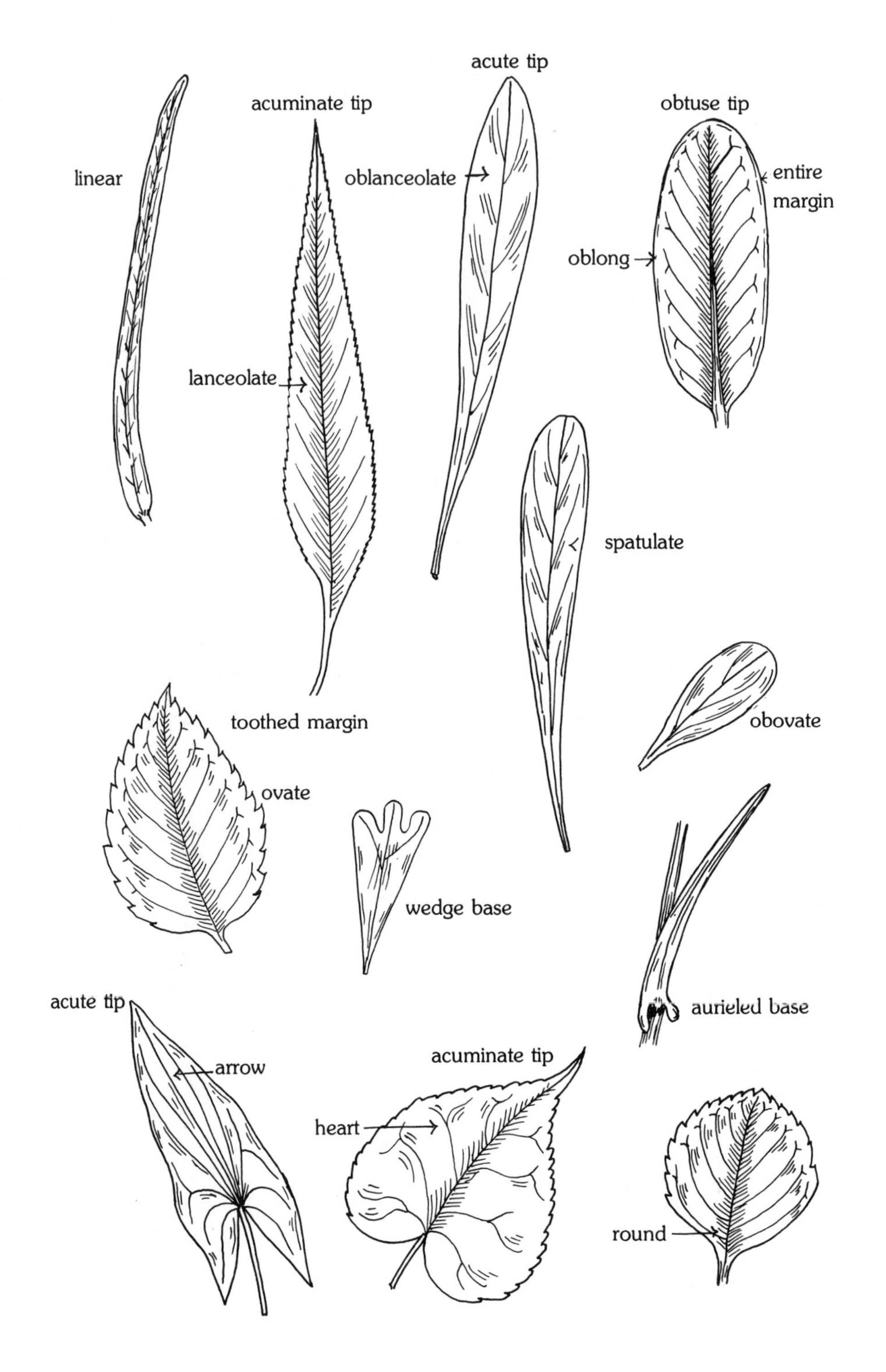

Plate C. Leaf Forms

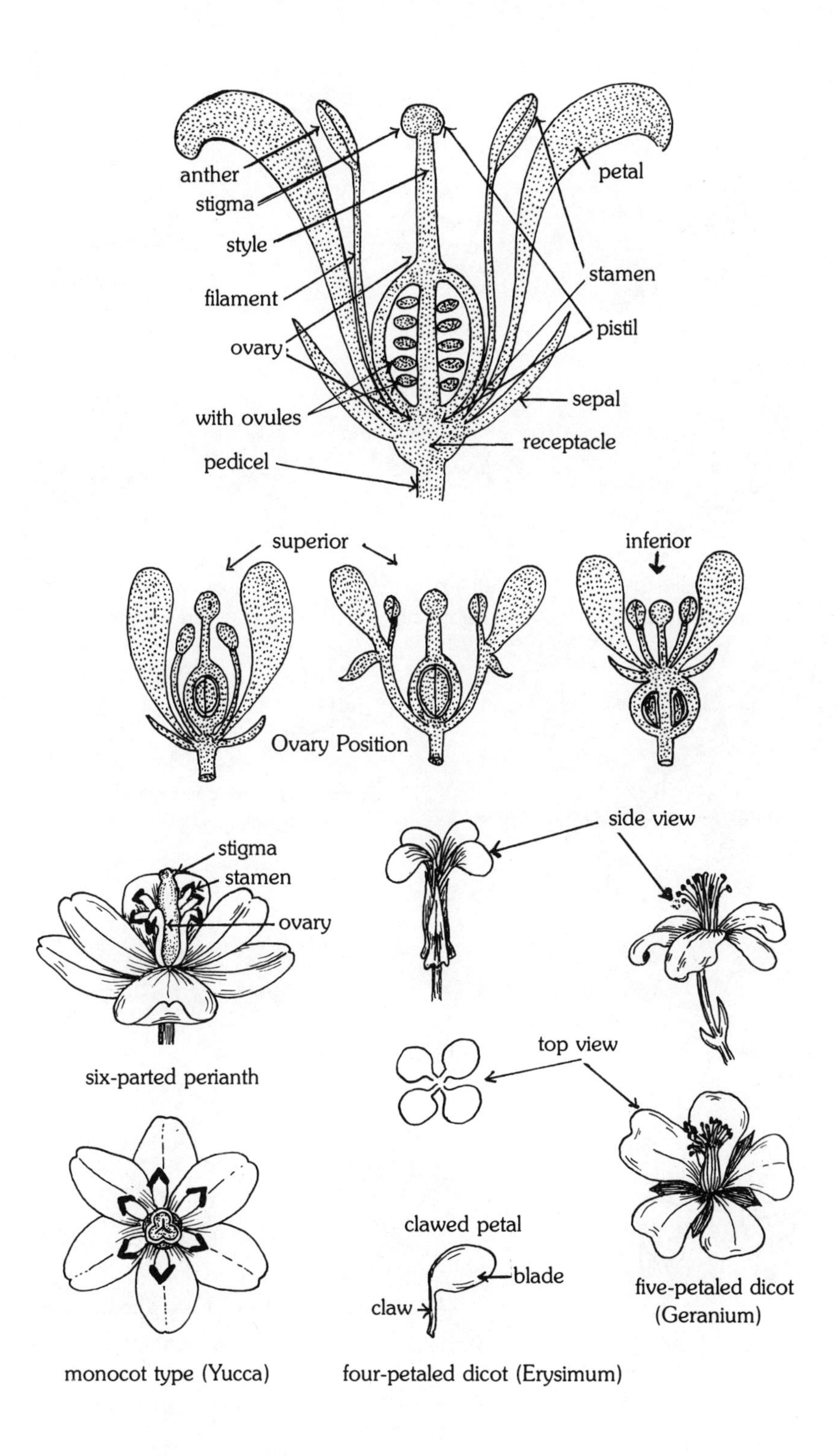

Plate D. Flower Parts

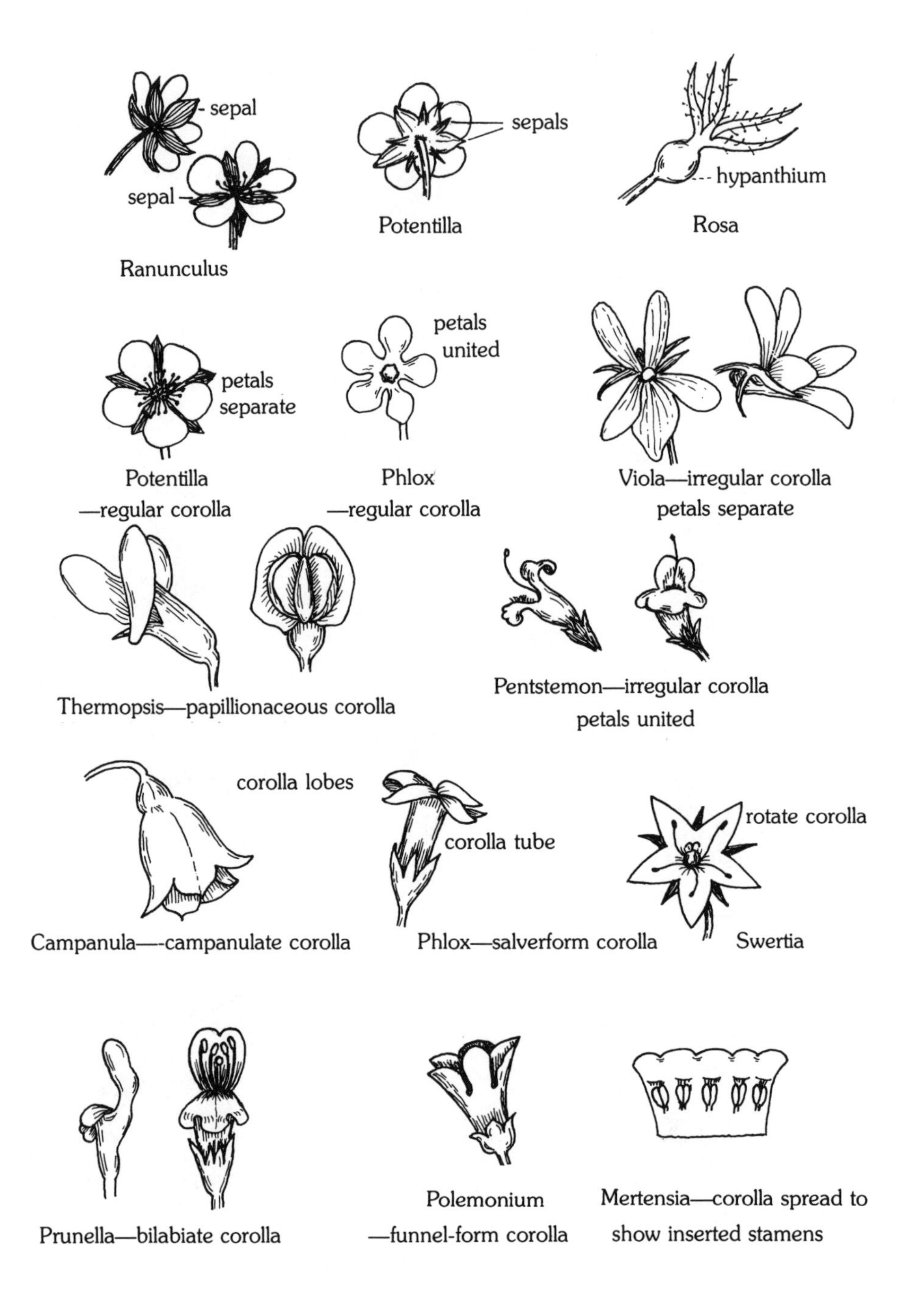

Plate E. Calyx and Corolla Types

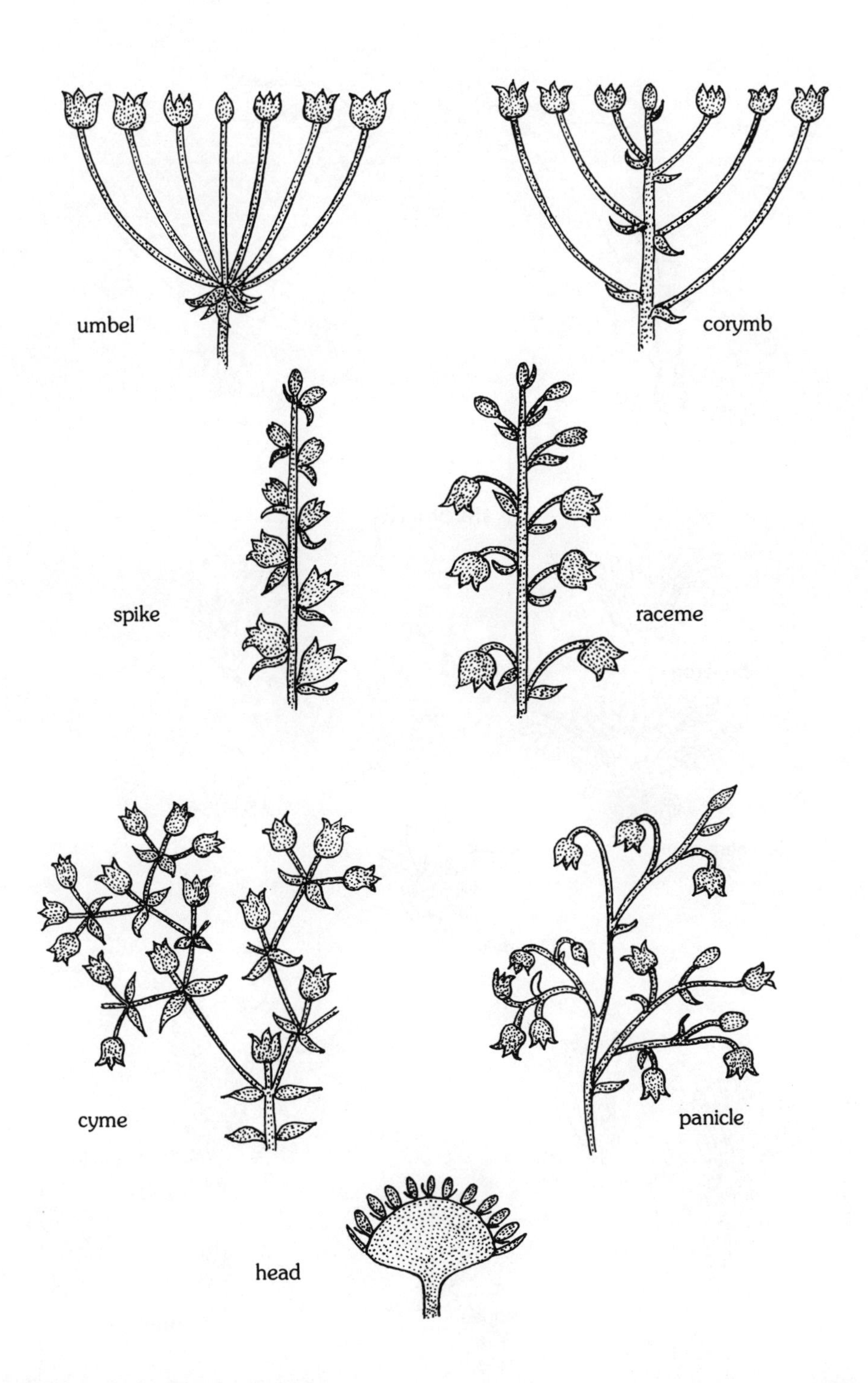

Plate F. Inflorescences

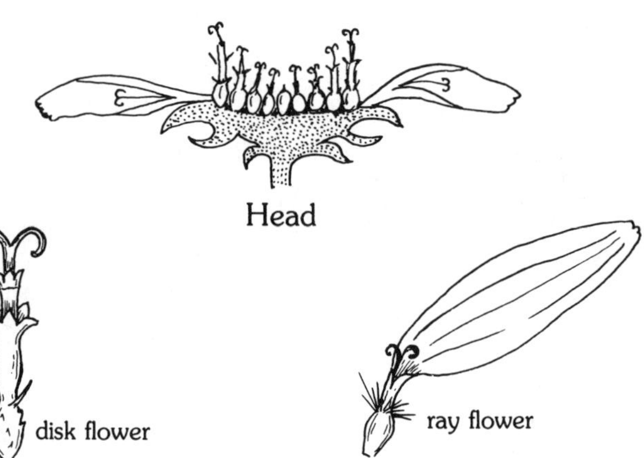

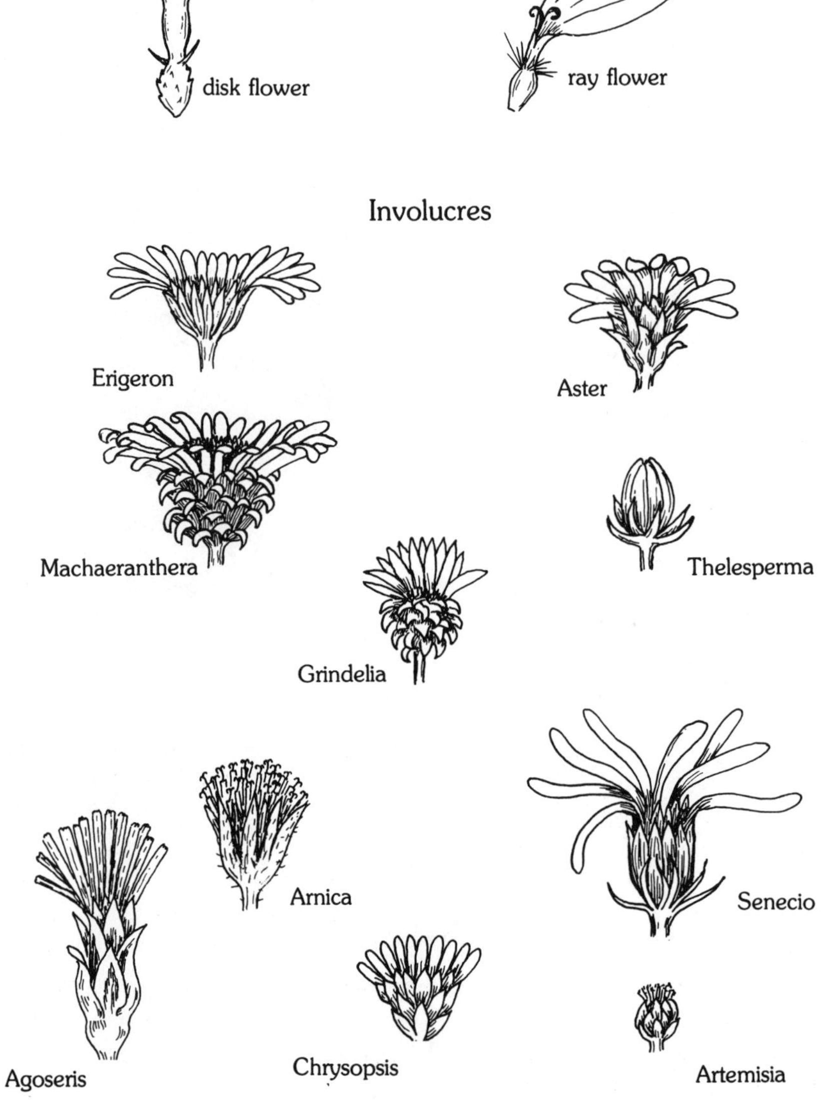

Plate G. Composites

Glossary

Achene. A dry, one-seeded fruit that remains closed at maturity

Acuminate. Tapering to a point at the end

Acute. Ending in a point formed by less than a right angle

Anther. The part of the stamen having pollen sacs

Auricled. With a basal, ear-shaped appendage or lobe

Axil. The angle above the juncture of stem and leaf

Berry. A fleshy, usually many-seeded, nonsplitting fruit

Bilabiate. Two lipped

Blade. Expanded portion of a leaf

Bract. Sessile leaf or leaves usually close below a flower or inflorescence

Bud. An undeveloped stem or flower

Bulb. A spherical, underground bud, with fleshy leaves attached to a flattened stem

Calyx. The outer circle of flower parts (sepals)

Capsule. A dry fruit with several compartments, each of which may contain few to many seeds. The capsule splits open when ripe.

Chlorophyll. The green pigment of plants

Cleistogamous. Fertilized in the flower bud

Cone. A spherical to cylindrical arrangement of bracts or scales subtending organs

Connate. Lke parts of plants that are firmly joined

Corm. An enlarged, solid, bulb-like base of a stem, usually underground

Corolla. The circle of flower parts (petals) inside the calyx

Corymb. A more-or-less flat-topped flower cluster of which the outer flowers open first

Cyme. A more-or-less flat-topped flower cluster of which the central flowers open first

Cymose. Having a cyme

Decumbent. Reclining or lying on the ground, but with the end ascending

Dentate. Having a toothed margin

Dicotyledon (dicot). Having two leaves as part of the embryo plant in the seed, as in beans

Dioecious. Having staminate and pistillate flowers on different plants

Disk flowers. The central tubular flowers of the head inflorescence in the composite family

Dissected. Cut or divided into narrow segments

Drupe. A fleshy, nonsplitting fruit with a stone-covered seed

Elliptic. A flat part that is oval, narrowed to rounded at the ends, and widest at the middle

Entire. Having a smooth margin (as of leaves)

Family. A group of plants having similar gross characteristics, especially in reproductive structures, such as flowers and fruits

Fascicle. A condensed or close cluster

Filament. A slender stalk, especially that of a stamen

Flower. A structure with one or more pistils, one or more stamens, or both

Follicle. A dry fruit that splits along one side when ripe

Fruit. A ripened ovary, sometimes united with sepals or receptacle, normally containing seeds

Genus. A group of plants made up of closely related species

Glaucous. Covered with a whitish substance that rubs off

Habitat. The kind of place in which a plant or animal lives

Hastate. Shaped like an arrowhead with narrow basal lobes pointing outward

Head. A cluster of sessile flowers on a short axis

Herbaceous. An annual or perennial plant that dies back to the ground at the end of the season

Indusium. The covering over the sorus on many ferns

Inferior. Applied to the ovary or seed pod when the calyx and corolla are placed on top of it

Inflorescence. The flowering part of a plant

Involucre. A whorl or set of bracts surrounding a flower, umbel, or head

Irregular. Describes a calyx or corolla in which the parts are not all alike (i.e., the calyx or corolla is not radially symmetrical)

Keel. The boat-like structure formed by the fusing of the two lower petals in flowers of the pea family

Lanceolate. Lance shaped

Latex. Milky sap

Leaflet. A segment of a compound leaf

Legume. A member of the pea family, also the fruit of a member

Lenticels. Wart-like, usually light-colored spots on the barks of trees or shrubs

Lenticular. Convex on both sides

Ligulate. Tongue or strap shaped

Linear. Narrow and flat, with parallel margins

Lobed. Divided into rounded parts, as of a leaf or a united corolla

Midrib. The central rib of a leaf

Monocotyledon (monocot). Having one leaf as part of the embryo plant in the seed, as in corn seeds

Node. A place on a stem from which one or more leaves or branches arise

Oblong. Two or three times longer than broad

Obovate. Reverse egg-shaped, with rounded end opposite the petiole

Oblanceolate. Reverse lance-shaped

Obtuse. Rounded at the end

Opposite. Two leaves at a node opposing each other

Ovary. The part of the pistil that contains the ovules

Ovate. Egg shaped

Ovule. The structure that contains the egg and becomes the seed

Palmate. Lobed or divided in a hand-like manner

Panicle. A loose, irregular inflorescence, profusely branching

Papilionaceous. Butterfly-like; used to describe flowers with petals expanding like wings, such as those in the pea family

Pedicel. A stalk bearing one flower

Peduncle. A stalk bearing several flowers

Perfect. Said of a flower when both female (pistil) and male (stamen) parts are present

Perfoliate. Said of a leaf, the basal part of which encircles the stem completely, so that the stem appears to pass through the leaf

Perianth. The two outer whorls of a flower (i.e., the calyx and corolla)

Petal. A division of the corolla

Petiole. A leaf stalk

Pinnate. Arrangement of the veins of leaves or the leaflet of a compound leaf on opposite sides of the axis, like the vanes of a feather

Pinnatifid. Cut into lobes or divisions that are pinnately arranged

Pistil. The seed-bearing part of the flower, normally comprising stigma, style, and ovary

Pistillate. Having pistils but no stamens

Plumose. Feather-like

Pollen. The grains in the anther that contain the male element

Pollination. The placing of pollen on the stigma

Pubescent. Covered with short hairs

Pyriform. Shaped like a pear

Raceme. An inflorescence in which stalked flowers are arranged singly along an elongated axis

Radiate. Having ray flowers

Ray flower. Strap-like flowers, arranged around a central disk or composing the whole head

Receptacle. The end of the stem on which some or all of the flower parts are borne

Rhizome. An underground, usually horizontal stem

Salverform. A corolla shape, having a slender tube abruptly expanding into a flat top

Samara. A winged fruit that does not split open

Seed. A ripened ovule

Sepal. A division of a calyx

Sessile. Without a stalk

Sinuate. Having a wavy leaf margin

Sorus (pl. sori). The fruit dots usually found on the undersides of fern fronds

Spathe. A large leaf or bract, below or around an inflorescence

Spatulate. Shaped like a kitchen spatula

Species. A group of individuals that actually or potentially breed with each other but not with other such groups

Spike. A flower that is sessile or nearly so on an elongated axis

Spine. A stiff outgrowth from the woody part of a stem, representing a modified leaf or a leaf portion

Stamen. Pollen-bearing organ of a flower

Staminate. Having stamens but no pistils

Standard. The upper, usually broad petal of a papilionaceous flower

Stigma. The top part of the pistil, which receives the pollen

Stipulate. Having an appendage or appendages at the base of a leaf petiole

Style. The part of the pistil that connects the stigma and ovary

Tomentose. Covered with densely matted hairs

Trifoliate. Applied to leaves with three leaflets

Tuber. A thickened, short, underground stem with numerous buds

Tuberculate. Having knobby appearance

Umbel. An inflorescence in which the peduncles or pedicels arise from a common point

Whorled. Leaves arranged in a circle around a stem, three or more at a node

Bibliography

Armstrong, Margaret, 1918. *Fieldbook of Western Flowers*. New York: G. P. Putnam.

Arnberger, Leslie P., 1974. *Flowers of the Southwest Mountains*. Globe, Ariz.: Southwest Parks and Monuments Association.

Clements, Frederick E., and Edith Clements. 1928. *Rocky Mountain Flowers*. New York: H. W. Wilson.

Collins, Barbara J. 1976. *Key to Trees and Shrubs of the Deserts of Southwestern Arizona*. Thousand Oaks: California Lutheran College.

———. 1979. *Key to the Wild Flowers of the Deserts of Southern California*. Thousand Oaks: California Lutheran College.

Cornett, J. W. 1988. "The Occurrence of the Desert Fan Palm, *Washingtonia filifera*, in Southern Nevada." *Desert Plants* 8(4). Superior, Ariz.: Boyce Thompson Southwestern Arboretum.

Craighead, John J., Frank C. Craighead, Jr., and Ray J. Davis. 1963. *A Field Guide to Rocky Mountain Wild Flowers*. Boston: Houghton Mifflin.

Dodge, Natt N. 1951. *Flowers of the Southwest Desert*. Globe, Ariz.: Southwestern Monument Association.

———. 1963. *Desert Wildflowers*. Globe, Ariz.: Southwestern Monument Association.

———. 1973. *Flowers of the Southwest Deserts*. 4th ed. Phoenix: McGrew Printing and Lithographing Co.

Ferris, Roxana S. 1962. *Death Valley Wild Flowers*. Death Valley, Calif.: Death Valley Natural History Association.

Heald, Weldon F. 1967. *The Chiricahua Mountains*. Tucson: University of Arizona Press.

Hill, Albert F. 1937. *Economic Botany*. New York: McGraw-Hill.

Jaeger, Edmund C. 1976. *Desert Wildflowers*. Globe, Ariz.: Southwestern Monument Association.

Johnson, W. T. 1988. "Flora of the Pinalena Mountains Desert Plants." *Desert Plants* 8(4). Superior, Ariz.: Boyce Thompson Southwestern Arboretum.

Kearney, Thomas H., and Robert H. Peebles. 1960. *Arizona Flora*. 4th ed. Berkeley: University of California Press.

Lehr, J. Harry 1978. *A Catalogue of the Flora of Arizona*. Phoenix: Desert Botanical Garden.

Mochel, Henry R., and Beverly Mochel. n.d. *Desert Flower Notebook*. Twenty-nine Palms, California, 92277.

Nelson, Ruth A. 1969. *Handbook of Rocky Mountain Plants*. Tucson: Dale Stuart King.

Parker, Kittie F. 1982. *Arizona Weeds*. Tucson: University of Arizona Press.

Patraw, Pauline Mead. 1977. *Flowers of the Southwest Mesas*. Phoenix: McGrew Printing and Lithographing Co.

Pool, Raymond J. 1929. *Flowers and Flowering Plants*. New York: McGraw-Hill.

Rickett, Harold William. 1970. *Wild Flowers of the United States.* Vol. 4, *The Southwestern States* (Pts. 1, 2, and 3). New York: McGraw-Hill.

Shreve, Forrest, and Ira L. Wiggins. 1951. *Vegetation and Flora of the Sonoran Desert* (publication #591, Vol. 1). Washington, D.C.: Carnegie Washington.

Sweet, Muriel. 1976. *Common Edible and Useful Plants of the Southwest.* Happy Camp, Calif.: Naturegraph Publishers.

———. 1979. *Wild Flower Guide.* P.O. Box 26767, Tucson, Arizona, 85726.

Swingle, Deane B. 1934. *A Textbook of Systematic Botany.* New York: McGraw-Hill.

Index

C

D

I

J

K

L

M

N

O

P

Q

R

S